RICHARD von MISES

# positivism

## A STUDY IN HUMAN UNDERSTANDING

•

DOVER PUBLICATIONS, INC.
NEW YORK

This Dover edition, first published in 1968, is an unabridged republication, with minor corrections, of the work originally published by Harvard University Press in 1951.

This book was translated from the German by Jerry Bernstein and Roger G. Newton, with the collaboration of the author.

*Library of Congress Catalog Card Number: 67-18741*

Manufactured in the United States of America
Dover Publications, Inc.
180 Varick Street
New York, N. Y. 10014

# preface

This book, essentially a translation of the author's *Kleines Lehrbuch des Positivismus* of 1939, is not a treatise *on* positivism, weighing the pros and cons of this kind of outlook on the world of experience. It is the positivist himself who speaks and argues, who tries to describe the world as he sees it. He addresses in the first place not the scholar interested in philosophical technicalities, but the open-minded educated man who feels a want for information that remains consistent even when it touches upon the most diversified areas of human knowledge. The table of contents will show the range of subjects discussed. The reader who likes to learn in advance where he will be led may turn to the short summary of results at the end of the book, or he may look through the introduction, which offers a preliminary survey of the principal ideas to be expounded later. The author was particularly anxious to avoid vagueness, and not to indulge in generalities—obvious dangers in a project of the present type. This is why, in a rather pedantic way, every one of the 195 paragraphs of the book is followed by a concise statement summarizing its content.

Some of the arguments and conclusions in the book may be found new and original, at least in detail, and the author does not want to shun responsibility. However, he considers himself only an interpreter of a certain line of thought that has developed through centuries of intellectual efforts of men. The very term "Positivism" has been taken over from Auguste Comte's *Philosophie Positive,* which itself is rooted in conceptions one can trace back to antiquity. From Comte a clearly distinguishable line leads to Ernst Mach and Henri Poincaré. The work of Mach has been continued and in essential points amplified by the so-called Vienna Circle, Carnap, Frank,

Hahn, Neurath, Schlick. It is *this* development which provides the basis for all comments on the various problems presented in the following text.

This preface should not close without a word of remembrance of a man who decisively contributed to the publication of the first edition. Otto Neurath, the founder of the Unity of Science Movement and of the International Encyclopedia of Unified Science, died prematurely in December 1945. He was an unusually clear thinker, a polyhistor, a successful writer and brilliant speaker, and he had a unique goal in life: the improvement of human understanding.

The author offers his book as a most modest contribution toward this goal.

*Harvard University*                                R. v. Mises
*August 1950*

# contents

# contents

## 11 the foundations of mathematics 125

## 12 the structure of physical theories 136

### PART IV · CAUSALITY AND PROBABILITY

## 13 causal propositions 151

## 14 probability 163

## 15 deterministic and statistical physics 177

## 16 miracles 189

### PART V · SCIENCE AND THE HUMANITIES

## 17 the alleged limitation of scientific concepts 205

... die kleinen, unscheinbaren, *vorsichtigen* Wahrheiten, welche mit strenger Methode gefunden werden, höher zu schätzen als jene weiten, schwebenden, umschleiernden Allgemeinheiten, nach denen das Bedürfnis religiöser oder künstlerischer Zeitalter greift.

... to value more highly the little, unpretentious, *cautious* truths, arrived at by rigorous methods, than those vast, floating, veiling generalities for which the yearnings of a religious or artistic era reach.

NIETZSCHE

# introduction

## I

The word "positivism" is used, as are all terms of this kind, with many different and partly contradictory meanings. Therefore it seems appropriate to say something about the sense in which it will be used in this book. But a complete discussion of the term "positivism" is clearly impossible here, since that would mean anticipating the content of the book. What we can attempt is only this: to start within a frame of reference familiar to the reader and to introduce him gradually, step by step, into the lines of thought which we call positivism.

Presumably the reader knows what he would regard as a reasonable or judicious attitude in most situations of life. No doubt a major component of such an attitude is, in the first place, to judge on the grounds of experience, that is, the remembrance of the contingencies of one's own life and the knowledge of those of others. Furthermore, such an attitude requires a continual readiness to give up a judgment once made or to change it if new experiences require. It also implies a lack of prejudice, superstition, obstinacy, blind trust in authority, mystical thinking, fanaticism. Evidently, nobody can be a perfect embodiment of all these qualities all of the time; but one should certainly be ready to repudiate actions and judgments as soon as one becomes aware that they were not consonant with those requirements.

As a first tentative and quite rough approach to the definition of positivism, we may say that whoever, when confronted with any practical or theoretical problem, acts as we have just described it, is a positivist.

For several hundred years there has been, in all civilized countries, an area of life in which positivistic conduct has become almost an unconditional rule. This is the realm of scientific research; and by this we by no means refer only to research in the natural sciences. Those who study the laws of phonetic development of the Romance languages, or try to clear up the circumstances under which Julius Caesar was murdered, are engaged in positive scientific investigation. The situation is more difficult in those sciences whose subject matter is closer to the life of the scientist himself or of those persons for whom he cares. The stars of the astronomer are detached enough, but the social sciences, which, if the term is used in the widest sense, include even theology, deal with questions that make it difficult for the researcher to maintain the disinterested attitude of the scholar. Nevertheless one can say that, apart from the most extreme cases, everybody who claims for himself the name of a scientist must accept, at least *in principle,* the rules that we have outlined above as the marks of "reasonable conduct." With this in mind, we may say, a little more precisely, but still in a very preliminary way, that he is a positivist who, when confronted by a problem, acts in the manner in which a typical contemporary scientist deals with his problems of research.

At this point it might be appropriate to say a word about what positivism in our conception is *not.* In the history of art the problem arises of determining the period of origin of a work handed down to us from a remote past. One scholar derives his assertions from a study of similarities and differences in artistic style, another draws his conclusions from a chemical analysis of the material. It is *not* positivism to accept the second method only and to reject, as a matter of principle, the first one. No procedure based on systematic observations from which conclusions may be drawn is declined by positivism. Those who demand that a physician, when he treats a patient, must use physical and chemical methods *only,* cannot claim a positivistic tenet as support. Even less than the method are the subject matter and the aim of research subject to limitations from the standpoint of positivism. The observations about telepathy so far seem not very promising; but positivism does not recommend that they be discontinued. Nor does a positivist think that man "lives by bread alone" or, for that matter, has only intellectual needs; but more about that later.

What are the things which in our mind definitely have to be regarded as antipositivistic? First of all is the idea that there exists an area of problems in which the intellect is not "competent," in which one *cannot* think or *must* not think. Next is the conception that there exists a realm of "truth" which cannot be shaken by any experience, previous or future. It is typical "negativism" to use the intellect in order to prove that the intellect is worthless and must not be used, either anywhere or in certain fields.

This book, however, will deal with much more subtle questions. It will turn out that deviations from "reasonable conduct" creep in almost everywhere, even in the work of the scientist in the so-called exact sciences, unless he continually uses the greatest care. The manner in which the means of language are applied in description and communication requires, at every period in the development of science, a new act of purification, a "purge," which usually lasts only for a short time. In every branch of science that really progresses, there arise continually new auxiliary concepts and the people who learn them are only too prone to misunderstand the tentativeness of their role. It is astounding to see to what degree men tend to misuse the intellectual (and, for that matter, the material) means that they have created themselves. A consequence is that those who go beyond narrowly limited technical fields, or areas of life in which they are at home, find themselves confronted by irresolvable contradictions, unless they are willing to change their conceptions every time. But neither contradictions nor continual changes of viewpoint are reconcilable with reasonable judgments and actions.

We now add to the previous conceptual delineations of positivism the more specific but just as tentative one: It is the aim of positivistic theory to review and to sum up the stock of experience acquired by men in a uniform picture so that mutually consistent judgments are possible in all situations of life.

## II

The first and greatest difficulty in striving for reasonable judgments and in constructing a consistent world picture lies in *language*. It is true and is often stated that our language contains deep wisdom, but it is the wisdom of the primitive, the childhood of mankind. All linguistic elements —words, locutions, grammatical rules—originate in the need to find one's way about in the maze of everyday life. They can be adjusted only with great difficulty to the complicated requirements set by our present stock of knowledge and experience. Anyone who knows a language takes words such as "cause" and "effect," or rules about contingent and causal sentences, as something given, and he can get along with these means in almost all practical situations. But as soon as one tries to go a little deeper into situations that are farther removed from everyday life, it turns out that the world is much less simple than men thought several thousand years ago (when our language was created). All school philosophers from Plato through Kant and Hegel to Husserl and Heidegger have tried to solve the unsolvable problem of deriving a consistent world image by using (and slightly modifying) the stock of ready-made expressions in their language. Present-day logical positivism (which has had rather early predecessors, too) starts from the fact that the "logic" stored in our language represents a primitive stage of science. The positivist, like everybody else, has to use colloquial language in order to make himself understood; but he uses it critically. He knows that all terms in use are conventions which refer to a limited area of experience and beyond that mean nothing. Over and over again he returns to the question: What are the actual experiences and observations that find their expression in a specific word, a sentence, or a theory?

For the positivist, every word, every phrase, of colloquial language means a dissection of the world into three classes. The first class consists of things or situations to which the word, according to the existing linguistic conventions, applies without any doubt. The second class comprises those things for which the word in question is definitely not meant; and the third is formed by all those phenomena for which the linguistic conventions are not sufficient to enable one to decide whether or not the given expression applies. This holds for the simplest words such as "table" and "bed," "above" and "below," "walking" and "running," as well as for more complicated terms such as "cause" and "effect," "body" and "soul," "good" and "evil." In most situations of everyday life and in wide areas of science, we can make use of these familiar linguistic means without having to fear misunderstandings. But these expedients are not sufficient if we go too far beyond the primitive experiences for which they were originally created.

The analysis and critique of language by positivism do not aim to restrict or to prohibit the legitimate use of the standard linguistic means in everyday life, in science, or in poetry. A simple analogy will make this immediately clear. For the greater part of our lives, we regard the earth not as a curved surface but as a plane. We measure distances, distinguish directions, we speak of mountains and valleys, of above and below, as though the surface of the earth were a flat disk. It is only when we undertake a trip around the world, or deal with the time of day on a different hemisphere, that we have to take notice of the spherical shape of the earth. All this is familiar today to everyone who has gone through grammar school. In the not-too-distant future, we hope, men will also understand that concepts such as cause and effect, body and soul, and other expedients of this kind, are not adequate concepts for the conquest of more difficult intellectual problems.

The metaphysician's attitude toward language is entirely different. He thinks that a word, e.g., the word "justice," corresponds, independently of all conventions, to some specific entity, and he seeks to *discover* this entity, i.e., to find the "true" and correct definition of justice. To the positivist the question "What is justice?" can mean only one of two things. Either one wants to find out what in the course of time was denoted by this word within different cultural areas (historical semantics), or one seeks, with a specific aim in mind, to fix a new concept of justice, that is to say, to suggest a new linguistic convention for use within some limited field of action or of science. In the exact sciences the second procedure is the common one. What in mechanics is called "force" or "work" can in no wise be derived from the meanings that these words carry in everyday language.

## III

Everyone who makes efforts to gain knowledge in any field has the natural desire to see this knowledge secured forever. Since scientific assertions are nothing but predictions about future experiences (in what sense this holds also for historical sciences and the other humanities will be explained later), this is nothing but another expression of the general longing for security in life. Hence it is no wonder that at a very early time, the ideal of an unchangeable *"eternal" truth* made itself felt.

For a long time we have known a class of assertions that seemed to satisfy this ideal—the mathematical theorems. That two times six equals twelve, or that thirteen is not divisible by any positive integer but itself and 1, seem entirely without doubt and certain for all future time. Most of Kant's and his successors' epistemology is devoted to the problem how one could arrive at results of the same absolute certainty in other areas, such as, e.g., astronomy. But in Kant's time and even before, there were wiser scholars (above all the English positivists such as Locke and Hume) who knew that these attempts were illusory. However, a satisfactory analysis of the whole situation was initiated only recently, by Ludwig Wittgenstein.

In his *Tractatus Logico-Philosophicus* of 1922, Wittgenstein shows that the theorems of pure mathematics or of logic say absolutely nothing about reality (about the experienceable, observable world), but are, in a specific sense of the word, *tautologies*. This of course does not mean that they are superfluous or self-evident. Sometimes they are very intricate transformations of certain symbol complexes according to fixed rules. Theorems of logic or pure mathematics are said to be "correct" if they are in agreement with the system of accepted definitions and rules, just as in chess only those moves are accepted which are in accordance with the rules of the game. One who knows these rules can decide *once and for all* whether a tautological assertion is true or false (unless there turns out to be an inconsistency in the system), but he has thereby said nothing about any matter of observable fact. That twelve is divisible by three, while thirteen is not, is absolutely correct, but a shepherd can no more divide twelve sheep than thirteen into three absolutely "equal" parts.

The last example also shows in what manner mathematical theorems are applicable to reality. The symbols and transformation rules of logic correspond as an *approximation* to certain facts and relations of everyday life. The wool of each group of four sheep in a flock is approximately equal and, if we are satisfied with this degree of approximation, it is possible to say that a herd of twelve is divisible into three parts and one of thirteen is not. But in this proposition there is nothing left of the absoluteness and exactness of the mathematical theorem. The situation is in no way different in the more complicated problems of geometry or physics in general. The theorems of Euclidean, as well as of non-Euclidean, geometry derived from different systems of axioms are both absolutely correct. The spatial relations, however, that are open to observation correspond only approximately to one or the other system of geometry. Which one we have to use in a given case is a question of better approximation, that is to say, of greater utility, and is thus to a certain degree arbitrary.

Our answer to the Kantian problem of epistemology is therefore this: One can construct in many ways tautological systems in which there exist —according to fixed rules—absolutely correct statements; but if one wants to state anything about relations between observable phenomena, e.g., in astronomy, then one is subject to control by future experiences. The application of mathematical methods can never guarantee the correctness of a nonmathematical proposition.

The opponents of positivism usually claim that we, the positivists, too, believe in certain dogmas and therefore contradict ourselves. Such a dogma of the positivist is allegedly, for instance, the statement: "There are no eternal truths." If we accept this, we are supposed to believe in at least one eternal truth (namely, the foregoing statement), and therefore we refute ourselves. The quoted assertion, however, does not appear in the vocabulary of positivism. As epistemologists we do nothing but what every scientist does: we describe what we observe. We see that there are tautological systems in which one operates with fixed symbols according to accepted rules. We see that the majority of all statements which play any role in practical life and in science originate in observations and are continually tested by experience. Aristotle's mechanics, according to which the circle is the natural orbit of a body, has been replaced by Newton's mechanics, in which the straight line is the path of a body left to itself. In order to take later observations into account, Newton's theory has been replaced by Einstein's, which one can interpret by saying that the inertial orbits are straight lines in a space with a non-Euclidean geometry. Whether or not, sooner or later, even this conception will have to be modified, is something we certainly do not know, or care to make assertions about.

But we also observe that metaphysicians make propositions which are framed in such a way that they neither form parts of an established tautological system nor are testable in experience. Such propositions, if stated by one author, are as a rule opposed by all, or almost all, others. Sometimes they find a group of disciples that is geographically and temporally limited. If one wants to give to these theories, or to one of them, the name "eternal truth," then this is a manner of speaking whose usefulness everybody may judge for himself.

## IV

We do not claim that a scientific theory, either in physics, or in economics, or in any other field, is uniquely determined by the observable facts. Theories are inventions, constructions. A theory is useful if it predicts the phenomena correctly. Different theories may make the same predictions with respect to large areas of facts. Under otherwise equal circumstances one will prefer that theory which covers a larger field of phenomena or which from some point of view appears to be the "simpler." This preference is subjective, and accordingly the acceptance or rejection of a specific theory is to a certain extent arbitrary. The attempts, sometimes made, to decide the usefulness of a theory "scientifically," as for instance by means of the so-called calculus of probability, must be rejected. The calculus of probability itself is a scientific theory of the same kind as any other branch of the exact natural sciences. Its area of application is that of long sequences of repeating occurrences or of mass phenomena. But scientific problems and competing theories in any field do not occur en masse; therefore, it is not possible to ascribe to them a numerical probability. Experience teaches that all theories are constantly subject to larger or smaller modifications and that, as Ernst Mach expressed it, science consists of a continually progressing *adaptation of ideas to facts*.

The positivistic philosophy of science seeks, in the first place, to determine the features that all branches of science have in common. In this sense it speaks of a *unity of science* without overlooking the sometimes wide differences of methodology in the separate disciplines. We prefer not to propose a classification of the sciences in the sense of a hierarchy or a pyramid, because too many points of view cross each other and because the boundaries are unstable. This shows itself in every small sector; the experiment, i.e., observation under artificially produced conditions, plays the main role in physics and chemistry, but almost no role today in astronomy or geology. As far as the extent of the application of mathematical means is concerned, astronomy and geology stand perhaps at opposite ends. There is a continuous formation of theories in physics as well as in geology. The boundary between physics and chemistry is gradually disappearing, astronomy changes into astrophysics, and geology comes to use more and more the methods of physics. As time passes the situation changes quickly, areas split off, others grow into one, and, in the course of one generation, the map of the sciences may assume an entirely different appearance.

The main problem arises when we study the mutual relation of those two groups of sciences which, as a rule, are regarded as complete opposites and even as incompatible: the natural sciences and the humanities. According to a conception that predominates primarily in Germany, not only are these two groups distinct in their methods of research and in the principal meaning of their results, but even the kind of "understanding" of matters of fact that each employs is allegedly totally different. The point of view of this book, which will be discussed in more detail in Part V, is essentially that this dichotomy is untenable. Physics, biology, psychology, the social sciences, history, form a complicated, interconnected web which cannot be bisected by a simple cut. The more we learn about psychosomatic phenomena, the less it is possible to split off a part of psychology as belonging to the "humanities." The social sciences, whose relation to psychology is becoming closer and closer, are accepting in many branches more and more the methods of the natural sciences. The idea that the use of mathematical formalism is a measure of the "scientificness" of a discipline is not shared by us.

Since the time of Ernst Mach, natural scientists have known that the explanation or the theory of a group of phenomena is only a description of the facts on a higher level. In history, the advocates of dualism claim that there are no theories at all but only pure and objective descriptions of occurrences. But such an "objective" report does not exist; otherwise, new historians could not always give new expositions of the same happenings. Even if we leave aside such explicit theories of history as that of Marxism or that of Spenglerism, the theory of a historian consists inherently in the selection and correlation of the facts he mentions. He implies that from certain premises which he reports the adduced occurrences follow and thereby he predicts or implies that under approximately the same circumstances in the future approximately the same thing will happen again. The meteorologist proceeds in the same manner when he describes the course of the weather, which, as a whole, is just as unique an event as the history of men and peoples or the history of the earth, the development of animal species and human races. It is always the search for, and the exposition of, typical and recurring elements *within the unique course of the world* that is the subject of science.

## V

The positivism represented in this book tries to avoid some exaggerations of which other authors in earlier or even recent times have been guilty. For us, metaphysics is not nonsense, poetry is not superfluous, the fine arts and music are legitimate forms of communication among men.

So-called "logical positivism," which was created in the first quarter of this century, has carried through for the first time the idea that epistemology is nothing but a logical study of the language in which scientific results are expressed. Among the founders of the "Vienna Circle" it was particularly Carnap and Neurath who developed in detail the theory that the scientific language can be built up in a consistent manner from uniform simple elements. The element sentences are short, immediately understandable statements about simple sensations (receptions). Later (in Part II) we shall see that this theory is only another form of Mach's doctrine of elements. It is also closely related to Bridgman's so-called "operationalism."

The Vienna scientists have drawn from the logical analysis of the language of science the conclusion that the propositions of metaphysics which cannot be constituted in the above-mentioned manner are meaningless and do not say anything. This is the point in which the present book does not follow the logical positivists. In our conception the decisive concept is that of *connectibility*. The statements of science and the carefully formulated sentences of everyday language are connectible among each other and with a certain stock of linguistic rules. The assertions of metaphysics do not belong to this area. With them the single words or groups of words do not have the meaning that can be derived from or traced back to element sentences. Nevertheless, metaphysical statements can in most cases be given a more or less vague meaning; this is due to the fact that here, too, within limited areas a certain connectibility exists, namely, between the works of a limited metaphysical school and certain rules of language which for them (and only for them) are accepted as valid. In other words, if two physicists talk about the phenomenon of heat conduction they always mean the same thing by the same expressions; but if two metaphysicians develop theories about cause and effect, they usually speak about different things.

The aim of intellectual endeavor of man may in the last analysis consist in the attempt to arrive, for all phenomena that are of some interest, at a description that is connectible across the boundaries of all fields. We are very far, at present, from achieving this final aim. In the meantime the gaps are filled by nonscientific theories, i.e., theories that are not connectible with the language of science. They appear in the form of metaphysics or of religious systems or of poetry. But we do not mean to say that these types of intellectual activity will disappear within the foreseeable future. Anyone who knows a little physics is aware that men continually use up the store of energy of the earth and that the entropy of the planet on which we live continually increases. But the prophecy that sometime all available energy will be exhausted and that we will have to suffer an entropy death does not frighten us. We do not make such extrapolations since *all* conditions change in time; the word "eternity" does not appear in scientific language.

Expressions such as *"eternity"* and *"the beyond," "beauty"* and *"love,"* are familiar words in another language which is called the language of poetry. We do not think of lyrical poetry only or of verses in general, but of all those communications to which the concepts truth and validity are applied in a different sense than to the assertions of everyday life. The story of a novel is not true in the historical sense, but one ascribes to it validity if it agrees with certain experiences of life and if the author has given us insights that stand the test of later experiences. Even lyrical poetry, so far as it is to be taken seriously, expresses experiences of a specific sort. Connectibility is even more limited here than in metaphysics, if one thinks of different single works of poets. But certain basic elements of the poetic language are familiar to such a wide circle of educated men that what is expressed in it seems understandable to more people than scientific theories.

Science and art are much more closely related to each other than the popular (and also the logical) positivism will have us believe. Every work of art can be considered as a *theory* of a specific small section of real life—at any rate, much better as a theory than as an imitation or reproduction. A drama describes the development of a human character by showing us a few single actions or a few moments of his life. A sculpture with the title "The Thinker" even shows only a single face and a single position and claims to tell us something about the nature of an individual engaged in intellectual work. A work of art is neither true nor false, but it can, to a greater or lesser degree, agree with our experiences, previous or future.

Evaluations of works of art are customarily framed with expressions that are related to the word "beauty." Today there will hardly be anyone who still believes that there exists a standard of beauty valid for all times and all peoples. It is the task of a sufficiently general sociology to study in what manner esthetic judgments depend upon the race, the environment, the education, and the personal experiences of the individual. The same holds for all "valuations" in metaphysical systems. At any rate, the positivist does not deny the existence of esthetic needs and he is not opposed to undertakings directed toward their satisfaction.

## VI

Most of the expositions of positivism avoid dealing with the complex of questions pertaining to the modes of conduct of men, usually called *ethics*. We shall not limit ourselves in this way here, particularly since we do not see a sharp dividing line between the intellectual endeavors of men directed toward regulation of general conduct and the other subjects of our investigation.

If an engineer computes the relation between the dimensions of the girders of a bridge and the load that the bridge can stand, he can phrase the result in the form: The bridge *must* have these dimensions. If the physician determines by scientific tests that a certain drug kills certain bacteria, he can make the prescription: The patient *ought to* take this drug. If sociological studies lead us to believe that a specific way of rearing children badly influences their development at a later age, one may fix by law: This kind of upbringing is *prohibited*. In all of these cases the connection between statements of fact and the ought-sentences derived from them is evident. We can formulate it thus: Ought-sentences are elliptic statements; they suppress one part of the implication.

Common opinion has it that there exist also imperatives of another kind. It is felt that the commandments: Thou shalt not steal, or, Thou shalt not kill, are more than expressions of the general experience that the community life of men would be decisively disturbed if stealing and murder were to be practiced to the full extent. Just what this "more" consists of that these ought-sentences allegedly imply is not commonly agreed upon. Some think that certain ethical rules are inherent in men, much as the ability to breathe is. Others believe that certain groups of rules of conduct were communicated to men at a specific historical period by revelation, i.e., without interference of their own intellect.

The first of these assumptions is contradicted by the fact that there are primitive peoples who simply do not know some of the rules of life that seem self-evident to us. The second, religious, conception of the moral laws is invalidated by the fact that the allegedly revealed commandments are so vague and incomplete that their application requires continually new interpretation which, after all, is a work of the intellect. Nobody can say with certainty whether the seventh commandment allows the lending of money at an arbitrarily high rate of interest, whether the fifth commandment includes the case of suicide, of self-defense, of killing in war, and whether it prohibits the sacrifice of an unborn infant in order to save the life of the mother. There can be no doubt that the rules according to which we live and act are an elaborate result of tradition, of continued control by experience, and of conventional decisions.

One usually regards as the main task of ethics the setting up and justification of systems of norms. A justification of a prescription can, as we have seen, only consist of statements that express the relation between the prescribed conduct and certain consequences. Among these consequences the acquisition of feelings of security, of an inner satisfaction, of peace of mind or peace of soul, of general recognition, and so on, take a particular place. Since the reaching of such an aim depends essentially upon the extent to which the same or similar norms of conduct are accepted by others and followed by them, the dispersion of uniform systems of ethics among large communities is a prerequisite for their existence. As a matter of fact, only a few religious doctrines—and these are not so very different from each other in their ethics—have historically survived. Nobody will deny the tremendous influence which the Hellenistic, the Jewish-Christian, the Islamic, the Buddhistic religions and Confucianism have exerted upon the civilization of mankind. But we see no reason in this fact why every single assertion of such a doctrine should not be subject to the same kind of logical critique and continual control by experience as any claim of a scientific theory.

Questions of ethics are frequently raised in connection with the concepts of *value* and *evaluation*. People think that it is possible not only to ascribe to single actions and to the total conduct of a man expressions such as good and evil, but even to bring all actions into an ordered sequence of increasing moral values. Now, it is very easy to order a group of a hundred individuals according to their height or weight, but very difficult or hardly possible in a consistent manner to determine their order with respect to their strength. Further, if one asks for the degree of bodily or mental health of the hundred individuals, the uncertainty and the variety of incompatible points of view become so large that agreement without the explicit introduction of arbitrary standards is entirely unthinkable. In our conception, it is only *one more step* in the same direction if a classification of moral conduct is sought. The question whether there "exists" an objective standard which we just do not know, may be neglected by us. It is certain that agreement on moral values, except in quite rough cases, can be accomplished only within limited communities that have a great part of their life experiences in common.

The introduction and the discussion of such standards of value which fulfill some useful purpose (to which, of course, the satisfaction of feelings of happiness belongs) is without doubt a worthy task; but no useful purpose is served if one tries to mislead oneself or others about the fact that *all* moral systems, including their justification, are creations of the human intellect of a similar kind to scientific theories.

## VII

The most serious objections raised against accepting the positivistic point of view are that it leaves unsatisfied essential needs of men, and that it often proves preferable in one's life not to act strictly according to logic and the scientific method. To a certain extent both of these points are well taken.

As to the first we may make our answer very brief. The aim of a scientific exposition can never be other than an intellectual one, that is to say, to offer information, enlightenment, elucidation of relationships, no matter what feelings of pleasure or displeasure result from these for an individual. Other types of communication, such as poetry, have, in addition, the purpose of creating pleasure, by stimulating certain vague associations with one's previous experience. We are quite aware that a strict delineation of these various forms of mental endeavor is impossible, and we maintain that, as we have stressed above, positivism does not stand for the elimination of any of them. Those who seek satisfaction of their esthetic wants (in the most general sense of the word) from sources other than scientific discourse do not thereby stand in opposition to positivism as we understand it.

To discuss the matter of the pragmatic value, or lack of it, of positivism is much more difficult. The criticism here comes from so many directions and can take on so many different meanings that it is hardly possible even to enumerate them all. We can mention only the most important of these antipositivistic approaches.

"Too clear an insight into the limitations and uncertainties of a theory hinders the creative scientist in his work, which is mainly guided by instinct." Many valuable scientific discoveries, it is true, are due to men who, consciously or unconsciously, kept free of philosophical scruples, who had absolute faith in the validity of the currently accepted auxiliary concepts, and who did not care for questions of epistemology at all. Textbooks of any branch of science are an intertwined mixture of definitions (tautological elements), statements of observation, inductive generalizations, and conclusions of various degrees of exactitude. Not every specialist in a field can analyze or have a full understanding of this entire complex. But it cannot be denied that the great turning points in the development of science were decisively influenced by advances in philosophical enlightenment of a positivistic nature. Newton's creation of the structure of deterministic physics was, in its origin, not independent of the principles of clearness and distinctness of ideas proclaimed about fifty years earlier by Descartes. And in our time, everyone knows that the theory of relativity and the ensuing reorientation of all of physics had their roots in Mach's critique of the foundations of Newtonian mechanics. Presumably it will take another step in the positivistic direction to clear up certain difficulties and inconsistencies in quantum physics, and thus to bring to perfection the present phase of the development of the physical sciences. In the small, in the individual steps or in routine work one may question the usefulness of positivism; in the large it is indispensable.

As far as ordinary happenings in everyday life are concerned, the situation is not much different. Undoubtedly in many cases an instinctive, unpremeditated act is successful, while careful examination of all pros and cons leads to failure. However, what we today, in civilized society, call instinct is to a large extent the product of early training, upbringing, and education, which become effective in not too unusual situations. If one is confronted by difficult tasks, by circumstances that deviate more noticeably from the normal, one seldom relies on intuition or inspiration and is very rarely successful with them.

Occasionally one hears the assertion that the practical consequences of positivism have been invalidated by certain newer results of natural science. Psychoanalysis has uncovered the role of the unconscious in human conduct, and the so-called uncertainty relation of quantum physics, it is alleged, has proved that even in the realm of physics not everything can be subject to measurement. The answer to this is that the "unconscious" of psychoanalysis and the "uncertainty" of quantum mechanics are entirely rational concepts; they may be interpreted in terms of metaphysics only in the same sense in which previously people saw a metaphysical element in the "action-at-a-distance" of gravitation or in all electrical phenomena. In the same category belongs the quaint belief that certain psychosomatic phenomena, once they are thoroughly studied, will be something else than just a new chapter of the rational explanation of nature.

The most decided opposition to the positivistic point of view comes from those circles which claim the existence of an absolute (religious) authority for the solution of all vital problems. As pointed out above, a system that anticipates all situations that might ever occur is impossible, and a new interpretation of the laws of religion by intellectual means continually proves necessary. History shows how much, in spite of all its apparent conservatism, the practical position of the Church with respect to factual questions (e.g., in the treatment of heretics) changes. Those who close their eyes to such changes and, in their daily lives, follow the prescriptions of their Church as they stand at the given moment can gain peace of soul and happiness to which positivism has nothing comparable to offer. However, whether a Christian Scientist who later becomes aware that, by neglecting rational actions, he has caused permanent damage to his own or other people's lives can keep his peace of soul, is, to say the least, questionable.

Positivism does not claim that all questions can be answered rationally, just as medicine is not based on the premise that all diseases are curable, or physics does not start out with the postulate that all phenomena are explicable. But the mere possibility that there *may* be no answers to some questions is no sufficient reason for not looking for answers or for not using those that are attainable.

This is particularly true for that complex of questions so vital to all of us that arise from the community life of large and ever larger groups of people. The problem has been the same for thousands of years: to find a just balance between, on one hand, the social requirements of planning and organization made necessary by the steady increase and the growing density of population, and, on the other hand, the desire for individual freedom. The two strongest political powers of the present take pains to emphasize exclusively either one or the other of these two extremes, and each regards those who pay heed to the other side as mortal enemies. On both sides scholars try to prove, by what are apparently the available scientific means, that this one-sidedness is justified. In the last analysis, they base their attempts (not with full justification) upon ideological systems of an extremely metaphysical character—the one side upon the doctrines of the Church, and the other upon Hegel's absolutistic world of ideas. If this goes on, the predictions of those who believe that the next step toward the solution of the basic sociological problems must come from the physical annihilation of one of the two groups of people will be borne out.

In our opinion the only way out is less loose talk and more criticism of language, less emotional acting and more scientifically disciplined thinking, less metaphysics and more positivism.

# language

Unsere ganze Philosophie ist Berichtigung des Sprachgebrauchs.
All our philosophy is improvement of language.

*Lichtenberg*

Une science n'est qu'une langue bien faite.
A branch of science is nothing else than a well-constructed language

*Condillac*

# introductory remarks

1. *The Question.* Almost all communications between men, and above all those between an author and his readers, are by means of language. This fact determines to a large extent not only the form but also the content and the limitations of these messages. It is therefore reasonable that a treatise whose intent is that of enlightening and of furthering insight first of all casts a glance at the difficulties arising from the use of linguistic means of expression. It will soon become apparent of what decisive importance for our problems the examination of the properties of language is. However, we shall not pursue here any linguistic, philologic, or literary investigations in the narrower sense, but discuss language only in so far as it forms the essential *tool* of our study. Later we shall return to its use as a means of art, in poetry (Chapter 23), and to other questions connected with language. In this first Part we are only interested in this:

*To what extent and in what way do the actual structure of language and the limitations of linguistic expression influence what we have to say in this book?*

2. *Speaking about Language.* We immediately encounter a peculiar difficulty: that everything we say *about* language has to be said by *means* of language. It might seem that this situation prevents any reasonable treatment of the problem; and indeed many authors have given up all hope of the possibility of a solution. However, an analogy from an entirely different field may serve to show how unjustified this pessimism is.

We may consider the situation as it presents itself in any branch of today's so highly developed industrial technology. In order to make a mechanical tool one has to use a great number of *equal or similar* tools. But even more, the construction of an elaborate instrument, e.g., a rolling mill, presupposes the existence of many other industries, plants, railroads, and mines, for whose construction in turn rolling mills were used. We know that this quite complicated system, however difficult it may be to *look through* all its details, functions well, and we are convinced that its gradual development can be analyzed in a rational way. What can be manufactured at one time depends upon what was manufactured before. At first men used simple, natural means as tools, e.g., sharp stones, for the construction of commodities. Then, by using the objects thus manufactured, *beyond their original purpose,* for the creation of new tools, men gradually came to have at their disposal the most complicated instruments of manufacture, such as a rolling mill.

Likewise, the human language originally consisted of natural sound reflexes and was, as Nietzsche said, "used only in order to communicate the simplest troubles of life among the sufferers." From these beginnings, step by step, developed today's civilized languages. At every intermediate point of the development the means of expression at hand were used, beyond their original scope, to complete and improve the language by new conventions. The creation of new linguistic agreements which lead beyond the existing state is a part of the function of language at any stage of its history. In the last analysis the attempt to discuss by means of language the limits of linguistic expression is only a part of this never-ceasing process of new "conventions."

*To speak about language is not, then, a contradictory process, necessarily leading to confusion; on the contrary, it forms a legitimate, and as we shall see later, decisively important part of all scientific activity, i.e., of all endeavor directed toward information and enlightenment.*

3. *Change of Usage.* If one seeks an insight into the process of the creation and development of language, one has three means at his disposal, which have to be used concurrently. In the first place there is the study of the historical linguistic documents, especially the oldest records; then the examination of the still living, more or less rudimentary languages of primitive peoples; and finally the observation of children and adults who are learning a language. In addition, one might mention experiment, that is, observation under artificially created circumstances. Research along these lines has uncovered valuable details, most of which are outside of what we are interested in here. There is a remarkable point of view, mainly held by English scientists, according to which language in the beginning was to be understood not only as a means of communication between acting and suffering men, but as an action itself. Among the modern German philologists it was above all Hugo Schuchardt who gave factually well-founded explanations of the origins of language. These are laudably distinguished from the older fantasies which usually strayed into metaphysics.

As far as language as a tool is concerned, the following idea presents itself in extension of the analogy introduced earlier. For material work we know E. Hartig's so-called law of the "change of usage," which governs the development of mechanical tools: Every existing tool is tried out, at some time or another, for new, not originally intended, purposes and thereby undergoes certain changes directed toward these purposes, which then lead to the creation of a new type of tool. In the same way, one tries continually to express by means of the existing linguistic elements (word roots, word forms, word and sentence combinations, modes of expression) every new experience. But for adaptation to the new situations, one often has to introduce little changes, which sometimes last, replacing the old form or, perhaps, adding to it. In this fashion the language is continually modified and enriched by adaptation in the "change of usage." Hermann Paul calls this in his *Principien der Sprachgeschichte* "deviations in the individual application from the usual which gradually become the usual."

This process of adaptation is by no means limited to the formation of language in the narrower sense. Ernst Mach recognized as the essential mark of the development of science, that it consists in a continual adaptation of thought to newly discovered facts. In this case too we see the functioning of the law of the "change of usage." The creation of language is, indeed, only the forerunner of the creation of science and we cannot draw a sharp dividing line between the two. "It is originally language which works at the formation of concepts, at later times it is science" (Nietzsche).

*Language develops, as does science later, primarily in such a way that existing means are modified for the sake of adaptation to new problems; part of these changes are retained and serve to enrich the stock.*

4. *Magic of Language.* Since we have touched, even though only as an aside, on the earliest steps of the development of language, we cannot completely pass over a phenomenon traces of which can still be found even in the contemporary use of speech. Among primitive peoples certain names, words, syllables, or sentences have a magic *connotation.* The mere pronunciation of these words, or their pronunciation in connection with certain actions, is supposed to have immediate observable effects, that is, effects that occur without the interference of persons who perceive the words and react upon them. Explorers of distant lands, as well as students of our own early history, tell of these magic formulas, conjurations, and oaths; not to speak of numerous remainders still existing in our own environment. We know today that the assumption of such effects is false, i.e., they are not confirmed by repeatable, critical observation. However, the striking thing worth stressing here is the degree to which men are capable of misunderstanding the meaning of an instrument which they—although unconsciously and through generations—have created themselves.

This phenomenon becomes even more pronounced in the case of a written formula than of a spoken one. Writing undoubtedly developed much later and in a much more advanced state of culture, as a means of communication between persons apart in space or time or both. The incidental formation of the belief that by means of the written word, even without the intervention of a person who reacts toward the message, one could effect changes in the external world can perhaps be explained as an unsuccessful attempt at a "change of usage." When in the fifteenth century a new technique of communication was created in the art of printing, enlightenment was already too far advanced; otherwise someone might have been struck by the idea that by printing a curse in a thousand copies an enemy could actually be destroyed.

From these naïve fantasies about the magic effects of language and writing we have to distinguish clearly the question of the influence upon the speaker or writer himself. A prayer spoken in a low voice to oneself, a thought formulated in writing, these create factual situations which influence the mental condition of the agent and through this channel may act upon the external world. The detailed examination of such effects is certainly an interesting problem of psychology; but it lies outside our present study.

*We shall, in the following, study language only in so far as it serves as communication between different persons; "magic" effects of words, etc. and their reaction upon the speaker will remain outside of our investigation.*

5. *Instinctive Learning.* From now on we shall limit our observations to contemporary languages, by which we mean, unless explicitly stated otherwise, one of the known civilized languages, e.g., that of this book. We shall later (Chapter 4, 2) return to the point that the differences existing within the thus limited group of languages are not of decisive importance for the problems that interest us here. In what, then, consists the *learning* of such a language?

The child who does not yet know any other language assimilates connections between different experiences on the one hand and a particular class of experiences, those of hearing and formulating linguistic expressions, on the other. Certain phenomena open to the child's observation adults accompany by sounds and the child gradually begins to imitate them. An enormous number of linguistic rules are almost unconsciously impressed upon the youthful mind. We can mention here only the most important categories of such rules: the demarcation of the meaning of nouns; the grammatical expression of relations between things, persons and their actions; the mastery of the I-you-he; the appearance of abstracta, of such expressions as "ought," "want," "may"; rules of word formation, the inconveniences of homonyms, synonyms and ambiguity; finally, the construction of sentences and sentence groups, governed by rules of a logical kind. All this, offered without order and system, becomes gradually, by a process of assimilation, the property of the child learning his mother tongue and is soon handled without difficulty. Small wonder that after this almost instinctive and certainly unconscious assimilation of the linguistic means the vast majority of mankind confronts its language without any readiness for critique. One is quite justified in saying that he who has not learned at least one foreign language under conditions other than those of childhood is hardly prepared for any kind of scientific research (Chapter 4, 1).

*No attempt at comprehension and mental re-creation of the world —and only that is the purpose of science—can be successful as long as language is handled uncritically, i.e., as long as one relies upon what he has instinctively learned in childhood and does not go back to the original relation between the elements of language and the experiences coördinated with them.*

6. *Limitation to the Written Word.* In the following chapter we shall consider how the best-known school philosophers have dealt with the problem of language. But first let us formulate a little more precisely what will be the exact object of our inquiry.

One usually distinguishes between a spoken and a written or printed text, in that the former shows a much greater variety, since there the distinctions of pronunciation and emphasis are added. We shall now agree that in what follows we are going to mean by a word, a sentence, or a text, only its image fixed by the script or print. That is, we shall neglect all modifications due to a varied manner of articulation (diction, stress, dialect). Of course, we accept the customary conventions concerning the equivalence (mutual interchangeability) of different sign forms like a, *a,* **a,** etc. Only in abbreviations, including mathematical formulas, may a and *a* mean something different. But if we suppose in these cases that the abbreviations are written out as "roman a," or "italic a," then we can keep the above-mentioned conventions.

The limitation to the written image in the foregoing sense is indeed a far-reaching and essential simplification of our problem. For every linguistic expression is thus reduced to a combination of a finite number of different signs: the letters, a few punctuation signs, signs for the end of a word (interval), signs for "capital letter," "new paragraph," "italics," etc. While one may perhaps be justified in supposing that the spoken words form a continuous manifold (and also show a much greater differentiation in their immediate effect upon the listener), in the case of the written text one always deals, according to the conventions of interchangeability of signs, with a finite number of combinations. On the other hand, there is no reason to be afraid that by this confinement to the written text we may lose or exclude anything essential for a scientific critique of linguistic expression. All sentences that form a part of science must in their written or printed form be totally and completely discernible by anybody who knows the conventions of the writing in question. The amount of knowledge or experience one needs for the *interpretation* of what one has read is an entirely different question. (These considerations are not applicable to the Chinese script; there the correspondence of the written to the spoken word is a much looser one.)

*The objects of our analysis, in so far as we deal with "language," are the combinations of conventional signs, which are "read" according to certain rules of mutual equivalence, and the relation of these groups of signs to the remaining world of experience.*

7. *Improvement of the Use of Language.* To the foregoing discussion of the finitude of linguistic expressions we shall now add another short note which will close these introductory remarks.

One should not expect that all possibilities of human experience form a "countable" class, i.e., that it should be, in principle, possible to account for everything that can be experienced by men in an ordered fashion, one after the other. For instance, we believe that the sensations of color which the eye transmits to us form a continuous manifold of at least several dimensions (perhaps of infinitely many). Even richer, it seems, are the possible gradations of our feelings; here the thought of a countability, of a "numerability," of all feelings seems actually absurd. Remembering, in contrast to this, that everything that can be expressed in writing is only a combination of a few scores of different signs in a great but nevertheless finite number of possibilities, one is necessarily driven to the conclusion of the extraordinary inadequacy and poverty of language. Many philosophers and other writers have indeed been profuse with the most pessimistic and desperate lamentations in this respect.

On the other hand, we also know the most enthusiastic praise, coming especially from poets, of the unbounded possibilities of expression, of the flexibility and adaptability of cultivated languages to all imaginable experience. Many works of poetry really make one confident that, at least in certain areas of feeling, there is hardly any experience that would not be open to linguistic expression.

There is also the widespread belief that by the use of words much more is accomplished than meets the eye. Morris Cohen, a contemporary, otherwise judicious writer, who accepts the viewpoint of positivism in many respects, confesses:

I am a mystic in holding that all words point to a realm of being deeper and wider than the words themselves.

He does not elaborate on what this realm consists of.

A composed, more factual appraisal of the situation will keep us from extreme pessimism as well as from an easy overenthusiasm for what has so far been accomplished in developing our language. We learn in mathematics that with a formula consisting only of a few signs one often commands much more than a "finite" area of thought. On the other hand, we also see that there are limits which one cannot transcend. Thus we summarize in short form what we have said so far and what will be borne out in the following text:

*Language, created by men for certain purposes and being in continuous development, is a tool whose application shows many shortcomings. We are as disinclined to camouflage these shortcomings romantically as to infer from their presence the impossibility of the application of language to our problems. But it seems imperative to us to test the tool critically over and over again in so far as it is used. In a certain sense everything contained in this book is, to speak with Lichtenberg, an attempt at an "improvement of the use of language."*

### CHAPTER 2

# language in the school philosophy

1. *The School Philosophers.* We accept the expression "School Philosophy" in the sense introduced by Philipp Frank, as an abbreviation for the entirety of doctrines usually taught in the philosophy courses of, for instance, a contemporary university. As everybody knows, these theories are in great part in mutual contradiction, much more so than the valid results of a positive science, e.g., geodesy. In addition, the line of division is often uncertain between what belongs to traditional philosophy and what belongs either to a positive science or to reflective poetry, or forms a part of the class of statements to which nobody pays much attention at all. Nevertheless, there is a common core, not so much of the content of statements as of outlook, in which the majority of philosophers agree; witness the existence of philosophic congresses as well as the fact that there is agreement in the personal recognition of a number of outstanding representatives of the school philosophy of the past. The elements common to school philosophy on the whole are most easily recognizable and distinct in the philosophy of the so-called German Idealism. We shall therefore mostly refer to this line of thought when we speak about school philosophy in this book.

Let it be explicitly stated here that neither the choice of the expression "school philosophy" nor the way in which we are henceforth to quote its views implies any deprecatory intentions. We shall show (Part VI) that even that section of classical philosophy, known under the name "metaphysics," which seems farthest removed from our own point of view, fulfills a quite distinct and important role in those endeavors directed toward an intellectual comprehension and classification of experience with which this book is concerned. On the other hand, we do not aim at any kind of historical completeness, and we shall never claim in any respect to have given full valuation to earlier accomplishments of philosophy. We may express what we intend to do thus:

*We shall discuss in this chapter, incidentally and without intention of complete historical recording, some points of view of past and present competent philosophers, in so far as we think that this may throw light upon the questions with which we are concerned.*

2. *Kant's Analytical Judgments.* Kant, the originator of the so-called critical philosophy, treated language less critically than most of his predecessors and successors. Many of his doctrines, indeed, are comprehensible only on the supposition that the customary expressions of everyday language, or at least of the language used among educated people, have a fixed, "objective" meaning beyond all possible doubt.

For instance, in order to explain the difference between an analytic and a synthetic judgment, this being one of the essential points of the *Critique of Pure Reason*, Kant gives us the following example:

> That bodies are extended is not an empirical judgment, but a proposition which stands firm a priori . . . I can cognize beforehand by analysis the conception of body through the characteristics of extension, impenetrability, shape, etc., all of which are cogitated in this conception.

Note that he says "cognize" and not "define." Then he goes on:

> Now I extend my knowledge and, looking back on experience from which I had derived this conception of body in the first place, I find weight at all times connected with the above characteristics, and therefore I synthetically add to my conceptions this as a predicate and say: "all bodies are heavy."

This exemplifies quite unambiguously that in Kant's opinion what one has to understand by a "body" is definitely fixed from the start. Somehow it was decided or predestined by the nature of our mind that the properties of extension, impenetrability, shape, etc., belong to the concept "body," i.e., to the entity denoted by this word of our language, but that the property of weight does not belong to it (although *all* bodies, according to Kant, are heavy). Kant does not seem to have realized that one could as well use a different delineation of the meaning of the word "body" such that, for instance, impenetrability does not belong to the concept itself. The concept "body" is, in Kant's opinion, "abstracted from experience" and in this way unambiguously determined.

In the last analysis this expresses an old idea dating back to Aristotle, according to which one can assign to every noun a "definition" which *discloses* the "essence" of what is denoted by the word.

Surely one can in various ways form sentences in which the synthetic character of the law of gravity is immediately apparent; for instance, one can say: "A stone in the vicinity of the earth is subject to the force of gravity." Here it is unimportant how one delineates in detail the meaning of the word "stone"; the connection between being near the earth and the gravitational attraction contains obviously a fact of experience that nobody could call analytic. What, however, becomes impossible as soon as one foregoes the naïve idea of language as something absolutely given, is this: to formulate a purely analytic judgment in Kant's sense. We may perhaps say: "A river contains water." And that is analytic if we think of the customary everyday meaning of the words "river" and "water." But if in the Asiatic oil lands oil flows in a river bed, or if one is reminded that the word "water" is not as unambiguous as it seems at first sight, then the nicely "analytic" statement loses not only its analytic character, but also even its general validity.

We shall return later to the *factual* questions connected with the distinction between analytic and synthetic judgments (tautologies and statements from experience; Chapter 10, 1). Here we shall only state:

> The concept of analytical judgments in Kant is founded upon the tacit assumption that the words of colloquial language have a definite fixed content of meaning which does not depend upon more or less arbitrary convention.

3. *Definitions and Theorems.* It is a peculiarity characteristic of the entire school philosophy that the borderline between terminological and factual questions, between definitions and contentful statements, is continually neglected. This conduct has its deeper root in the uncritical treatment of language. We shall first illustrate it with another example from Kant.

In the *Critique of Judgment* (Part I, Chap. 5), we find, for instance, the following:

> That which gratifies a man is called pleasant; that which merely pleases him is beautiful; that which is esteemed or approved by him . . . is good.

One could take this to be merely a definition of the concepts "pleasant," "beautiful," "good," if one could assume that the other expressions appearing in the sentence, such as "gratify," "please," etc., are already known to the reader. In that case the meaning of the sentence would be this: Whenever in the ensuing theory the word "beautiful" is used, its meaning shall be the one just stated. But later we find this sentence in Kant:

> Beauty is the form of the purposiveness of an object so far as this is perceived in it without any representation of a purpose.

Is this supposed to tell us that for the entire meaning of the concept "beautiful," as it was fixed by the previous definition, this new statement is true? Kant, of course, does not wish to say that. For him none of these assertions is a pure definition and none is a pure inference from any definition. Every statement that he makes is a coördinated part of an assertion or a description of something that exists independently of any arbitrary definition and that is generally called "beauty," just as the zoölogist enumerates the qualities of the genus *Canis domesticus*, each of which can be verified by observation of a specific object.

The tacit assumption is, as we see, that the legitimate use of the word "beautiful" covers an entity that can be described as precisely as one wishes, in analogy to the way one could describe a zoölogical genus. (The restriction "legitimate" is necessary; for idiomatic expressions like "beautiful weather" or "a beautiful piece of work" are, presumably, outside of Kant's considerations.) We are not concerned here with the content of Kant's esthetic theory (see Chapter 24, 3), and neither do we intend to deny all merit to his point of view. But it remains remarkable that Kant never mentions and probably is not even aware of the fact that the whole problem is *created* by a certain parlance which may be somehow justified but which is, by its very nature, vague and changing. In fact, various philosophical schools fight (at times in the most vigorous manner) about what beauty "really is," whereas it can be only a philologic-historical question to determine what contents of thought have been connected with this word during a certain period and within a certain community of language and culture (see Chapter 24, 3–5). This fight about words is the starting point of all of esthetics as a philosophical discipline, and the situation would be exactly the same in the science of mechanics if it were to use as point of departure an explanation of what motion "really is."

Present-day school philosophers have not changed much in this respect. William James, whose Pragmatism has a distinctly empiricist trend, devotes an entire book to the *Meaning of Truth*. One of the questions that he discussed at considerable length is this: Suppose *A* and *B* are two mutually exclusive states of affairs of antediluvian planetary history and we accept the proposition that it is never to be known which one of the two, *A* or *B*, has taken place; is there a truth at all about these facts? In our opinion this is a purely linguistic question. Whether the answer is yes or no, it is in either case a statement only about the conventional use of the word "truth," contributing nothing to our knowledge beyond a detail on the usage of language (see also Chapter 3, 1).

*Many problems of school philosophy are of this type: Expressions, referring in ordinary language to a very vague and varying content of experience, are supposed to have some "objective" meaning and then attempts are made to "disclose" this meaning by a kind of definition.*

4. *Linguistic Carelessness of Schopenhauer.* In the first part of his main work, *The World as Will and Idea* (Chap. 9), Schopenhauer presents a "little incidental discussion" of the delineation of concept meanings and of the importance of such investigations for philosophy. There we find, among other things, accompanied by little drawings, the statement that the

concept "horse" is contained in the concept "animal"; that the concepts "flower" and "red," on the other hand, overlap one another, etc. Then there follows a big table showing the relations between the concept "traveling (peregrinari)" and about two dozen other concepts. Among them are *utile ditans, quaestuosum, negotia promovens, ad quaelibet idoneum reddens,* and others. Each of these concepts is represented in the drawing by a little circle and the various overlappings of these circles form the subject of the discussion. Nowhere does the author mention that he is dealing only with *words* about whose exact content probably no two philosophers would agree.

It is quite intentional that Schopenhauer chooses Latin words instead of German ones for the denotation of the various conceptual areas. He escapes in this way the effects of the temporal variation of meaning, i.e., of the continuous change of content to which any expression of a living language is subjected. Today, indeed, about a hundred years after the publication of his work, hardly any of these terms would be understood exactly as Schopenhauer intended them to be, had he quoted them in German. If a dead language is used, the interpretation is based upon the usage of the word in the recorded and preserved literature, to which nothing more can be added. But nevertheless, what vagueness and uncertainty still remain! The idea that by fixing the conceptual spheres in their mutual relations only a first step has been taken toward a definition, toward a more or less *arbitrary* delineation of the conceptual content, does not occur to Schopenhauer at all.

One may think that these remarks apply only to a rather unimportant point in Schopenhauer's philosophy. However, in criticizing Kant Schopenhauer says:

> He who is himself clear to the bottom, and knows with perfect distinction what he thinks and wishes, will never write indistinctly, will never set up wavering and indefinite conceptions, compose most difficult and complicated expressions from foreign languages to denote them, and use these expressions constantly afterwards . . . as, for example, "transcendental synthetic unity of apperception."

This shows that it was one of the fundamental principles of Schopenhauer to get along with words of an ordinary language and not to introduce specifically created terms which then are consistently maintained, as one finds frequently in Kant and everywhere in science (see Chapter 4, 4 and 5). Quite characteristically, Schopenhauer thought that the meaning of expressions of everyday language is less vague and uncertain than the meaning of artificial terms. Thus he believed that when he talked about the "will in nature" he did not create a new, modified concept of "will," but that he subordinated new matters of fact to the already existing customary concept "will." Even the most daring statement of his philosophy, "The world is our will," he wants to have understood in such a way that the word "will" denotes in this connection

by no means an unknown quantity, something arrived at only by inference, but is fully and immediately comprehended and so familiar to us that we know and understand what will is far better than anything else whatsoever.

Time and again, at the most essential parts of the theory, we find him appealing to an insight on the part of the reader that in the last analysis rests upon nothing but the knowledge of customary language. We see that:

In fundamental doctrines, on which their entire system rests, philosophers sometimes use seemingly familiar but actually vague words, whose ordinary meanings are most difficult to comprehend, as if they were self-explanatory.

5. *Misunderstood Terminology.* We shall add here an example from the newer philosophical literature which shows how sometimes quite incidental and unessential details of language give rise to far-reaching philosophical assertions. Hans Vaihinger, the Kant critic and creator of the widely known *Philosophy of the "As If,"* deals in his main work with, among other things, the so-called mathematical "fictions." In the following particular case he wants to show as an example that the assertion "the circle is a special case of an ellipse" is such a *fiction.* In this connection he discourses about "circle" and "ellipse" as follows:

The conceptual formula for the ellipse includes, for instance, the existence of two foci, which then, of course, must be a finite distance apart. The distance itself is undetermined and it may be arbitrarily large or arbitrarily small. As long as this condition is satisfied, we have an ellipse. But now it is an objective and undeniable fact that the closer the foci move to each other, the more nearly the ellipse becomes a circle. From this it follows that, if this distance has disappeared altogether, the ellipse has become a circle . . . However, this last transition from one kind to the other is only possible by a sudden jump, which leads into a quite new territory. The definition of an ellipse demands that it have an eccentricity, in that it have two foci $F$ and $F'$ with the distance $2e = m$. We get an entirely different shape if this distance disappears. Between the existence of $m$ and its nonexistence there is absolutely no third possibility. The concept "ellipse" contains $m$ as a variable element. I can increase or decrease $m$ in arbitrary intervals, and the ellipse remains always an ellipse; as long as $m$ has a finite value I stay in the same class. If I omit $m$, I enter a new territory. Thus there is no continuous transition from the ellipse to the circle. The transition from the ellipse to the circle is undeniably discontinuous. As much as I change the ellipse quantitatively, I will never effect by this a change in quality, i.e., in kind. Ellipses and circles are not connected with each other without a discontinuity. There is a clear break across which there is no bridge. There is nothing intermediate between a decrease and a disappearance or between something and nothing.

The mathematically trained reader will find fault with this long-winded discussion in that the transition from an ellipse to a circle is exactly what is called "continuous" in mathematics according to precise definitions. However, that is not essential here. For the definitions of mathematics and the mathematical usage of certain words are by no means obligatory outside the area of mathematical deductions. The mathematician gives for the word "ellipse" a definition that leaves open the question whether the eccentricity $m$ has a positive value or is zero; thus *for him* the circle falls under the heading "ellipse." If Vaihinger wants to adopt a different definition and call "ellipse" only a curve for which $m$ is not equal to zero, that he has a perfect right to do. Then he *has* to say that the circle is not an ellipse. He has thereby merely introduced a certain linguistic usage for himself. In no case is there a need for his long discussion of the difference in "kind." But there is still more to be said about Vaihinger's comments.

The so called equilateral hyperbola stands in exactly the same relation to the general hyperbola as the circle to the ellipse; for the former, the difference between the two semiaxes (the real and the imaginary) is equal to zero, while for the general hyperbola it has an arbitrary value. Hence there are the possibilities of defining the hyperbola in such a way that the zero case is excluded or included. The only difference between the situation in the case of the ellipse and in the case of the hyperbola is this: There is no separate *word* in use for the equilateral hyperbola in analogy to the word "circle." It therefore does not even occur to Vaihinger to find fault with the assertion that the equilateral hyperbola is a special case of the hyperbola and to claim that there is a clear break between the equilateral hyperbola and all others. If there were a customary name for this curve, e.g., "quadrix," then Vaihinger would have to declare the statement "the quadrix is a hyperbola" to be a fiction, exactly like the fiction that calls the circle an ellipse. Those familiar with the history of nomenclature in mathematics know how much the introduction of a name often depends upon mere accident. This example shows to what extent a philosophical theory like that of the "as if," or of fictionalism, is based upon purely linguistic states of affairs which from the point of view of the discipline in question, here mathematics, can only be called accidental, and in any case are quite unessential.

*Many a philosophical theorem is based merely upon a misunderstanding of the nomenclature, i.e., of the assignment of certain terms to specific states of affairs, often due to mere historical accident (see Chapter 4, 6).*

6. *Predilection for Generalities.* We may now quote a contemporary philosophical school that seriously attempts to clarify the relation between the words of colloquial language and the phenomena they represent; this is

the school of phenomenology, founded by E. Husserl and today enjoying a large following in all countries. A large part of the *Logical Investigations* of Husserl deals with this question, but his treatment is very different from the one in our book. A short sample may suffice to show this; Husserl says:

I speak of *my inkwell,* and immediately the inkwell itself stands in front of me; I see it. The name denotes the object of perception and denotes it by means of the significant act expressing itself in kind and form by means of the name. The relation between name and that which is named shows in this unitary state a certain *descriptive character,* which we have already noticed: the name my inkwell, so to speak, "applies itself" to the perceived object. It, so to speak, belongs to it intimately, so that one can *feel* it. But this belonging is of a unique kind. After all, the words do not belong to the objective relation, here the physical-material, which they express. In that they have no place. They are not meant as something in or on the things they denote. If we go back to the experiences, we find on the one hand . . . the acts of appearance of words, on the other, the similar acts of the appearance of things. In the latter respect we are confronted in the perception by the inkwell. According to our repeated stress upon the descriptive nature of perception, this means phenomenologically nothing but that we experience a certain sequence of happenings of the class of perceptions, made one by such and such a determined consecution and spiritualized by a certain act-character of "comprehension" which lends them an objective meaning. This act-character has the result that an *object,* just this inkwell, appears to us in the manner of perception. And in a similar fashion, of course, the appearing word constitutes itself in an act of perception or imagination.

This short excerpt can certainly not give a complete picture of Husserl's frequently rather subtle investigations. But it does give us an insight into the manner—so different from ours—in which the school philosophy treats its problems, which are partly also ours. We too believe that words are "not meant as something in or on the things they denote," but are rather their names. However, we do not think that one can elucidate this fact by a very great number of words each of which is the name of an extremely vague situation, impossible to determine exactly, e.g., "spiritualized (durchgeistigt)," "act-character," "to lend an objective meaning," etc. It is not that the problems raised by the philosophers seem to us simple or trivial. It will surely take a great deal of intensive research work before we shall have a clearer insight into the correspondence between words and the rest of our experiences, or between the appearance of words and the appearance of things, as Husserl puts it. That one can anticipate this research work by constructing an involved scheme of words that works only because *their* relation with things remains largely undetermined is the belief characteristic of the school philosophy, and we cannot accept it.

One could object that every explanation of a matter of fact must make use of linguistic expressions which are themselves not entirely explained.

However, the example of the positive sciences shows that a construction step by step *is* possible, such that, even though vagueness cannot be completely eliminated, undefined and undefinable general terms do not form its basis. If a physicist explains the necessary parts of a radio, or the linguist, the rules of shifting of consonants from Latin to French, then both are moving within an area of speech in which communication is practically unambiguous. It is the position of this book that in all questions that we admit, only discussions of this "factual" kind should be allowed.

*Characteristic of the school philosophy—in contrast to the positive sciences—is the belief that by the use of specially created but not definable general terms like "essence of things," "immanent truth," "spiritualizing," etc., difficult situations can be clarified.*

7. *Mauthner's Critique of Language.* If we now close this short sequence of quotations from some representatives of school philosophy, the reason is not that we think the subject matter is thereby exhausted. On the contrary, time and again we shall return to this theme (which will turn out to be a *leitmotiv* of our discussion), namely, to what extent all so-called philosophical problems are connected with the actual limits of linguistic expressibility. On the other hand, we could without difficulty multiply the cited examples, by going back further in history as well as by considering more recent publications. However, only two quite short notes may be added.

One of the oldest and most popular doctrines of school philosophy is that of the Platonic Ideas. "There are," says Plato in the tenth book of the *Republic,* "many tables and many bedsteads . . . but there are only two concepts of these objects: that of *the* table and that of *the* bed." Thus, he concludes from the existence of the word "table" and the multitude of the really existing tables, all of which are different from one another, that there must be something else—something that shares with the *word* the "unity," and with the visible tables the "real existence." This hypothesis will be examined more closely later on (Chapter 3, 1 and 2).

From Plato down to our day, school philosophers have almost continually struggled with the difficulties of language. Finally, in recent years, from their own ranks arose a severe censurer, Fritz Mauthner, who in the six volumes of his *Contributions to a Critique of Language* reached some results that we can certainly accept. But neither his basic position nor the majority of his discussions emerge in our opinion sufficiently from the compass of traditional school philosophical prejudices—in spite of the inexorable way in which the author seems to criticize most philosophers. His main idea, "that cognizance of the world is impossible by means of language . . . that language is not fit as a tool for knowledge," is not acceptable to us, as we have already mentioned (Chapter 1, 7). For we have no other means of communication than language and it can therefore only be our task to eliminate so far as possible the effects of its shortcomings in the endeavor of building up a scientific structure. Mauthner seems to enjoy the pleasure of accusing language of its frailties, faults, and contradictions; but he tests its services almost entirely with problems of school philosophy, which are by their very nature unsolvable, such as that of the "objective investigation" of the "real world," etc. He also believes rather firmly that results of the positive sciences can be replaced or anticipated by the outcome of philosophical speculation. Nevertheless, however great its weaknesses, it would have been beneficial to the advance of knowledge if the professional philosophers had not ignored almost entirely Mauthner's critique, which perhaps for the first time showed how much the *whole* of philosophy is a question of language.

*From the beginning to the present day, it has been a characteristic trait of school philosophy that it deals with language uncritically, i.e., that it employs the means of ordinary language without hesitation for purposes for which they are neither meant nor suited. Mauthner's attempt at a Critique of Language is not successful, because he takes the basic ideas and problems of school philosophy for granted.*

### CHAPTER 3

# some points of logical grammar

1. *Denotations in Ordinary Language.* We now want to consider a few simple facts about the use of language, the discussion of which will be helpful for our later studies. In a certain general sense one may call such propositions "grammatical" rules, even though at times they go beyond what is called grammar in linguistic science. Occasionally the expression "logical grammar" has been suggested, and for the sake of simplicity we are going to adopt that name here.

Everybody who knows the English language knows what the word "table" denotes. That is, about most of the things confronting him he can decide without difficulty whether or not the word "table" is applicable to them. But it is also certain that any knowledge of the English language, however perfect, is not sufficient to enable one to make such a decision about *every possible* object. Is a box, turned upside down, upon which dinner is served, a table or a box that "serves as a table"? A table for children, a table for dolls: these are still tables. But is this true of an object of the same shape being only a tenth of an inch high? Is a bedside cabinet, sometimes also called a bedside table, a table or not? Where are the limits? Are they dependent upon size at all, or only upon shape, or upon the purpose for which the thing is used either momentarily or at length?

None of these questions can be answered unambiguously; but that does not constitute an essential shortcoming of language. Every single instance, e.g., the case of the box turned upside down for use as a table, can be adequately described, if necessary by using several further words and compounds. It is only the precise question "Is this a table or not?" which may in some cases necessarily remain unanswered. The convention according to which certain objects are assigned the word "table"—a convention tacitly accepted by us when we learned the language—does not contain any indication which in the above-mentioned exceptional cases could lead to a decision. The situation is like that of a faulty contract, not providing for all possibilities that might arise under its provisions.

In the vast majority of practical applications of the word "table," however, the hole in the linguistic usage will not be noticeable at all, and where it does become noticeable, one can easily patch it up by other linguistic means of a more complicated kind.

Apart from the somewhat vague rules for the application of the word "table" we have just exemplified, which are given by conventional usage, there is *nothing* at our disposal that could be applied to answering a question of the kind, "what is a table 'really,' or 'essentially,' or 'precisely speaking'?" One can, of course, create a precise definition for the concept "table," and that can be done in many ways; but this definition *must* be somewhat arbitrary. It is impossible that it should cover the whole range of ordinary usage exactly. This usage is too vague for that. Every definition, in whatever form it may be stated, is a *new* agreement—like a new contract which is written in such a way that it does not contain any gaps, and therefore cannot, of course, be identical with the one that did contain the gaps. Aristotle's conception, mentioned in Chapter 2, 2, according to which the definition is an unraveling, a disclosure of the true "essence" of a thing, cannot be accepted by us.

This situation has occasionally been expressed by calling a word an "open set" of experiences (this being reminiscent of a related concept of mathematics). Another analogy would be this: The question what a table "really" is cannot be answered better than the question: How many yards is the distance from Vienna to Paris? The words "Vienna" and "Paris" denote such large areas that the distance between them can be given only in miles as long as one does not add *arbitrary* assignments of "centers" of both cities. We summarize perfunctorily:

*Words of ordinary language correspond to areas of experience of a rather vague delineation; giving a definition, i.e., assigning exact boundaries to the area, always implies an arbitrary addition to the linguistic usage.*

2. *The Core Area and the Area of Indeterminacy.* One could object to the foregoing or its generalization on the grounds that even in everyday language there are *some* words that have an unambiguous meaning. For instance, the words "square" and "rectangle" are hardly ever used, at least by literate people, in any sense but that fixed by the geometric definitions. We may leave it open here to what extent this is really the case. At least, one will hardly find any agreement in the linguistic usage as to whether "square" denotes the area or the boundary, or whether one may speak of a "square with round corners," or of a square on the surface of a sphere, etc. But we are quite ready to agree that in certain cases ordinary language has taken over strict mathematical definitions and more or less resigned itself to using the corresponding word in no sense other than that of the def-

inition. Mauthner calls these definitions "restraints of the free development of language." For us, only this is essential: that the strict definition did not originate from the question, "What does the word 'square' 'really' mean? How do we *have to* define a square?" On the contrary, in the system of geometry it proved useful to introduce a certain conceptual delineation and then to attach to this new creation the name "square" (which may have existed already as a vague concept in everyday language). If afterwards, owing to the great extension of elementary-school training, this scholastic usage of the name was generally accepted, that does not prove anything about the possibility of assigning nonarbitrary, unambiguous definitions to all words of ordinary language.

What we said above about the name of a thing, "table," is still more true of all abstract expressions, such as "truth," "right," "economy," "mind," etc. Other classes of words, e.g., adjectives like "pretty," "round," "red," etc., and also prepositions like "between," "within," etc., are subject to the same rules. There is always a narrower area of experience in which the applicability of a word is universally prescribed by linguistic usage for everybody. But around this *core* there forms a wide *zone of indeterminacy,* in which there is no agreement as to the applicability or nonapplicability of the expression. Unambiguous communication by means of ordinary language is possible only if the application of every expression is limited to its core of meaning; as soon as one crosses over into the area of vagueness, the ambiguities of speaking or writing begin. A means of avoiding them is the use of paraphrases (in which one remains in the core of meaning as far as the additional words are concerned).

The essential conclusion from these considerations is that questions of the kind: What is "fundamentally" truth? What is "really" right? What is "precisely speaking" red? are senseless questions, because they contradict the facts of language. One could only ask: What concept of "truth" do we *want* to form for certain practical or theoretical purposes? How shall we paraphrase the concept "right" exactly in order to derive from it a complete system of juridical norms? How can we draw the border lines between different colors so that we can assign an unambiguous area to the expression "red"? In the same way, as already mentioned, one cannot ask, "What is the *exact* distance between two large cities," but only, "How can one, by a suitable assumption about the end points of measurement, obtain a useful measure of the distance?" Our results are:

(a) *Clear communication by means of language does not depend upon exact definitions, but upon using every single linguistic expression only within a certain core of meaning in which there exist, at least, a nearly unambiguous agreement about the applicability and nonapplicability of this expression.*

(b) *Definitions that aim at answering a question like, What is a table really? or, What is truth? are just as impossible as the problem of measuring the distance between two big cities exactly to the yard, without arbitrary assumptions.*

3. *Sentences and Sequences of Sentences.* It may be added that everything said so far about words or single linguistic expressions is also true for sequences of words, sentences, and sequences of sentences. In fact, to an isolated word as such there does not always correspond an area of experience, and almost never is there an area of correspondence that does not depend upon the place in which the word appears in the context of the speech. The essential thing is that the correspondence remains vague and undetermined, i.e., there is always a sometimes smaller, sometimes larger class of experiences for which the linguistic convention does not decide whether the expression is an adequate description or not.

In the two statements, "Smith left his house twice yesterday" and "Smith left his wife last year," the word "left" has two quite different meanings, determined by the two contexts. Each of these meanings is vague and has a certain area of indeterminacy, although with respect to almost every action of Smith it is clear whether it is covered by the word "left," taken in the first or in the second sense. For the second sentence the ambiguity is quite evident, and nobody will doubt that the expression is inexact and may give rise to differences of opinion. As far as the first statement is concerned, one has to think of such borderline cases as Smith's having stepped over his threshold only for a moment, or only with one foot, etc.

As we already know, this vagueness of expression by no means makes the language unsuitable for the needs of everyday life. One can always make oneself clearly understood by limiting the application of every expression, every idiom, every sentence, so far as possible, to an area in which the linguistic convention is sufficient; and outside this area suitable paraphrases can be used. But attempting to find the "true meaning" of a sentence, and signifying by that more than an examination of the (tacit, often unconscious) conventions among those who use the language, would contradict the facts of linguistic usage. One cannot define the "table" or the "truth" without arbitrarily adding something to the linguistic usage, nor can one paraphrase a statement like "thou shalt not kill" exactly without some such arbitrariness; in any case, there remain situations in which the applicability of the statement is questionable.

The state of affairs described above may also be characterized by saying that two different sets of words (a word and its definition; or a sentence and its explanation) never are exactly equivalent. If we assert that a certain sentence expresses this and that, then we equate expression (I) to expression (II), where the words and groupings that appear in (II) are more closely confined to their core of meaning, i.e., to the area where there is sufficient agreement about usage. That is the role of every linguistic explanation.

*Sentences and sequences of sentences of ordinary language correspond only to vaguely delineated areas of experience, just as do single words; the question of the "precise, complete, truly objective" meaning of a sentence contradicts the fundamentals of linguistic usage.*

4. *Grammatical Rules.* The rules on which linguistic usage is founded are manifold and complicated, and have not yet been much studied. A certain part of them is covered by ordinary grammar, which we call "linguistic" grammar. Usually it is said that linguistic grammar contains the "formal" rules of language. However, the word "formal" often corresponds to no factual judgment at all, but to a value judgment, and usually to a deprecatory one. In what follows we shall examine some of the different kinds of linguistic rules a little more closely.

Grammatically, we are not permitted to say "The children eats sugar," although hardly anybody would misunderstand that; but we are permitted to form the sentence "The book eats sugar," which has no meaning at all. It is one of the conventions determining the meaning of the word "children" that one is dealing here with a plural. English grammar (but by no means that of every language) requires that the verb take a corresponding form. But linguistic grammar is indifferent to the fact that the word "eat" belongs to the class of verbs whose subject must be a living creature. In the *logical* grammar, "to eat" is a verb of action, i.e., the sentential function "$x$ eats" is defined only for such variables (subjects) $x$ as can act, and is not applicable to other subjects (Chapter 6, 2).

The practical role of the above-mentioned rule of linguistic grammar, and of many similar ones, is to make a text more quickly comprehensible and more easily understandable. By the requirement of a certain correspondence of number, genus, etc., the determination of how the parts of a sentence are related to each other is facilitated. But none of these rules is indispensable, as is witnessed by their partial absence in many languages. The majority of the rules of linguistic grammar have, as we shall see, yet another character—that of creating efficient abbreviations. It is just to alleviate the very difficulties arising from the introduction of these abbreviations, or to compensate for them, that we have the rules of accordance. These prescribe the repetition or resumption of previously expressed elements, so that the same idea is really expressed several times. In some cases, as for instance in the case of the modes of verbs in subordinate sentences, the two purposes of abbreviation and clarification overlap.

*A small part of the rules of linguistic grammar prescribes the repetition of an element of expression and serves principally to facilitate the comprehension of the relation of the different words in a sentence.*

5. *Typification by the Linguistic Rules.* By far the most important effect of the grammatical rules is to build up an ingenious structure of linguistic abbreviations. An obvious example of this is the tense of verbs. In order to express that an action is to take place in the future or has taken place in the past, a small change in the word is introduced. One says "he wrote" or "he will write" instead of "he writes" and thereby the statement has been confined to a certain period of time—with all the vagueness and ambiguity inherent in every linguistic expression. (What, for instance, is the meaning of the perfect "has been confined" in the previous sentence?)

A language could be imagined that would express a localization of action (in the proper, spatial sense) by a change in the form of verbs instead of by adverbial phrases like "in this vicinity" or "far away." One cannot object that a large part of our sentences are actually meant without any spatial reference, for many of our statements are without reference to time either, and it is only a custom to put them in the present tense. In the sentence "This tree bears fruit" the present tense has to be understood quite differently from the one in "Charles enters the house." (Note that in English the gerund could be used to mark a difference; but this is not possible in German, for example.) The first of the two propositions does not imply a temporary reference at all (see Chapter 4, 3).

The inflection of nouns in Latin and German, and its substitute of case expression by prepositions in English, provides us with another, similar example. "The book of the friend" is the book belonging to the friend, or written by the friend; on the other hand "friend of the book" means somebody offering friendship to the book. The genitive has many different meanings and which one of them is referred to in every special case has to be inferred from the connection in which it is found. Logical grammar would, for instance, have the task of investigating the various forms of relations abbreviated by the genitive and, on the other hand, of finding the limits of their applicability. It is impossible, for example, to speak about the "foot of the law," although, according to a special linguistic rule, one may speak of the "arm of the law."

The formation of so-called subordinate sentences also fulfills the function of an abbreviation. Instead of saying, "What was said just now happened at the same time as the following," it is sufficient to introduce the second sentence by the conjunction "while," possibly accompanied by a few little changes having the character of repetition, as discussed above, for the purpose of clarification. Another case, which will be treated in detail later (Chapter 13), is that of sentences starting with "because." Here a complicated theory of the happenings in the world, abstracted from long experience, is compressed into a short formula. The result is that by learning the language everyone becomes unconsciously possessed of a theory of whose difficulties and problems he has no idea. Thus grammatical forms establish certain types of relations which to those who take the language for granted appear as fundamental and indisputable, perhaps even as existing prior to all experience.

*It is the essential role of grammatical rules to fix certain types of relations in the form of conventional abbreviations, which cannot be exactly paraphrased; everything one wishes to express in that language has to be reduced to these typical relations.*

6. *Derivations of Words.* Closely related to the grammatical rules in the narrower sense—the conjugation, inflection, formation of sentences, etc.—are the rules for the derivation of words from given roots. These also result in abbreviations by stressing certain types of relations, but the connection here is somewhat looser. The boundary line between the two groups of rules is vague and depends only upon how far one wants to go in the admission of "exceptions." The derivation of the comparatives "bigger," "smaller" from "big," "small" is still regarded as a grammatical rule, and one calls the transition from "good" to "better" an exception. On the other hand, in the present state of language the formation of antonyms like "uneven," "undetermined" from "even," "determined" are called derivations of new words, because otherwise too many exceptions such as "uniform," "nonuniform"; "narrow," "wide," etc. would have to be admitted. The same holds for the derivation of expressions like "hatter," "teacher" from "hat," "teach," etc. But one can hardly claim that these relations are less uniform in content and therefore less suited to grammatical fixation than those expressed by the application of the genitive. It would still require very extensive linguistic research to discover in what way, in one case the weaker, and in the other case the stronger, typification of relations originated in the language. Incidentally, different languages by no means behave uniformly in this respect.

A peculiarity of the German language that was not without influence upon German philosophy is the automatic substantivation of verbs by putting an article before the infinitive. According to grammatical rule one can form almost without exceptions "das Kommen und Gehen," "das Suchen," "das Schenken." On the other hand, one can still say, e.g., in French, "l'aller et venir," but for "das Suchen" one cannot get any closer than "la recherche," and "das Schenken" can only be translated by "action de donner" or something similar. As we see, in French we have to deal with formations of new words instead of changes of grammatical form. In English two forms "to give" and "the giving" are available, but they are not much used. Admittedly, even in German the substantivized infinitives belong more to the written than to the spoken language. But a writer in German has the substantives provided by grammar at his disposal, while the Frenchman has to contemplate first what shall be expressed by the substantive. The German philosophical litérature, accordingly, formed with great ease, in addition to "das Sein" (which can hardly be translated by "l'être" or "l'existence"), the "Nichtsein," even the "Sosein," the "als ob sein," etc. The possibility of forming such words misleads one into putting them into all relations grammar permits for substantives. Thus originate sentences like "Das Nichtsein ist, das Sein ist nicht" (roughly translatable as "Nonbeing exists, being does not exist") and similar ones, which sound extremely deep, but have hardly any accessible meaning.

*In addition to the grammatical rules proper, the rules for the derivation of words serve as typifications of relations, although of a weaker kind; the example of the substantivized infinitives in German shows that in some cases a wealth of opportunities provided by the grammatical rules can also have detrimental effects.*

7. *Temporal Changes.* It is not our task here to unravel the tremendously involved rules to which the use of language is subject. Some interesting facts, especially pertaining to the differences between various languages, will be discussed in the next chapter. At this point we only want to say a few words concerning our position toward etymology, or the history of words.

Mauthner's critique of language, which we mentioned in Chapter 2, 7, remained almost entirely within the etymological realm. For the purposes of the present book, which regards historical study never as an end in itself, it is of no great importance in what succession the meanings of a word have developed and changed. That is the problem of so-called historical semantics. What we are interested in is the *present* state of ambiguity, indeterminacy, and obscurity, as expressed by the present rules of linguistic usage.

If we talk about rules and even at times about regulations, this must, of course, not be misunderstood as meaning that there is somebody who *makes* the rules or orders the regulations. We are dealing only with a description of concrete, observable facts, the facts of language; and what we call a "rule" is nothing but the short description of a group of individual facts. The subject to be studied (if what we have only touched on here is carried out in detail) is the totality of conventions existing among people who talk a common language, conventions that concern the relation of words and other linguistic elements to the world of experience.

These agreements are not made explicitly, but are contained in the bulk of communication absorbed while one is learning a language. In this respect one must not think that the learning of one's mother tongue is completed during childhood; rather, it is continued through reading and scientific study by the adult. We have stated before that all rules are to a large extent vague and, as to their content, limitation, and meaning, uncertain. At this point we must add that all grammatical rules change also *with time* continuously.

Since any regulation of linguistic usage, except the few rules of conventional grammar, is only given implicitly by its application, it follows that in principle *every* use of a word or idiom in speech or writing changes the language for all those who are ever reached by the written or spoken message. One need not add that this is true only for a *new* use of the particular expression; since the convention of semantic relations is in a way a statistical effect, the total picture is changed by an accumulation of usage in a certain direction. The total gradual change of the meaning of a word and the development of the whole language is composed of an infinity of such small alterations (see Chapter 1, 3). This temporal dependence further increases the vagueness and uncertainty of all communication. But, as we have stressed before, we do not draw the conclusion from all this that language is not suited to describing the world of experience. All we conclude is that questions which do not take this characteristic property of language into account and lend to a word or sentence significance beyond that of a changing and never exactly determined convention—and such questions form a large part of what today is called philosophy—are not answerable and hence are futile. Only studies which in their fundamentals take the uncertainty of language into account—and that is characteristic of most positive sciences—are not subject to this criticism. We shall discuss this point later in more detail (Part III).

*The relation between a linguistic expression and outside experience changes continuously with time and is modified by every use of the expression. This increases the uncertainty of language beyond what we have already pointed out and forces us to reject all theories that do not take this uncertainty into account from the very beginning and do not try to formulate their problems in such a way that this vagueness is avoided as far as possible.*

### CHAPTER 4

# differences among languages. the language of science

1. *Untranslatability.* So far we have almost always talked about "the" language and we have had in mind either the modern civilized languages in general, or specifically the mother tongue that every one of us learned without conscious effort—as it were, without even awareness. We shall now consider certain differences between various languages, first considering the entirely different situation in which an adult finds himself when he acquires the knowledge of a foreign language.

If one language is known already, another is learned at first mainly by "translation," i.e., by assimilating the relations between the foreign words, idiomatic expressions, etc., and the ones known before. When one advances far enough, one gradually succeeds, by practice and custom, in finding a direct connection between the foreign expression and the experiences related to them. The final aim is to have the new words appear in one's mind immediately as a reaction to the corresponding external stimuli. Many modern methods of teaching attempt to exclude the intermediate stage of conscious translation entirely and to teach a language to the adult in the same way as the child learns its first language. We may leave open the questions to what extent this is in fact possible and whether this method can be extended to those parts of the language which are required for the understanding of difficult scientific lines of thought.

The essential point to note is that in learning the second language one unavoidably notices the incongruencies that are for the most part the result of the indeterminacy of the connection between linguistic expression and experience within each single language. This effect by no means disappears after one acquires the highest degree of assimilation of the foreign language. It is not the delineation of meaning of the single words that presents the difficulties. It is easy to learn that in English the German "Hof" is largely translated by "court" and sometimes by "back yard"; and that on the other hand "court" has to be translated into German often by "Gericht" but sometimes by "Hof." But what difficult problems arise if expressions like "reine Anschauung," "absoluter Geist" are to be translated. According to a very widespread opinion all such words correspond to certain realities which "exist" independently of their denotation by a word. If this were so the only question would be that of finding or even creating the "right" expression in the foreign language. We know, however, from the preceding discussion that the situation is quite different. A word of any language only corresponds to a very vaguely delineated class of experiences and is defined by a very uncertain convention, leaving the question of application in many cases undetermined. Exactly equivalent conventions do not in general exist in the other language, because the conventional demarcation of meaning rests upon the totality of previous usage of the particular expression and hence is a creation of the particular linguistic community. As we have seen, even within one language two different expressions can never have exactly the same meanings (Chapter 3, 3); and this is true to a much greater extent for expressions in two different idioms.

The inadequacy of interpretation in different languages, especially in so far as works of poetry and philosophy are concerned, has long been a commonplace, formulated usually in the saying "traduttore—traditore." If we mention this fact here, it is only because, according to the customary conception, in contrast to our position, this is due to some "irrational moments," "imponderabilities," "holistic phenomena," etc.

*The simple basic fact that the meaning of every linguistic expression depends only upon incomplete, uncertain, and temporally shifting convention within a community of language has as its necessary consequence that equivalent reproduction of a text in a foreign language is impossible.*

2. *Mutual Assimilation of Civilized Languages.* It can be readily stated that most living languages have already adapted themselves to each other to a high degree. The similarity of ways of life, general outlook and religion, scientific activity, and other professional work creates the prerequisite for a roughly parallel development of logical grammar, at least within all not too remote fields. We should call the logical grammars of two languages congruent if the two were *entirely* translatable one into the other. For this to be so, the semantic delineation of all words and idioms as well as of all relations fixed by rule would have to agree, while articulation might be completely different. Although this state has nowhere been reached completely, the contemporary civilized languages show much more similarity with respect to their logical grammar than phonetically. Even close relationship, i.e., common origin not too far removed in time, did not prevent certain languages, e.g., German and Dutch, from becoming so very different phonetically that mutual understanding is not possible directly.

On the other hand, the common cultural history of the European nations had the effect of rendering the logical differences between English, German, French, Dutch, Italian, etc., comparatively unimportant. Later we shall meet some examples of quite essential deviations in logical grammar between languages belonging to different cultures.

The parallelism of the logico-grammatical rules is, incidentally, due not only to the congruence or similarity of environment but also to direct exchange and traffic. Witness the similarity of many idiomatic and metaphorical expressions in the different civilized languages. Translation of foreign works influences the linguistic usage in the receiving country, and this effect is more pronounced when the subject matter is further removed from the predominant interests of the country, and hence from the center of its linguistic practice. There is no doubt that the translation of a great number of works from German philosophical literature within the last hundred years has influenced the French philosophical diction.

But it is in this very field that the most profound differences of logical structure between the two languages still subsist. We have already mentioned the many possibilities of substantivation in German (Chapter 3, 6). There is no comparison between the abundance of words for philosophical abstraction in German and French. Thus, as an example, for "Bewusstsein," "Bewusstheit," "Bewusstwerden," "Bewusstmachung," etc., there is only one word in French, "conscience," which means "conscience" as well as "consciousness"; or for "Kenntnis" and "Erkenntnis" there is only the one word "connaissance." But if we consider with what vagueness and inconsistency the German expressions are used, then we cannot help suggesting that this abundance is accompanied by a severe shortcoming, a want of lucidity, which is more easily avoided in a language where one is forced to paraphrase explicitly. The individual author may be able to go a long way in avoiding the worst consequences of existing linguistic usage, but on the whole he cannot get rid of all influences from the actual state of the logical grammar of his language.

*Similarity in mental development, direct contact, and translations all had the result that the important European languages, despite their phonetic disparity, are to a large extent assimilated to each other in logical structure; more distinctly marked differences appear only in special fields.*

3. *Examples of Deviations.* It is instructive to consider an example to the contrary, namely, a language which belongs to a culture somewhat distinct from the West-European and which shows quite noticeable deviations in its logical grammar. In Turkish there are two different expressions for "to be," one for the existential sense and one for the auxiliary verb. In the two sentences "The room is dark" and "There is noise in the room" the "is" has to be translated quite differently. This difference does not cause

any difficulty of speech even to a child, or to anybody however uneducated; on the contrary, people cannot understand the foreigner who confuses the two meanings. The expression for "being" in the existential sense (and also that for "not-being," which is by no means expressed by the mere addition of negation) is a *verbum defectivum,* which allows only the third person and only the present and perfect tenses. For the future tense the form of the auxiliary verb "being" is used that has the connotation of "becoming." While in French the auxiliary verb "avoir" is used to paraphrase "being" (il y a), there is no "have" at all in Turkish. One has to translate the sentence "I have a book" by "There exists a book which is mine" (two words suffice for that purpose). Obviously, this exemplifies the presence of fundamental structural rules quite distinct from our own.

Another peculiarity is that the Turkish language contains a tenseless form of the verb, a real aorist. The sentences "The clock shows the hour" and "The clock shows the fourth hour" contain the verb in two different forms, and similarly in the sentences "He does not see (us now)" and "He does not see (he is blind)." Again one observes that distinctions which seem very difficult to those who are used to a different language, and which *seem* to be logical subtleties, appear quite easy and natural to natives even if they are completely ignorant of logic. Through learning his mother tongue everybody acquires a certain stock of logical ability, which he uses quite unconsciously. Many Frenchmen are able, without much trouble, to make such subtle distinctions as that between the transitive and the intransitive use of the verb "vivre": "Les jours que j'ai vécu" and "Les beaux jours que j'ai vécus." Incidentally, it seems that nowadays in the Turkish language, which is being more and more influenced by translations, the original meaning of the aorist is gradually becoming less and less pronounced.

Turkish syntax is essentially different from that of the European languages. It is characterized by the fact that it does not admit the most common subordinate sentences, namely, the relative sentences. "The house in which we live" and "The house which we shall build" are expressed by having the word "house" preceded by a special form of the verb "live" or "build," which refers to the first person, plural, and the tense, present or future. There is no distinction between the accusative in the second sentence and the locative in the first. Hence there is no way of distinguishing between "the book which I read" and "the book in which I read." Such losses of expressibility always appear if one measures one language by another.

*Peculiarities which distinguish the Turkish language from the West-European ones show us what the possible differences in the logical structure of languages may be and how the faculty of making certain logical distinctions is impressed upon people by the language they speak.*

4. *The Formation of Scientific Languages.* The inadequacies of ordinary language for the purpose of a more precise and reliable description of facts appeared early in history. At least part of the people who used the language became aware of them. Thus a special development, lacking the characteristics of spontaneity and generality, gradually branched off from the general current of natural evolution of language. In addition to the constant changes of linguistic usage in the entire linguistic community, of which we have spoken exclusively so far, there began the conscious development of a "scientific language," limited to a smaller group.

Of course, there is no sharp line of division between science and systematic, reasoned thought of a nonscientific or prescientific kind. (Such a line of division could be drawn only if an arbitrary definition of the word "science" such as could serve only some special purpose were introduced.) Therefore, it is impossible to distinguish sharply between scientific and ordinary language. But even though one cannot say exactly where one or the other branch of a stream dividing itself into two arms begins, on the whole the distinction can be justified. In this sense we can talk in what follows about a "language of science" without risk of being misunderstood. The relation of this new concept to that of nationally distinct languages we will discuss later (Chapter 4, 7).

The first step in the movement toward conscious improvement of language for the purpose of science consisted in the creation of a scientific *terminology* in certain disciplines. The best and most instructive example of this appears in what used to be called natural history. The urge to distinguish, describe, and name the animals with which human beings come into contact is an eminently practical and a very old one. For the first and simplest needs the names of ordinary language were sufficient (one may wonder in what way these are connected with the names in the animal fables), but then came a time when people noticed their disturbing vagueness and their geographically limited range of applicability, which often did not even extend over the whole nation. If we consider only the western European civilizations, we can trace back the first attempts at a conscious terminology and hence at an artificial system of nomenclature for the purposes of classification, to the sixteenth century. After a long sequence of intermediate steps, to which the history of zoölogy bears witness, certain international conventions, which are still in use today, were finally arrived at near the end of the nineteenth century.

It would be a large task to analyze these conventions from the point of view of the logic of science (or logical grammar—these concepts verge on one another), and we cannot undertake to do that here. We shall return to some special points in Part V of this book. There are various types of conventions with which one has to deal. The gamut of terms in the classification: phylum, subphylum, class, subclass, order, family, genus, species, race, variety (and their equivalents in other languages) was chosen in connection with linguistic usage but is by no means uniquely determined by it. No one is told by his linguistic intuition, for instance, that "class" is more general than "order." The delineation of these order concepts is influenced by theoretical considerations which have changed extensively with the years and, in particular, the concept of "species" is still subject to continuous refinement (Chapter 19, 6). The practice of naming a species by a grouping of the genus name, an additional explanatory adjective, and the citation of the discoverer, is well known. The name of the genus, usually agreeing with some customary denotation, is unique; the additional adjectives, defining the species, are in general taken out of a fixed stock and repeat themselves in different genera. The whole thing seems like the construction of a personal name, with first name, last name, and possibly the addition of the bearer's origin. The choice of Latin for the nomenclature of the species originated probably with the urge for international communication. Its logical function, however, is primarily to allow for the independence of scientific terms from the unavoidable changes of linguistic usage in living languages. There are many things to be said about this that we cannot go into here. We summarize:

*The inadequacy of ordinary language leads to the branching off of special scientific languages, resting upon conventions within small groups of people, but reaching across national boundaries. The first step in such a formation out of the general linguistic development is the creation of a scientific terminology, of which the zoölogical nomenclature forms an example.*

5. *The Necessity for Scientific Languages.* Botany, and also in part mineralogy, possess a terminology constructed similarly to the zoölogical one. The chemical nomenclature, being much younger, has a slightly different character. It rests entirely upon a theoretical basic idea which is not much more than a hundred years old and is generally accepted today, namely, the idea that all bodies are composed of a finite number of elements in simple proportions. This makes it possible to denote every material by a short formula, consisting of a few signs, and the chemical "names" are expressions uniquely coördinated with the formulas; they are, so to speak, "pronounceable formulas." Here the precision of the connection between name and observation is much greater than in the case of the descriptive natural sciences; but one must not believe that it is a complete one. Stereochemistry, for example, breaks through the simple denotations by formulas of the first, primitive type. The discovery of isotopes a few decades ago and, even more, that of the transmutation of elements into one another by means of radiations, destroyed, in a certain sense, the logical foundation of the whole system, though not its practical utility. We cannot

doubt that the future progress of theoretical research will be accompanied by more such difficulties.

The mathematical or "exact" sciences go one step further in the direction toward a special scientific language; here one has to do not only with a terminology, but with the fundamentals of a specific linguistic structure. The creation of a language in jurisprudence and related sciences runs along different lines again. But the aim is always to attain a kind of unambiguity of meaning. In fact, one may define a scientific language as a language in which exactly equivalent sentences (P. Servien) exist, which is possible only when there are *complete* conventions, not allowing any zone of indeterminacy at all. All this will be the subject of more detailed discussions in the following parts of the book, where we shall deal with questions of scientific methodology. Time and again we have to point out that the development of everyday language finds its consistent continuation in the development of science (to which, of course, belongs the creation of a scientific language). There is no sharp line of division between the rules of logical grammar and those of scientific theory—witness the English expression "grammar of science."

At this point we may also take occasion to mention a rather unfounded objection frequently raised against the introduction of a specific language of science as distinct from the ordinary language. Some people claim that the use of special scientific terms and even more the use of separate scientific forms of language makes it unnecessarily difficult for the layman to gain access to sciences and to understand scientific results. In some countries, particularly in Germany, this idea is related to the tendency to suppress "foreign words" ("Fremdwörter"), i.e., words whose roots originate in a foreign language. After what we have said so far there seems to be no need for a long and explicit argument if we reject this objection as being contrary to the needs of the development of science.

Only the replacement of the vaguest expressions of everyday language by more precise ones makes it possible to attack the problem of unambiguous description, which is first a task of language and then of science. The rejection of artificial improvement of a language, i.e., an improvement that is not worked out unconsciously by the totality of the people speaking it, would make impossible any comprehension of the happenings open to our experience that go beyond the ordinary level of the man in the street. Moreover, it is quite erroneous to think that the use of a foreign or otherwise strange expression for the denotation of a scientific concept is detrimental to understanding. It is a matter of indifference to the one who does not know the conceptual structure of the pertinent parts of mathematics whether one says "differential quotient" or "derivative." And if English were used instead of the Latin expressions for names of plants in the botanic system in America, one would only promote confusion through the unavoidable associations carried by every word of the usual spoken language.

*Every scientific discipline must necessarily develop a special language adapted to its nature, and that development represents an essential part of scientific work. The point of view which holds that the introduction of special terminologies is dispensable or even detrimental is based upon a complete misunderstanding of the situation.*

6. *The Abuse of Technical Terms.* The misunderstanding of the role played by the conventional denotations of scientific concepts is extremely common, and its consequences appear in incidental articles in the newspapers as well as in the most serious works of philosophers. As is generally known, one calls in mathematics the square root of 3 an "irrational" and the square root of minus 4 an "imaginary" number. This has nothing whatever to do with the meanings of the words "irrational" and "imaginary" in the nonmathematical language. It is nothing but a historical accident that the two terms were not chosen the other way around. In spite of this, an outstanding contemporary philosopher saw as a serious problem the investigation of the "essence of the imaginary" in the sense that, for the explanation of the "only imagined" ($=$ imaginary), he made use of the mathematical concept of the square root of a negative number.

When in the nineteenth century the study of algebraic equations with integral coefficients was carried to a higher level, it seemed desirable to introduce a separate name for those numbers which cannot be solutions of such equations. Since the words "irrational" and "imaginary" were already appropriated, these new numbers were called "transcendental." But there is no factual reason whatever for not calling the square roots of negative numbers "transcendental." The otherwise customary use of the words "transcendental" and "imaginary" cannot be brought up as an argument in either case. According to Leibnitz, transcendental is "ce qu'un inventeur est à sa machine," and Kant calls transcendental "Grundsätze, welche die Grenzen der Erfahrung übersteigen" (principles transgressing the limits of experience). If one wanted to conclude from these or similar definitions what a transcendental number is, it would be like proving that love is stronger than war by citing the fact that the mass of the planet Venus is greater than that of Mars.

The choice of a name for a scientifically established concept is to a large extent arbitrary. As a rule one chooses a work that belongs, according to previous usage, to a somewhat related area of meaning. But as soon as the new usage has been established, the old meaning ceases to play any role at all in the scientific use of the word. (On the relation of the artificial language of axioms to natural language, see Chapter 9, 6.)

We have mentioned above (Chapter 3, 2) that the semantic delineation given a word in a special science is sometimes taken over more or less precisely into general linguistic usage. This is particularly true of concepts that are spread about by elementary education, and such a process fits exactly into our conception of the development of language and science. But there is also an abusive way in which ordinary language seeks to "enrich" itself by adopting scientific expressions. If things are called atoms or molecules, or more recently quanta and electrons, only because they are small, then we have a rather harmless example of such abuse. But a well-known, fashionable philosopher, who declares in a discussion of the relation between man and wife that "one must not see absolutes in polar coördinates," shows only that he once heard a vague rumor of the use of polar coördinates in geometry and thinks they are somehow related to "polar antitheses." At times the misunderstood use of an expression borrowed from some technical science becomes so extensive that a new expression of everyday language originates, which may be regarded as fully detached from its origin. Thus "dynamics" and "statics" were originally two chapters of the science of mechanics; now they are vague denotations for situations which either are or are not subject to violent changes. An art historian was so impressed by the use of the words "static" and "dynamic" in the critique of paintings that he was struck by the idea of looking for a deeper insight into the problems in which he was interested in textbooks of mechanics. We could increase ad libitum the number of such examples.

*The meaning of a technical term in a scientific language cannot be derived or guessed at from the meaning of the word in ordinary language. On the other hand, by borrowing scientific terms and using them without paying sufficient respect to their meaning in the technical language, everyday language frequently creates new expressions of vague and uncertain content.*

7. *Conclusions.* As we have already mentioned, the creation of a specific language of science works toward the facilitation of international understanding. This is partly because phonetically similar expressions (foreign words derived from the same roots) or identical terms (e.g., Latin names of plants) are used in all languages. But still more it is achieved by the standardization of meaning, of the correspondence between words and things. It is very simple for the mathematician of either country to use the words "derivative" (English) and "Ableitung" (German) side by side, because the definitions are *exactly* the same. A large part of the difficulty in handling a foreign language is eliminated if one works in a domain where the rules of logical grammar are the same.

Considerations of this kind, and in particular the situation prevailing in chemistry, induced Wilhelm Ostwald and others to suggest the creation of an *international language* for communication in all spheres of human activity and interest. Alas, such a problem is much more difficult. For here one would have to substitute an artificial creation for everyday language, with all its characteristic ambiguities and continual changes of meaning. This would be possible only if the international group forming the new linguistic community were really alive and ready to serve as the agent for the perpetual development of the conventions. A prerequisite is an extensive unification of logical grammar among the participating peoples. The practical advantages of such an artificial, unified language, existing *beside* the natural languages, would be so great that one could only agree with Nietzsche's remarkable prophesy (of 1886):

. . . at some far future time there will be a new language, at first in the commercial field, then a language for the intellectual intercourse of all people; that this will come true one day is as certain as that there will sometime be aviation.

So far, however, we do have aviation but we do not have such a utopic unified idiom. We must content ourselves with the ordinary national languages and the special technical languages, derived from them and limited to specific purposes. These constitute the only means at our disposal for the further discussion of our problems. Therefore, it will not be possible for us to eliminate entirely the vagueness and ambiguity of expression, or the dependence on temporal changes of meaning, or the difficulties caused by translation from one language into another. In addition, there is the compulsion to limit oneself to the typified relations fixed by grammatical rules, a compulsion that one can get rid of only slowly and to a limited degree, if one wants to make oneself understood.

If we summarize what was said in this introductory part about language and the role it plays in carrying out the task set before us, we may stress the following main points:

*1. The first, still unconscious, step in the urge for science, i.e., for intellectual comprehension of the world, is the creation of language.*

*2. Grammatical rules in the widest sense of the word are conventions which, corresponding to a more primitive stage of intellectual development, establish certain simple typical relations and force us to reduce, in some manner, everything that we want to express in words to these basic relations.*

*3. Progress in scientific knowledge is possible only if it is accompanied by a critical and conscious attempt at the improvement of language. The gradual creation of a comprehensive "language of science" is a part of this improvement.*

# analysis

Nihil est in intellectu quod non fuerit in sensu.
Nothing is in the mind that did not enter through the senses.

(Aristotle)

# negativism

1. *"Synthesis and not Analysis."* People who agree with the basic point of view of this book will find it quite natural for us to attack our problems by analysis, by dissecting complicated situations and reducing them to simpler ones. But it is just as true that there is a numerous class of people with a conception opposed to ours who regard everything called analysis, by its very nature, an evil, and at best an unavoidable one. The only worthwhile and praiseworthy task for the human mind is, according to this view, synthesis—synthesis of the branches of science, synthesis of ideas, experiences, rules of life, etc. But one will not find a chapter on synthesis in this book. We do not believe that the task of science is like that of a watchmaker, who takes a broken watch apart, looks it over, and puts it together again. It is not that the world is dissected by our analysis. But the picture we form of the events in the world in order to find our way about in it consists of simple elements, just as a world map is the result of surveying performed at many separate spots. We know of no other synthesis than the sum of all we have to say.

In many circles one finds opposition, and even hostility, toward the principle which we follow here and which may be simply called the *scientific* one, namely, the principle that knowledge is to be sought by examining isolated facts and focusing our attention upon single *sectors* of the world. In order to make clearer the meaning of the following inquiry, we must look for a moment at these trends in opposition to science, which at all times have had a considerable following, but which have received new and powerful impulses in recent decades. One may wonder whether this movement is still on the upsurge or whether it has lately passed its climax. A contemporary historian, J. Huizinga, says:

A systematic philosophical and practical anti-intellectualism as we see it today seems indeed to be something new in the history of human civilization.

The forms in which this anti-intellectual state of mind manifests itself are manifold. Besides the slogan "synthesis, not analysis" there are the favorite formulas "soul against reason" or "spirit versus intellect," or "living intuition instead of dead formalism," and expressions such as "holism," "reverence for life," "intuitive comprehension of the world," "Wesensschau," etc. Sometimes one even hears such statements as "This may be logically correct, but it does not stand up against the facts of life," or "The sterility of thinking has to give way to a stronger feeling for life," and other similar things. Phrases of this kind are built up into entire philosophical systems. They dominate the relevant columns in newspapers and literary magazines and at times provide the basis for the formation of organized groups. An excellent critique of the consequences of this modern anti-intellectual movement has recently been given by Lancelot T. Hogben in his lecture on *Retreat from Reason.*

There is so far no uniform, comprehensive name in use for these various viewpoints which are more or less directed against the application of reason. Since we find it desirable to give them a tag, and since the points of view in question have in common that they are directed against what is called by us positivism, we propose the name "negativism" for them. Of course, this denotation and the rather vague definition are to be taken with all the reservations that follow from our discussion of the shortcomings of language in the previous chapter.

*We denote collectively by the name "negativism" such theories and attempts at theories as are directed toward restricting and depreciating the role of reason and analytic thinking in our efforts at comprehension of our environment.*

2. *Skepticism and Faith.* In this chapter we shall discuss a few examples of negativistic tendencies in contemporary authors—again without making any claim to historical completeness or to a thorough evaluation of the particular individuals, but only for the sake of elucidating what will be discussed in later parts of the book. First, however, it seems to be suitable to define the concept of negativism a little more closely with respect to certain philosophical doctrines with which it might be confused. We do not call everything opposed to our view negativism.

Above all, we do not include in the negativistic scheme the old conception, emerging again and again in philosophy since ancient times, which is customarily called *skepticism.* We may not agree with the claim that "we cannot know anything fundamentally," but that is mainly because we have no clear conception of what is meant by "knowing something fundamentally." If, on the other hand, the ancient skeptics claimed that one could not reasonably distinguish between the beliefs of Pythagoras, Heraclitus, the Eleatics, Democritos, and other Greek philosophers, and that there is no unique answer to the questions put by these philosophical schools, then we cannot help agreeing with them. The modern skeptic generally does not doubt the usefulness of the answers given in special branches of science to factual questions, but he is skeptical toward the answerability of questions of this kind: What is it that holds nature together at its innermost core? or, what is the true essence of animation? Anyone who has understood what was said in the first part of this book will have no doubt about what to think of such questions. Furthermore, the decisive reason for not putting the skeptic into the class of negativists is that he does not think one can get answers *by other means* than those used in the positive sciences, the systematic collection and examination of experiences.

The *believer* is often regarded as diametrically opposite to the skeptic, but we do not count him among the negativists either. If somebody says that he believes in the existence of a heavenly being of superhuman intelligence, then he means that this belief is in agreements with experience. All religious precepts are as a rule given in such a form that, in the first place, they cannot be immediately refuted by observation, and secondly, they do not offer answer to questions that science asks and solves. The fact, however, that the area covered by science expands more and more as time goes on forces the sphere of belief to recede continuously. Difficulties arise where a rectification of the boundary has not taken place in time. Thus it happens that the world conception based upon religion sometimes contains claims that we have to reject as in contradiction to experience; yet on the whole religion does not pretend that it can arrive at answers to scientific problems by nonscientific means. Also, the followers of religion usually argue more for a clear delineation of the boundaries (see Chapter 27, 5) than for effacing them.

One could object that the doctrines of faith are not based upon observation and experience, but upon sources of knowledge of quite a different kind. But that is not decisive; for the larger part of what we regard as scientific knowledge, too, is acquired, as far as the individual is concerned, by tradition, the hearsay of teachers, and hence is largely based on faith. The only essential is the willingness to test by sincere observation what one has accepted as true, as often as there is a possibility of doing so; and in general, the believer is not opposed to this.

*Neither philosophical skepticism nor religious faith is in a proper sense a form of negativism; both leave, at least in principle, the sphere of science out of their consideration.*

3. *Bergsonism.* We regard as the most influential modern representatives of negativism the French philosopher Henri Bergson and his followers. In French literature Maurice Maeterlinck, as well as others, represents with great consistency the same line of thought. In England, Bernard Shaw sides with Bergsonism. Among the German popular philosophers it is mainly Ludwig Klages who has lately made much of his

negativistic point of view; many schools, as for instance the "holistic" philosophy (Chapter 22), are in close relation to him. There is also a widespread organized movement governed by theoretical ideas of this kind, which was founded by Rudolf Steiner and is called *anthroposophy* (see Sec. 5). Furthermore, as was mentioned before, certain basic elements of negativism can be found throughout contemporary literature.

Bergson's philosophy is fundamentally hostile toward the intellect. In one of his main works, *L'Evolution créatrice* (1907), he says, for instance,

> The intellect, so clever in the treatment of inert matter, shows its inadequacy as soon as it touches the living. Whether one deals with the life of the body or of the mind, the rigidity, sharpness, and crudeness of an instrument which was not created for that purpose is always immediately apparent. The history of hygiene and pedagogy is full of examples of that. If we think of how much it is our main interest to preserve our body and perfect our soul . . . if we think, on the other hand, of the obvious harm done by the shortcomings of medical and pedagogic practice, we are crushed by the extent and especially by the durability of the errors. One must recognize the basis for this in the fact that we treat the living as dead and think of reality, however fluid it may be, as something fixed and forever changeless. We are at home only in the discontinuous, the motionless, the dead.

All that is conceded to the intellect here is at most that it is capable of dealing with dead, physical matters (although the criterion of motionlessness and discontinuity does not seem to be very aptly applicable to, say, the theory of electric waves). For biology, however, and its applications to medicine, the use of the intellect, according to Bergson, results only in error and harm; the fruits of scientific research in these fields are examined by the philosopher and found wanting! Bergson does not hesitate to state what means should take the place of the intellect when one deals with questions of living matter: it is "instinct" which "works organically instead of mechanically like the intellect," which "lives the knowledge and does not think"—instinct which, "when it becomes conscious of itself, is called intuition" and which then "can recognize and supplement what is inadequate in the intellect." At the same time, intellect and instinct are two totally "divergent, but equally excellent solutions of the same problem." According to this we must assume that it was the intellect by means of which wireless telegraphy was invented, but instinct that found insulin and penicillin therapy—unless the latter also belong to the great harm done by the intellect, of which the history of medicine is supposed to be so full.

Perhaps, historically, one can find some explanation for Bergson's view (his first book was published in 1888) if one remembers how general scientific thinking in the final decades of the last century had degenerated into the superficial philosophy of Herbert Spencer in England, and of Ludwig Buechner, Ernst Haeckel, and others in Germany. But it remains entirely incomprehensible what sense it makes in view of modern (and even ancient) natural science to contrast two distinct forces of the mind, one capable of working in the physical, the other in the biological sciences. The only reasonable conception seems to be that, to varying degrees, instinct, intuition, and weighing and analyzing reason concur in all discoveries, not only physical and biological, but also in such areas as philology and history (see Chapter 5, 7). The whole concept of an opposition between instinct and intellect seems so artificial to us that we think it is due neither to a lucky instinct, nor to a sharp intellect.

*Bergsonism holds the view that in certain positive sciences (the biological) the application of reason is harmful, and that here, as opposed to the sciences of dead matter, instinct, intuition, etc., have to take the place of the intellect.*

4. *Time and Duration.* We shall stay a little longer with Bergson's philosophy in order to examine, by discussing one of its concrete theses, what meaning is given to the principle of the negation of intellect. Bergson points again and again to his conception of time and duration as the crucial and basic idea of his philosophy.

According to Bergson, one has to distinguish between two fundamentally different things: on the one hand there is the *time* of the mathematical and physical sciences, measured by clocks, dissectible into sharply distinguished intervals, and flowing uniformly, while on the other hand there is *duration* or psychological time which alone plays a role in real life and which flows nonuniformly and is neither measurable nor sharply dissectible. "As soon as we speak of time," says Bergson, "we think mostly of a homogeneous medium in which our states of consciousness succeed each other, are placed beside each other as in space, and form a manifold of distinct points." As contrasted to this, the real, psychological time (duration) is not homogeneous, but entirely inhomogeneous; it does not contain any intervals equal to one another. "Pure duration," he says,

is nothing but a sequence of qualitative changes, smoothly transforming into each other, penetrating each other, without exact contours and without any tendency to remain foreign to one another, without any relation to numbers: pure inhomogeneity."

The experience of this pure duration is most perfect in the state of dreaming or while we listen to a melody, or in general when we do make no attempt to establish relations between the present state of consciousness and a former one.

In our opinion there have been much more abstruse things said about time, e.g., by Hegel, who, in order to derive Galileo's laws of freely falling bodies "from the concept of the thing itself," can be read as saying:

But now time is the moment of negation, of being by itself, the principle of unity; and its measure—any empirical number—is to be taken in relation to space as unit or denominator. Space, on the other hand, is the being apart from one another, and that of no other entity but the entity of time.

The characteristic and interesting fact about Bergson's theories is that they are not entirely unacceptable, although not very clear, and sometimes contain very good insights; the only thing one does not understand is why these obviously well-considered and reasoned propositions are supposed to have originated not in the intellect, but in some different source.

What are the concrete claims that Bergson finds incompatible with the basic concepts of the physicist?

It is known to everybody who thinks in terms of natural science that there exists a *feeling* of time or sense of time which stands to the measurement of time in the same relation as the sense of heat to the temperature scale and the sense of space to geometry. Ernst Mach dedicated to the sense of time a short section in his *Analysis of Sensations* (the first edition of which in 1886 appeared before Bergson's *Essai sur les données immédiates de la conscience*). There, among other things, he examines very clearly what Bergson calls the inhomogeneity of "real" time: that the subjective valuation of a time interval depends upon the totality of states of consciousness passed through during that interval. This idea is much further developed in Mach than in Bergson. That a melody as it runs through time is perceived as a unit, as a whole, also follows from Mach's theory as one of the essential characteristics of time sensation. Mach says, at another place:

The basis of all cognition is intuition which may refer to sensual feelings or to only intuitively imagined things, or to potentially intuitive concepts.

In short, the physicist is not the bad boy the negativists make of him, continually staring at his formulas and figures and seeing nothing but mathematical abstractions. Physicists are aware that any theory can give only a one-sided and simplified picture of reality and that it never exhausts the full measure of experience. But they are convinced that only by a steady continuation of research with the same intellectual means that have proved themselves so far, will the picture of the world be completed more and more and in yet finer detail. It is the intention of Mach to serve such progress of theory by drawing into the discussion the characteristics of time sensation, as opposed to time measurement. And more than that, namely, to add yet another hue to our incomplete world picture, cannot be the task of Bergson either, however many beautiful words he may choose for the purpose. A large part of his discourse on the concept of time could be taken as a reasonable contribution to the analysis of time sensation, if it were not for the continuous attacks on his supposed enemies—numbers, mechanics, thinking, exactness, the physicist, etc.—which interrupt them.

*The factual statements of Bergson, in so far as one can assign to them a clear meaning, contradict the concepts of science much less than they seem to at first sight; yet the contrast is stressed artificially by continually emphasizing the alleged opposition of instinct to intellect, and by incessant polemics against an imagined "dead" mechanics and its proponents.*

5. *Goethe and Anthroposophy.* The brilliant style and persuasive diction of Bergson's writings put them close to poetry, which one does not usually judge by a criterion other than that of the pleasure it gives to the reader. From the other side, the same border region is approached by the philosophical writings of some poets, for which we have quoted as an example Maeterlinck, an extreme negativist. The master of French symbolists cannot find enough words to praise obscurity and rebuke clarity, while valuing highly only those matters which are comprehended "better by the absence of reason than by reasoning." One must not underestimate the influence of works of this kind upon the advancement and stabilization of negativistic ideas in wide groups of people. We know of hardly any analogous support by contemporary writers of attempts at sober and judicious thinking.

But times were different and the greatest German poet was proud to say, "We profess we are of the kind that strives from darkness to light." And he gave expression not once, but on many occasions and in the most diverse forms, to the fundamental principle of scientific research: "If you want to comprehend the infinite, just explore the finite in all directions." Goethe wrote to Jacobi on May 5, 1786, "God punished you with metaphysics and put a thorn into your flesh; He blessed me with physics." In his own scientific studies Goethe relied exclusively upon observation and experiments, which he carried through with the most painstaking care and inexhaustible diligence. "It would have to be shown," he says incidentally,

which is the true way of research in natural science, how it rests upon the straightforward pace of observation, the observation being raised to experiment, and how this, finally, leads to results.

And:

One must allow neither myths nor legends in science. These should be left to the poets, who are called upon to use them for the benefit and pleasure of the world. The scientist must confine himself to the nearest and clearest present.

It was a peculiar twist of fate that led to Goethe's name becoming a symbol for almost all undertakings in the sphere of German intellectual activity that follow negativistic lines of thought. The most powerful of these is the widespread anthroposophic movement founded by Rudolf Steiner, which calls its central place of cult in Switzerland "Goetheanum" and branches out to the American continent. Anthroposophy apparently was never recognized by the representatives of school philosophy as an equal, but it may well have found more active followers all over the world than many a famous school of philosophy. In any event, it is one of the characteristic signs of our time, and the diffusion of these and similar theories in public life is often a greater hindrance to the reception of clear scientific thought than scholastic metaphysics.

According to Rudolf Steiner, human beings have the capacity to form an immediate intuition of a spiritual world by means that are basically different from the ones used in science. The "first, still shadowlike manifestation of comprehension" is "pure thought," a form of "apprehending consciousness." Above this first level lie the higher spiritual powers of intuition; far below it are found the methods of profane science, namely, observation, experimentation, and carefully reasoned conclusions drawn from them. Yet on all factual spheres the most valuable and important results are obtained only by the activity of the highest form of the powers of intuition! At the same time a sufficiently deep and genuine concentration upon the inner apprehension can even replace the otherwise prerequisite training. The entirety of knowledge gained by these higher means constitutes the "spiritual sciences." These methods open to humans "higher worlds," the first of which is the "imaginative world, which lives in living pictures" and borders on the real world; the next is the one "that lives in the element into which we strive to get by inspiration." On the other hand, the spiritual sciences lead to highly concrete conclusions for practical purposes; e.g., they demand a certain trisection in matters of human society, and they teach us to reject certain artificial medicants like aspirin and to prefer others that originate in the "insight into the whole man."

An explicit examination of the contents of these and similar theories may be omitted here. We merely wish to indicate their existence and the comparatively wide publicity they have received. The use of Goethe's name can be explained in the first place on grounds of propaganda. In addition, it is true that Goethe as a scientist was, even according to the standards of his time, a dilettante and that he did not distinguish clearly in his optical studies between physical questions and those which belong to the physiology of the senses. Not having the requisite training for an understanding of Newtonian physics, he let himself be carried away by a critique of Newton that was factually unfounded and, for the defense of his own work, by no means necessary. Thus he saw himself forced into opposition to some of the scholars of his day, and this is one reason for his being claimed by the negativists. Another reason can be found easily in some of the poetic utterances he made "for the benefit and pleasure of the world," in which he displayed ideas that may be interpreted in a negativistic sense.

*Anthroposophy is a widely diffused, popular species of negativism without any serious foundation. Its claim on Goethe cannot be justified, despite the many-sidedness and multiformity of Goethe's work, in the face of his unambiguous appeals for clarity and objectivity and his sober way of furthering natural science by means of observation and experiment.*

6. *Enemies of the Mind.* As an example of a doctrine with a decidedly negativistic slant, which has more the form of school philosophy, we cite a work by Ludwig Klages, a philosopher who enjoyed a great following in Germany during the last few decades. The determined will to attack everything intellectual is exhibited in the very title, *The Mind as Enemy of the Soul.* Klages started from a discipline, denoted collectively by "Ausdruckswissenschaft," to which belong physiognomy, graphology, etc. There are interesting problems in this sphere, lying on the borderline between psychology and physiology (see Chapter 16, 3), which deserve serious scientific treatment. But having hardly been touched by the earlier development of the sciences, they became the field of more or less dilettantist attempts and attracted a circle of researchers and semiresearchers who find themselves forced into a certain opposition to science and scholarship. The wish, so predominant with dilettantes, to arrive at practically useful results by passing abruptly over all difficulties at the start, provides an excellent opportunity for the development of doctrines directed toward a rejection of analysis and the cult of the "whole."

Klages' philosophy is mainly based upon the idea of contrasting the two concepts "mind" and "soul." The soul, at times being simply identified with "life," is "intuitively devoted to what happens," and what it "lives through in unique form" is incarnated and becomes reality. Vision is "the inner counterpart of a continuously changing reality." On the other hand, it was the mind that posited the concept of the unextended mathematical point, which does not exist in reality at all. This positing has been the mind's main function since the time of ancient Greece and it still remains a miracle and a riddle how it was possible for this "inflexible nothing to be applied to the current of becoming and changing." Klages constructs a complicated theory in order to make the breaking of the mind into life at least half-way understandable: life is oscillating and, so to speak, at its turning points it comes to rest and gives way for the breaking in of the mind into the living soul. The main point, however, for which Klages claims all the prerogatives of discovery, is the insight that the mind, with its "inflexibility and narrowing point-likeness" is destroying the soul, falsifying its natural drives, and leading to delusion and error, to slavery and the overpowering of life:

> Mind and life . . . are two fundamentally hostile realities . . . There is no third of which they might be parts or aspects.

All "logocentric" systems, including religion, philosophy, and natural sciences, are incapable of providing real knowledge. They aim away from the "world's essence and result in a conceptual grammar of the dead."

One can see the kinship to Bergson—Klages likes to revel in a vast exaggeration of the negativistic aspects of Bergson's philosophy—but there are also touches of Rudolf Steiner's anthroposophy with its customary appeal to Goethe's Weltanschauung. The new contribution of Klages is to take up the active fight against the "noxiousness of the mind." Klages regards man as a schoolboy who, through an overdose of intellectual training, wastes away and perishes. Hence he declares school, teachers, teaching, and everything that is connected with them, objectionable, and demands their complete abolition. Such a demand may be made by the entirely uneducated or by those who think that they stand high above such things. Klages indubitably, and perhaps rightly, counts himself among the latter. He most surely claims that his book will not be considered unintelligent, unreasonable, and illogical. But those who are on the other side of the fence and are fought by him do not advocate a "deification of the mind," as he thinks they do, if for no other reason than that they cannot accept the two-fold personification which this slogan implies. And those opposed to Klages can only hold that everything said or advocated in a book as a doctrine should be clear, reasonable, and logical—in short, that it should satisfy the demands of the intellect so deeply despised by the negativists. "The mind" or "the intellect" plays, in our opinion, no other role than this: One may abstain from formulating doctrines about the world or parts of it, but if one choose to make such formulations, one cannot do it in contradiction to reason and intellect.

*Klages' philosophy, which is an exaggeration of certain Bergsonian ideas, combats alleged claims of the personified intellect toward "domination of the world" and "suppression of life." But we see in the intellect merely the ability man has to use when he collects and organizes knowledge and wants to communicate it in a reasonable fashion. Whoever does not like this kind of activity because it disturbs him in pursuing other goals of life may abstain from it; but one cannot partake of it without the use of the intellect.*

7. *Fixation of Our Point of View.* We have not exhausted by these few examples the number and multiformity of negativistic doctrines which

at the present time abound in all countries. The German "existentialism" and its French version by Jean-Paul Sartre, and the widespread Christian Science movement on the American continent would offer striking examples. But we do not strive toward a complete enumeration anyway, and wish only to characterize a mood, a general climate, with which at present any new theory that reaches the public has to reckon. Every expression that points toward a view incompatible with negativism, such as positivism, empiricism, operationalism, etc., has from the start a bad sound in the ears of the public.

If we disregard the extreme exaggerations that some authors have added to the negativistic idea, the following remains as the core of it: All that is understood by scientific method, logic, reason, intellect, mind, is insufficient to provide an adequate picture of the world in which we live; one has to use for that fundamentally different qualities, such as instinct, intuition, feeling, vision, sense penetration into the universe, devotion to life, etc.; the only really valuable results are won exclusively by application of the latter extraintellectual means. We shall attempt to test this claim and to sketch our view of this matter, as far as this is possible at this early stage of our book.

In the first place, one notices that all the terms collected in the two groups above are among the vaguest that the language contains, and that it would be very difficult to reach agreement upon what meaning each expression would have to be assigned, i.e., to which area of experience it refers. Moreover, the grouping and confrontation of the two sets of terms already represent an anticipation of the most essential part of the claim. It was pointed out earlier that we find the basic position of Bergson's philosophy, according to which instinct and intellect are contrasting, mutually exclusive capacities, entirely unfounded. The same holds for the other contrasting pairs, like logic and intuition, etc.

Let us see concretely how scientific progress in a single instance is achieved. When the mathematician Fredholm found his method for the solution of integral equations, which became the starting point of a famous theory, instinct and feeling for certain analogies with other problems led him to set up tentatively a formula; then he had to spend much effort in deriving the formula by way of logical deductions, i.e., to connect it with previously accepted mathematical theorems. Once provided with logical proof, the formula is incorporated in mathematical literature and comes to be known by others. But these, if they are productive mathematicians, not only assimilate the content and the proof, but also form a vivid apprehension of the whole line of ideas. All these steps combined constitute the scientific or positivistic activity, or, if you will, embody the scientific method. In another case, the medical scientist, on the basis of long observation of a certain pathological symptom (of which he may not even be completely conscious) may instinctively conceive a new therapy. Then he starts to test it systematically, by the classical method of isolation and combination of effects, until he thinks he can give a first empirically founded evaluation of its applicability, which will then in turn be subject to further tests by experiment and observation of others. In the same way, a historian who has acquired a deep insight into a historical epoch by a careful study of the literature and all kinds of available records may come upon the trace of a new conception; this then serves as the basis of diligent examination and comparison, and only on the grounds of these finally becomes an object of a scientific communication and a part of science.

In each of these examples one notices how all the means that the negativists so sharply contrast with each other—instinct and reasoning, vivid intuition and careful experiment etc.—concur toward one goal. Not always does an act of the one group precede a step of the other, for the instinct that leads the scholar on the trace of a new idea often grows out of careful preparation of a logical or experimental character (Chapter 23, 5). The contributions of different kinds may vary in importance from case to case, but a piece of knowledge, a theory, or a practical result that is achieved without any contribution of the intellect is unknown to us.

Negativism challenges this very conception. It regards everything in whose creation the intellect was decisive as worthless if not harmful; this refers to theoretical abstractions as well as to the consequent practical results. The negativists hold that both theory and practice, at least in certain spheres, can achieve essential progress only by emotional and instinctive methods. Thus the line of demarcation between our view and that of negativism has been drawn, and we do not regard it as our task to do more than that. What we have said in this chapter will be completed and elucidated further by following discussions, and we briefly summarize:

*At the present time many ideas are being advanced and widely publicized (here called negativistic) which are directed toward assigning to the intellect a subordinate or even harmful role in life, and which expect any progress of humanity only from the use of fundamentally different qualities, like instinct and vision. In contrast to this, we maintain that all knowledge of a theoretical, as well as of a practical, kind is gained by the coöperation of the various—and by no means opposite—human capacities, and that no substantial result can be reached in a way that is incompatible with the demands of the intellect.*

### CHAPTER 6

# connectibility

1. *Delineation of the Problem.* If one wants to examine scientific theories or other utterances of men more closely, one faces as the immediate object of study a specific linguistic expression—a sequence of sounds, words, or sentences. Such an expression can always, as we noticed in Chapter 1, 6 (rejecting differences in pronunciation, etc.), be taken as a combination of a finite number of different signs (letters, punctuation marks, etc.). But one cannot, the other way about, consider every arbitrary combination of signs of this kind in the same sense as an object of such study. There is general agreement that from the start certain groups of signs can be neglected.

We shall in the first place neglect all those combinations that have no corresponding articulate sounds connected with them, as, e.g., Wv.?;zx. In the second place, we also do not care about those compounds which, although they may be pronounceable, do not form words of the language we choose for discussion or admit to it, e.g., Yapamam fela bint. There remains a comparatively small number of groupings which consist of single correctly formed words of our language, e.g., cornered sleep knowledge. Then we perform another, more difficult cut, by rejecting all those groups of words which do not satisfy the rules of ordinary (linguistic) grammar. This is difficult, because the range of the grammatical rules is not fixed unambiguously. But the difficulty can usually be surmounted since we can agree, without losing anything essential, that we shall admit for our present consideration only expressions which *without any doubt* satisfy the grammatical rules. Sentences that are uncertain in this respect are then for the time being excluded; however, in special cases we are going to admit certain relaxations of the rigor of grammatical rules (Chapter 8, 2).

Now we arrive at the threshold of other and more decisive difficulties. The following sentences, for instance, are grammatically correct: (*a*) the rose is a red flower; (*b*) the rose is a black animal; (*c*) the rose walks on the house of the roof. One can easily make the decision that of these grammatically correct sentences (*a*) is true, (*b*) is false, and (*c*) is meaningless. The question arising here, whose treatment is a prerequisite for any analysis of cognition, is this: How is it possible, within the totality of the sign combinations now admitted, i.e., within the totality of grammatically correct sentences, to find a useful classification, whether according to categories of true and false or meaningful and meaningless?

One will notice that from our point of view it is not the distinction between true and false that is the serious problem, but rather a demarcation of those sentences to which the criterion "true or false" can be applied at all. It is easy to see that the sentence "John Smith died on the 17th of May" belongs to the first category, but the sentence "John Smith died on the 34th of May" to the second one. But how can one classify sentences like the following, which can be found in abundance in so called philosophical writing: "The nothingness penetrates the universe," or also "The universe penetrates the nothingness"? Do we have to introduce beside the "true" and "false" another disjunction, "meaningful" and "meaningless," or a new category, such as "symbolically" valid sentences?

Of course, one will not demand that in every case the decision must be possible for a single isolated sentence (sentences in the grammatical sense). But even for a sequence of sentences, a whole context, the decision is often no easier, and may be even more difficult. If a discussion of the "essence of cause and effect" ends with the assertion that "world never *is,* but worlds," ("die Welt *ist* nicht, sie weltet") then anything preceding these words will hardly contribute much to clarify the meaning of this sentence.

*We see our task in the analysis of statements (by no means of "reason"). Such an analysis of linguistic expressions must begin with a suitable classification of those sentences or groups of sentences which are admissible from the point of view of linguistic grammar; in particular, we are looking for a demarcation of those among these sentences to which the criterion "true or false" is applicable.*

2. *Consistency with Linguistic Rules.* The simplest method of handling the above-mentioned problem (a method already used to a certain degree in our previous discussion) is to classify all sentences and groups of sentences as true, false, and meaningless. Then the first two categories together would be called "meaningful," while the last one is "devoid of meaning." This bisection is also applicable to shorter groups of words which do not form sentences. For instance, the introduction into a sentence of the words "on the 34th of January, at 16 o'clock A.M." is surely not meaningful. Here the expression contradicts without any doubt the generally accepted conventions about the length of the month of January and the division of the day into hours.

This last example suggests that we seek the criterion for the "meaninglessness" of an expression in the fact that it contradicts the conventional rules of the usage of language (compare the concept of "logical grammar" introduced in Chapter 3). One could assume—and this indeed corresponds to the view of modern logistic—that only those sentences are admissible, i.e., not meaningless, which satisfy all rules of the logical grammar. For instance, one logical rule covering the use of the genitive case could be paraphrased thus: the genitive determines the relation of part to the whole unilaterally; therefore it is possible to form the phrase "roof of the house" but not "house of the roof."

A very fruitful concept of logic in this connection is that of the sentential function. How this concept is used may be explained as follows.

In the arithmetic of real numbers the symbol $\sqrt{x}$ (square root of $x$) is defined only for positive values of $x$. Hence it is meaningful to speak of the square root of seven, but meaningless to speak of the square root of minus seven. Similarly, the statement, $x$ is a prime number, is defined only for such $x$ as are integers. Among the sentences, 7 is a prime number; 8 is a prime number; 8½ is a prime number, the first is by definition true, the second false, and the third meaningless. One may call the sentence "$x$ is a prime number" a sentential function and say that its "range" consists of the integral natural numbers. In the same way, one may say of the sentential function "$x$ is red" or "$x$ has the color . . ." that it is only defined for, or has the range of, those $x$ which are denotations of things. Among the sentences, blood is red; snow is red; justice is red, the first one is thus true, the second false, and the third meaningless. If one knew the range of functionality of all possible sentential functions, i.e., if all these ranges could be completely described by suitable linguistic expressions, then at least a large part of the work of distinguishing between meaningful and meaningless statements would be done.

But we also see that with the demarcation of sentential functions alone we would not have accomplished very much. There would still be a need for many other conventions to regulate the vast variety of existing relations from the point of view of logical grammar. Think, for instance, of the difficulty of the concept "genuine pearl" now that there exist the so-called Japanese or cultured pearls, which are artificially produced but naturally grown. What is important for us to learn in this example is that a complete listing of all rules for the use of language is not feasible before we possess, somehow, all possible knowledge, present and future. Although the rules of logical grammar would still leave undecided the question of the truth or falsity of a statement, there is no way to anticipate the rules without knowing at least the general frame of future experience. We need only think of the examples about the square root. As long as one knew only real numbers, the expression "square root of $x$" was meaningless for a negative $x$; the later theory of complex quantities changed the use of language by introducing for a certain class of operations the convenient expression "imaginary number." Phenomena which in the domain of an exact science are clearly recognizable often occur in other areas in more complicated form. The fact is that the rules of the usage of language cannot be developed in any area of knowledge to any significant degree before one knows the answers to the factual questions of the discipline in question.

*It is not possible to base a classification of sentences or sequences of sentences with respect to being meaningful or meaningless upon the criterion that they agree or do not agree with the entirety of rules for the use of language (the logical grammar), because this would presuppose possession of almost all essential knowledge.*

3. *Connectible with . . .* The modern logistic movement—with which we agree in many points—advances the view that the sentences of so-called metaphysics are "unmasked" as meaningless, because one can prove that they do not satisfy the rules of (logical) grammar in the wider sense. Rudolf Carnap, one of the main representatives of so-called logical empiricism, presents the following line of thought.

The sequence of words "Caesar is and" appears to us according to ordinary grammar unacceptable, because at the place where the "and" stands should stand a predicate and not a connective. The sentence "Caesar is an emperor" is grammatically correct but false. The sentence "Caesar is a prime number," however, is grammatically correct and meaningless, because in a more complete, logical, grammar one does not consider the words "prime number" and "emperor" merely as substantives, but distinguishes between them according to their "syntactic category." Then the rule would have to be added that "prime number" can be predicated only of numbers, and "emperor" only of persons. Once one has regulated the whole language by fundamental rules in this fashion, then, according to Carnap, the rejection of the sentence "Caesar is a prime number" results automatically, and the same holds for all metaphysical sentences, as for instance the famous statement by Hegel, "Pure being and pure nothing are therefore the same" ("Das reine Sein und das reine Nichts ist also dasselbe").

After what has been said before it is clear that we cannot accept this way of looking at the situation without reservation. We do not think it possible to anticipate the rules of language in any exhaustive manner before knowing the sentences that will have to be tested by them in order to decide their admissibility or inadmissibility. A language is not complete before all possible sentences have been pronounced. One can at most examine a specific given sentence to determine whether it is compatible with rules that either were explicitly formulated or are derivable from another use of the same terms. Moreover, in many cases the "rules of language" are by no means distinct from statements of factual content that play a role within the theory. It is so in the previously cited example: "In the arithmetic of real numbers, sentences dealing with the square root of $x$ are meaningful only if $x$ is a positive number." There are many cases where one cannot draw a sharp line between rules of language and factual statements.

For these reasons we prefer to suggest a formulation that is slightly different from Carnap's. In the first place, we want to relativize the concept of logical admissibility of a sentence; the decision depends in each case upon a more or less arbitrary choice of the "rules of language" that are taken into account. At the same time, we think it advisable to avoid a denotation which, like the terms "meaningless" and "void of meaning," has from the start a disparaging connotation and therefore needlessly provokes objection. We propose to call a sentence *connectible* if it is compatible with a certain totality of statements which regulate the use of the words and word forms appearing in it. The statements of a branch of science are connectible with each other (in so far as they can be regarded as rules of language or give rise to such rules) and with most of the customarily accepted rules of the ordinary use of language. The connectibility of scientific statements beyond the limits of the special field is generally aspired to, but not always achieved. (The conception, proposed by some representatives of logical empiricism, of a "physicalistic language" tries to serve this purpose.) The statements of metaphysics are often connectible among each other only within a very narrow range, and the smallness of this range makes them of relatively little use (see Chapter 21).

To what extent the concept of connectibility is related to the problem of distinguishing between "true" and "false," and many other details, still remain to be discussed; a large part of this book can be regarded as amplification of the concept "connectible." For the present we shall state the definition in this form:

*We call a group of words (sentences and sequences of sentences) "connectible" if they are compatible with a system of statements which, it is assumed, regulate the use of language—connectible, that is, with respect to this system. Strictly speaking, one would always have to say "connectible with . . ."; this addition can be omitted only if the system of reference is supposed to be known.*

4. *Connectibility as such.* In many cases the use of the concept "connectible" here introduced is immediately apparent. A sentence that starts with the words "On the 32nd of January" is not connectible with the rule of language: " 'January' is the name of a month that contains 31 days, as denoted by the numbers 1 to 31." The sentence "Anton is a proper fraction" is not connectible with the rules: "Anton" is the name of a person; "proper fraction" is the denotation of a class of numbers. The sen-

tence "Napoleon was the victor at Sedan" does not contradict any rule of ordinary language, it is "connectible" within everyday language, but it is false.

There is another class of cases which can easily be settled: the propositions of exact science. A sentence in which the words "Conformal mapping of the infinite plane . . ." occur seems meaningless to the nonmathematician, because he recognizes it, and rightly so, as unconnectible with customary rules for the use of the words "conformal," "mapping," "infinite." We know, however, that technical language (Chapter 4, 4–5) is characterized by the fact that in it different rules are at work. The statements of mathematics are connectible with the rules of mathematical language (which are mostly mathematical propositions too) and with all rules of the ordinary use of language not explicitly altered by specific conventions (e.g., by definitions of technical terms). This second part is often omitted because one feels that it is not necessary to make any reference to the ordinary use of language within purely mathematical contexts. To what extent that is possible we shall examine a little further on (Chapter 8, 6).

In any case, the example of mathematical statements shows that one must be rather careful with the claim that a sentence as such is unconnectible or "meaningless." Even such an extremely obscure proposition as Heidegger's "The nothingness itself nothings" ("Das Nichts selbst nichtet") cannot be dismissed by simply pointing out that, according to the rules of ordinary language, one cannot assign a predicate to the subject "nothingness" and that "to nothing" does not denote a predicate. One must carefully investigate to what extent the particular philosophical work or philosophical school has founded a new parlance. In most cases one will then come to the conclusion that connectibility exists only within extremely narrow limits. The situation is largely such that the author concerned disregards the ordinary usage of language without explicitly stating in what respect he intends to do so and without substituting clearly new rules for the discarded ones. When this occurs there is nothing for the logical critic to do but state the fact and delineate as accurately as possible the limits of connectibility. If one wants to reject theories because they are not connectible with a certain class of linguistic rules, then this is an arbitrary decision or a judgment of value which cannot be justified logically.

Let it be explicitly stated here once more that our term "connectible" points only to compatibility with (logical) rules of *language* and by no means to a possible incompatibility of two factual theories. The question "true or false" is not yet decided even after a proposition is recognized as "connectible." When in what follows we occasionally say of sentences that they are "connectible," without referring to a specific system of language, we mean this:

*There exists a sphere of generally accepted linguistic rules, though not exactly defined and never explicitly formulated, on which ordinary language is based. The technical languages explicitly cancel some of these rules, or change them. Whatever is in agreement with the stock of linguistic rules thus formed is simply called "connectible as such" (meaningful).*

5. *Verifiability.* The attempt at an exact distinction between "meaningful," or, as we prefer to call them, "connectible," statements and others has understandibly been a subject of study by epistemologists for a long time. A particular line of thought which in recent times has found many proponents is insistence upon the criterion of *verifiability.* While we have asked the question how sentences to which the distinction "true or false" is applicable can be characterized, the followers of that school assume that it is immediately apparent whether or not a sentence is verifiable. All statements are rejected as "meaningless" that do not contain, either explicitly or implicitly, the rules by which they may be verified or falsified. The meaning of a statement is, according to Schlick, the method of its verification. This formulation, however, is subject to many objections.

If one writes the sentences: This (exactly denoted) man is 58 inches high; or: The distance of the moon from the earth is 700 miles, then in both cases it is clear that one is dealing with something verifiable. Though many definitions, explanations of methods of measurement, the units of measurement, and many other things have to be taken for granted, there is the possibility that, by carrying out a certain procedure of testing, one can assign to these sentences one of the predicates "yes" or "no" ("true" or "false"). But how about, for instance, the statement: This man has a good character? Whether or not this is a verifiable statement depends upon what one means by "to have a good character," that is, upon the rules regulating the use of this expression. One may imagine that in a specific, rigorously constructed system of psychology there are accurate and, in all or most cases, applicable criteria fixed for the truth of the statement. Under these assumptions one would recognize the sentence as a verifiable one. If, however, we do not have such a definition at our disposal but must rely merely on the vague and changing usage in ordinary language, then it is hardly advisable to call the sentence simply "void." We have already remarked in Chapter 3 that the vagueness of everyday language by no means makes it useless—otherwise neither this book nor any other one dealing with general questions could be understood. Perhaps those who claim verifiability as the principal condition of "admissibility" will admit that in such cases a limited, incomplete verifiability is still acceptable. We prefer to say: The sentence referred to is connectible with the rules of ordinary language; in the specific case of the above-mentioned system of psychology it would also be connectible with the rules of this branch of science. The latter fact may under certain circumstances increase the value of the statement—but our goal here is not to appraise values.

The theory of verifiability has recently been the subject of much discussion. First, Karl Popper pointed out that general statements like "all bodies are heavy" cannot be verified, but at most falsified, since it is not possible to check *all* bodies. This, however, is not correct since in a factual statement the term "all" can refer only to a limited set describable in observational terms. Most other objections, such as those raised by Bertrand Russell, C. G. Hempel, and others, can be met by a more cautious formulation of the verifiability principle, e.g., this: A factual statement has significant meaning if it is possible to describe in observational terms two different states of the universe—one that takes place when the statement is true, and another one when it is not. This would sufficiently discriminate metaphysical sentences as nonsignificant ones.

It is clear, however, that before verification in any sense can be thought of the linguistic form of the statement must be found adequate. A statement not connectible with a certain stock of rules that constitute a language suitable to describe experiments is certainly not verifiable. On the other hand, it is hard to see why a more exclusive criterion should be needed.

*It does not appear expedient to accept verifiability (or perhaps in the unilateral sense, falsifiability) as the sole criterion of a sentence's admissibility, because the question of verification depends upon the accepted definitions, and hence upon the linguistic rules; thus, in the last analysis, verifiability is determined by the fact that the sentence in question can be embedded in a totality of sentences which for it take the place of linguistic rules.*

6. *Questions and Commands.* Another reason for not accepting verifiability as the ultimate criterion is the necessity of the consideration of sentences or word groups that do not form statements in the ordinary sense, such as, e.g., questions and commands. The sentence "Thou shalt not kill" corresponds to rules of language which, as far as the word "shall" is concerned, are rather involved and peculiar (see Chapter 25, 3). But apart from these difficulties we may say that the sentence "You must not be similar" is unconnectible, because the predicate "to be similar" cannot be used without further specification (indirect complement). The verifiability of shall-sentences in general might be a subject of special investigation, but any answer depends upon a previous analysis of the concept "shall." Compatibility with a limited system of linguistic rules is more easily established and, at the moment, suffices for us as a criterion.

The situation is similar as far as interrogatory sentences are concerned. There are many examples of illogical or impossible questions, such as: Is the duck a fish or a mammal? Is this table brown or round? In the first case the "or" is combined with an incomplete disjunction; in the second, with a nonexistent one. The use of the word "or" (particularly in the German language) is little regulated and it depends upon conventions, which are to a certain extent still undetermined, whether we call the one or the other of the two forms of question connectible, i.e., compatible with the accepted linguistic conventions. Then there are interrogations which include an incorrect statement: Will this apple tree again bear cherries this year? A rigorous formulation demands that the *question* as such, namely, the total sentence without the word "again," be separated from the *assertion* . . . bore cherries last year. The assertion is itself by no means meaningless; it is connectible if one takes as a basis the customary area of meaning of the word "cherry," etc.; whether it is verifiable or not, depends upon the position one takes concerning historical statements. The question as a whole must be taken as contrary to the above-mentioned rule of separation and hence as unconnectible.

All these cases are easily decidable and almost trivial. We mention them here only because we want to stress their analogy with other, more important ones. Questions such as: Is there a real world? Is nature benevolent? and similar ones form the basis of endless controversies and the contents of voluminous systems of philosophy. But what we regard as the problem here is not the question asked by these words; rather: are the few words assembled above to form a question in any sense contentful or connectible? In the first sentence the words "there is" stand for something extremely vague and it would require a large number of rules to explain the use that is to be made of these words in this specific case. (In mathematics, or at least in certain parts of mathematics, we have a fairly clear concept of existence.) In the second case we find, above all, the word "nature" in a context outside of all linguistic order. The two interrogations are connectible at most with a set of linguistic rules regulating the most superficial everyday language, almost all of which are essentially invalidated in the positive sciences. The expression "nature" in a personified sense is not admitted in any part of natural science.

*The concept of connectibility applies immediately to sequences of words that form not actual statements but questions, commands, etc. This leads to a first attempt at the criticism of certain metaphysical questions.*

7. *No Valuation.* The concept of connectibility which we have introduced will undergo criticism and objections from two opposite sides. Those who stand consciously or unconsciously on the grounds of the traditional school philosophy will find bothersome any attempt at making a distinction between propositions of the technical sciences and metaphysics. Perhaps these critics maintain that the statements of metaphysics possess a "higher truth," but they will never admit that such propositions fail to

have any of the qualities which one assigns to ordinary scientific statements. On the other side, the view of the extreme representatives of "logical empiricism" demands that any statement which cannot be regarded as a sentence of some science must be dismissed as "meaningless." In contrast to this we want to make our view quite clear, as follows.

Above all, we are not proposing here a value judgment, that is, we are not concerned with a classification in an undefinable scheme of valuation which appeals to the entire world of human feeling. We are merely looking for a division of grammatically admissible sequences of words into two classes, one of which contains (among others) statements of the sciences and sentences of applicability generally agreed upon, and the other one of which contains (among others) entirely meaningless sequences of words. There is a need for such a division at least for those who would make a closer study of sentences, of one or the other kind, their task. Certainly the demarcation is possible in various ways. The main thing we have found is that it can be only *relative,* i.e., that the decision whether a sentence belongs to the first or to the second class depends upon previous conventions. Such conventions are determined, in our opinion, in such a way that a certain system of linguistic rules is set up which regulates the use of words and word groups over and above those fixed by the customary grammar. The sequences of words that satisfy a set of such linguistic rules are called "connectible (with this set)." All propositions not connectible with rules that are considered indispensable are called "meaningless" in the usual sense of the word.

In a completely formalized discipline it should be possible to point out all of the linguistic regulations. A part of them, however, would always have the implicit nature which we shall meet in our discussion of axiomatics (Chapter 9). This ideal case of completeness will scarcely ever be reached, but that does not invalidate our criterion. For if a specific sentence is given, we can test to what extent it is compatible with linguistic usage by looking for the rules that it *may* contradict. In most cases we shall, in this fashion, arrive at a more or less accurate delineation of the area within which the particular sentence is connectible. When this is found the general part of the problem is solved. A further study can be carried out only under consideration of the actual linguistic demarcations. We shall not exclude entirely from our attention lines of thought that we cannot regard as connectible with those of science. We shall also have occasion to return (Part VI) to concepts like that of the "symbolic meaning" of an expression.

The area, however, in which we are mainly interested is determined by the rules for the ordinary use of language, including the additions and alterations introduced by the various sciences. Everything that is connectible with this group forms the main subject of our book. The modern movement toward a "unified science" or a "unified language of science" can be understood in terms of the connectibility with a unified body of linguistic laws. In the following parts of the book we shall attempt to work out the main contours of a structure that incorporates simultaneously the basic propositions of the various sciences as well as the laws of their linguistic expression.

*By the introduction of the concept of connectibility we do not mean to discriminate against any aspect of intellectual life expressed in words. We wish only to find a suitable classification of meaningful propositions and to stress at the same time the desirability of creating a comprehensive body of scientific and otherwise important statements that are in every instance connectible with each other.*

### CHAPTER 7

# mach's elements

1. *Element Sentences.* The concept of connectibility as developed in the last chapter leads to the conclusion that the construction of a general scientific theory, i.e., of a system of mutually connectible statements about the world of observation is possible only if we start with the simplest sentences, the meanings of which are, so to speak, self-evident. On the basis of such sentences we have to develop a language, gradually advancing by testing each newly incorporated sentence to determine whether it is connectible with the previous ones. The ultimate goal of the theory is clear. It attempts to embrace everything that is open to our experience and observation, i.e., the phenomena of "nature" outside of us as well as those within ourselves, along with the actions of our fellow men which intrude upon us with their various reverberations in the past and present—in short, everything that can be meant by the terms natural and cultural sciences. But, we have to ask ourselves now, what are the "simplest sentences" that have to be taken as a start?

The word "simple," alone, is not sufficient, for there is nothing that is simple in itself. Simplicity is a relative concept. In general, things that serve the purpose of being compounded, that combine to form something new are called simple with respect to the use made of them. In our case, the use we have in mind is this: We want to derive and make understandable comprehensive systems of sentences that contain many words, concepts, and relations of concepts. Hence we have to start with sentences that are composed of as few different words and concepts as possible and only of those for which the correspondence between name and experience is immediately understood, i.e., is not controversial within a community of language. We do not believe, however, that this can be done completely or in a unique and definite way. We shall be concerned only with the attempt to attain, by a careful analysis of our experiences and language, a suitable *approximation* to a *Logical Structure of the World* (R. Carnap) or to the "constitution of the system of concepts."

In the search for immediately comprehensible expressions and sentences we readily arrive at those sequences of words that customarily describe direct sensations. There is no controversy among seeing people who know the English language about whether it is light or dark (light as day or pitch dark) in a room. Independent of all other experience and knowledge that the individuals concerned may possess, there is consent among them about the use of the words, i.e., about the assignment of the phonetic and written signs "light," "dark" to certain experiences, at least in a large core of application (Chapter 3, 2). In the same way one distinguishes unambiguously between a high-pitched and long-drawn-out sound on the one hand and a low-pitched and periodically interrupted one on the other. One agrees to give each of these sensations a name, consisting possible of several words. There are adequate linguistic expressions for whether a body we see is blue or red; whether, if it is in motion, it falls or rises; whether it feels ice cold or burning hot; and there exists agreement about their correspondence with experience—always disregarding the exceptions in which the boundary of the core of meaning of the word is overstepped. It is upon the existence of such largely unambiguous denotations of sensations that the possibility of mutual communication depends in the first place. And we recognize in these denotations the basic elements necessary for the logical construction of the conceptual world. The fact that the unambiguity is not without exception makes the task more difficult but does not doom it to failure.

*In attempting to arrive at unmisunderstandable basic sentences that can serve as starting points for a connectible system of knowledge, one finds as basic elements, which for the time being cannot be further reduced, certain denotations of direct sensations, of the form: I see blue, I feel cold, etc.*

2. *Mach's Elements.* Ernst Mach (1838–1916) made a successful attempt, a landmark in the development of science, at reducing the totality of the experiences open to us to simplest elements and ultimate components. His "doctrine of elements," often misunderstood and much misrepresented, is based upon a point of view differing slightly from the one just described. We shall easily see that the difference is unessential, and perhaps only apparent.

Mach does not start out to analyze statements, systems of sentences, or theories, but rather the world of phenomena itself. His elements are not the simplest sentences, and hence the building stones of theories, but rather—at least according to his way of speaking—simplest facts, phenomena, and events of which the world in which we live and which we know is composed. The world open to our observation and experience *consists* of "colors, sounds, warmths, pressures, spaces, times, etc." and their compounds in greater and smaller complexes. All we make statements and assertions about, or formulate questions and answers to, are the relations in which these elements stand to each other. That is Mach's point of view. What connection has it with what we have said in the beginning of this chapter?

In the following sections we shall have occasion to come back in more detail to the parallel, revealed mainly by Carnap, between the so-called "formal" and "material" modes of speaking. Propositions are often expressed in a form as if they dealt with matters of fact, or experiences, while, strictly speaking, they make assertions about words, sentences, and statements; or, to use Carnap's phrase, one formulates "syntactical sentences." For instance, one may assert, "Five is nothing but a number," when one means: The word "five" is a name of a number and not of a thing. Or one may say in the material mode: An atom is always found at a certain location in space. This means, translated into the formal language: In every set of sentences in which one speaks of atoms, one can also speak of their instantaneous coördinates. On the other hand, a simple, purely factual report is not translatable, such as, e.g., I feel cold.

If, then, Mach says that a body is a complex of sensations of a special kind ("sensation" here is only another word for elements; see Sections 3 and 4), surely he means this as a syntactical sentence. He wishes to assert that a statement in which there is reference to a body can be replaced by a sequence of sentences (of the same content) in which there is reference only to a certain complex of sensations. One can offer an even more precise translation in terms of the formal language: Every sentence containing the word "body" is equal in content to a system of sentences in which the word "body" does not occur but in its place there is reference to the elements in certain relations. If for the moment we accept the word "sensation" for "element," we have to translate the main contention of Mach's theory ("the world consists for us of a complex of sensations") into the formal mode as follows: Our statements, sentences, and questions about the world are reducible to statements, sentences, and questions about sensations.

Specific documentations for the admissibility of this translation can be found in abundance in Mach's writings. Those who are thoroughly familiar with his variously formulated but always consistent doctrines will hardly be in any doubt that our interpretation, i.e., the translation of his principle from the material into the formal mode, is not unjustified and not arbitrary.

*The reduction of the phenomena open to our experience to simple "elements," as proposed by Ernst Mach, means, translated from the material into the formal language, a reduction of all statements and theories, in the last analysis, to simplest elementary statements.*

3. *Denotation of the Elements.* Mach stated clearly the motives that led him to suggest the doctrine of elements—he sought a standpoint that he would not have to abandon when transferring from physics to psychology and physiology. In our way of expression this means that he was seeking a scientific language whose connectibility goes beyond each one of these three areas and embraces at least all three. Mach could have added that the solution of this problem includes that of a wider one, to gain a language connectible across *all* areas of science.

Certainly we are dealing here with more than mere terminology, or mere convention on linguistic terms that could be decided upon by scientific congresses. Language has to be understood in this context in a more general sense, as providing the possibility of description or characterization of matters of fact. To create a new language means here to introduce new concepts, hence, new syntactical relations. The chemist cannot fix a system of signs for the elements before forming an idea of what elements are and in what kinds of relation they stand to each other. Accordingly, purely terminological efforts are far from solving the problem of language that interests us here. The construction of a special terminology (Chapter 4, 4) is the most primitive means of the scientific improvement of language, and it can only be applied at quite specific points in the development of science. (Some philosophers think, nevertheless, that one would gain something if only people could agree which kind of statements are to be called "principles," which "laws," which "particulars," etc.)

The essential merit of Mach's doctrine of elements consists in the fact that it attempts to reduce the entire world of experience to uniform elements, and that it points out *approximately* the place where such elements are to be found. Such indication has necessarily to be vague, because it is certainly impossible to denote a completely new and original concept with a word taken out of the general stock of language and already having many different usages. Mach called his elements—and with explicit reservations—"sensations." He could not avoid the many misunderstandings to which this expression was especially subject since it has too many different meanings in psychology and physiology. Perhaps it would be better, always with reservations which we still have to discuss, to speak, instead of sensation, of "sense impressions" or in an even more neutral way of "receptions." This would point to the fact that we are dealing with single impressions which we *receive* and which then form the given, the data, with which we are trying to deal by means of the language and further theories. Here is a (necessarily inadequate) analogy. One could imagine a physicist sending a balloon, carrying recording machines of various kinds, to Mars and getting it back; then *everything* he can reasonably say about the situation on Mars must be reducible to the single phonographic, photographic, and other records he receives. The decomposition into elementary receptions is given here at first hand.

*The word "sensations" by which Mach sometimes denotes the elements is itself not significant and can easily be replaced by "sense impressions" or "receptions"; what is decisive is only that here everything experienced was successfully reduced to uniform elements or (translated from the material to the formal mode) that a language was successfully created which is connectible across all boundaries of the individual sciences.*

4. *The Double Purpose of the Elements.* Everything said so far about Mach's elements needs an addition without which our explanation will still be misunderstood. We mentioned that Mach introduced the denotation of the elements as sensations only with an explicit reservation, and the replacement of "sensations" by "sense impressions" or "receptions" proposed here can also be valid only within the framework of this reservation. With reference to this we offer the following remark:

Within the totality of the elements accessible to us, two groups are distinguishable even after the most primitive consideration: first, complexes of elements of which we say that they refer to external bodies—let us call these $A, B, C, \ldots$—and second, another group $K, L, M, \ldots$ which refer to one's own body. It is clear how the distinction originated. If, for instance, we reach with a finger of the right hand for a complex out of the $A, B, C, \ldots$ group, then we experience the sensation of touch only on that finger. But if we reach for a complex formed out of the $K, L, M, \ldots$ group, e.g., the left hand, the eyelid, or the ear, we are aware of further touch sensations and disturbances of the field of vision or hearing. If we investigate connections between elements $A, B, C, \ldots$ without paying any attention to connections with our own body, that is the $K, L, M, \ldots$ set, then we study physics. For instance, we may study the change that the color $(A)$ of a piece of iron goes through during progressive heating $(B)$, without paying any attention to possible changes occurring in our retina or our skin nerves. Proceeding in this way, it makes no sense to call the $A, B, \ldots$ set "sensations" in the customary sense of the word. It corresponds better to customary linguistic usage if we call the $A, B, C, \ldots$ group physical objects or realities. It is only because we are in a position to detect close and very important connections between the $A, B, C, \ldots$ group on the one hand and the totality of the set $K, L, M, \ldots$ on the other, and because most of the time we are immediately aware of the existence of these connections, that it is possible to say: the color is *my* sensation, a color sensation. There are not two simultaneous things—color sensation and also color as a physical reality. The important fact about Mach's elements is that they can be assigned two such different names out of the vocabulary or ordinary language as "sensations" and "physical objects." The explanation that Mach himself added to the introduction of the terms in the later editions of the *Analysis of the Sensations* is this:

> *When in what follows, besides or instead of the expressions "element" or "complex of elements," the terms "sensation" or "complex of sensations" are used, one must realize that the elements are sensations only in the connection and relation pointed out (namely, to one's own body). In another connection, they are physical objects. We use the auxiliary name "sensations" for the elements only because to most people the elements are much more familiar as sensations (colors, sounds, pressures, spaces, times, etc.).*

5. *Body and Substance.* In order to give a clearer impression of Mach's doctrine of elements, we are going to discuss in this and the following section the two applications that have always been considered most characteristic of his theory and that also became the crucial point of most critiques—his conceptions of the material body and of the personal ego. Mach was induced to deal with the question: what is a body or a thing? by the fact that physiologists of the nineteenth century considered it a natural and even vital problem to ask: how can the origin of sensations be explained as the action of moving atoms? Since Mach's interests embraced physics and physiology equally, one might not go wrong in assuming that it was just this problem—upon which the physiologist Du Bois Raymond based his famous "ignorabimus" (Chapter 17, 2)—that provided the point of departure for his far-reaching theories. The decisive explanations of this point can be found in the last pages of Mach's *Mechanics* of 1883.

Our outline of Mach's conception might well be preceded by Goethe's words: "One should not seek anything behind the phenomena; they are the lesson themselves." As soon as we speak of a body, a thing, an object that we can see, touch, or smell, we speak of certain impressions which we receive and which are connected with a specific space and time impression. Each one of these single impressions can change but we still do not cease to talk of "the same" thing, just as one calls an object of household furniture whose pieces have worn away and have all been replaced one by one still "the same" object. If the color of a thing changes, this means that in connection with a large number of other impressions which remain the same we receive a new color impression. If a great many qualities are changed at the same time, as in the transformation of water into steam or ice, then a sort of metaphysical problem arises, whether or not it is still "the same" thing. The question is of the kind mentioned in Chapter 3, 2, i.e., the linguistic usage is not unambiguous here; we have arrived at the boundary of the core of the customary meaning of the words. A supreme court, however, which could supplement the defective linguistic convention and could make a binding decision as to the absolute meaning or the "essence" of water, does not exist. In times when people used to believe in a superhuman or supernatural being who had carefully arranged everything in the world and was omniscient, it seemed necessary only to grasp just a little piece of the knowledge possessed by this being. Later, whole generations of philosophers made the most ingenious attempts to disclose the mystical "thing in itself" which hides behind the fleeting forms of illusory appearance. But how it is possible to make comprehensible with words something that is not accessible to observation remains obscure. The idea that there is nothing to be found in this extraphenomenal world, that the only thing to do is to investigate the relations existing between changing impressions, has lived through centuries in the minds of many intelligent men and became operative in the work of scientists, but it was left to Mach to have the clearness of mind and the courage to state it.

Mach's explanation of the concept of a thing is this: a body is a comparatively constant sum of tactual and visual sensations connected with the same space and time impressions. We outlined above how this sentence can be translated from the material into the formal mode (Chapter 7, 2). Perhaps the words "space and time impressions" are in need of some elaboration, and it may be better to speak here of space and time *receptions*. We perceive the position of an object in space as we do its shape and its dimensions. The child, just learning to move by itself, becomes familiar with space by touch, i.e., at first it experiences the connections between visual and tactual impressions, then their connection with certain linguistic terms such as "right" and "left," "above," "beside," etc. A statement like: The pointer stands to the right of the blue line belongs to the primitive sentences which, as we have said above, correspond to Mach's single elements. One could reduce spatial impressions to visual and tactual ones, if it were not for the collaboration of other bodily organs in providing orientation in space. In any case, it is by direct sensations that we become aware of whether two phenomena are visible in the same or in different places, simultaneously or at different times, as we know from everyday experience. That is why Mach's definition speaks of a complex of different sensations which are connected with the same space and time impression. Such complexes, which furthermore show a certain degree of stability, i.e., change on the whole only slowly and in small steps, we call bodies.

According to Mach's conception, which we follow here and which, incidentally, was partly anticipated in David Hume's *Treatise of Human Nature* of 1739 and touched upon even earlier by Thomas Hobbes (1655), "body," "substance," and similar expressions are auxiliary concepts, auxiliary words, whose extraordinary value for practical life nobody fails to recognize and which also have given indispensable service to all positive sciences. Nobody wants to bar these expressions from the language of science, but there are occasions on which one arrives at the limit of their applicability. Thus, questions such as whether water and ice, a caterpillar and the butterfly are still the same bodies, whether a gas is a body at all, and so on, can only be decided by conventions and not by reasoning "from the concept" of body or object. The attempt to reduce sensations themselves, from which the customary concept of a body is abstracted, to the motions of such bodies seems entirely preposterous. That would be tantamount to explaining the fauna of a country by the consonance of the Latin names of the animals, or the motion of the planets, by the dimensions of the telescopes.

*For certain complexes of sensations whose coherence proves to be vitally important, denotations like "body," "substance," "thing," etc. have been introduced. Thus, it seems a vicious circle to try to explain sensations as motions of bodies (atoms). On the other hand, in order to define a "thing in itself," disconnected from all sense impressions, one would have to use words that do not, in the last instance, correspond to sensations, and hence must remain unintelligible.*

6. *The Ego.* The application of the doctrine of elements to the customary ideas of body or substance found violent opposition from many of Mach's contemporaries. Its consequences for the concept of the individual, the ego, the single person, met with even stronger objections. In all discussions touching this subject there are often influences discernible which are far from scientific.

The critics would have objected less sharply if they had not been of the false opinion that from Mach's point of view *everything* that could be said about personality and the individual is exhausted by the few very enlightening words that he devotes to the origin of the "I"-concept. The goal of Mach's discussion is only to denounce certain pseudo problems connected with the word "I" and with related terms. In everyday language and (justifiably) in large areas of science, we use the word "body" or "thing" although it is not possible to point out exactly the totality of elements that constitute a body; and analogously, we indulge (and also justifiably for practical purposes) in a manner of speaking that presupposes one's own and a foreign "ego" as fixed, well-defined units. Nobody intends to bar from linguistic usage such expressions, which are of the greatest importance for the orientation in our environment and hence for our whole life. However, if questions like these are posed: Is the ego dissectible? Is an old man still the same individual as the child was? Does individuality live beyond bodily death? etc., then we have nothing to say but that there is no exact and binding demarcation for what constitutes an individual, and there can be none. Hume had shown in the above-mentioned *Treatise of Human Nature* that what we call "I" is nothing but a bundle or aggregate of different sensations which are in continuous flow and motion. Mach's assertion comes down to this, if translated into formal language: All sentences that state anything about the "ego," one's own or a foreign one, are resolvable into sentences in which only receptions (observations) are mentioned; these are connected among each other in a definite manner and have specific traits in common.

What "we are" we learn only by observations, which may or may not be intentional, but in any case consist of a sequence of "receptions." It makes no difference that this kind of observation, in contrast to others, is called "self-observation." A bodily pain with which we are afflicted, a flash of reminiscence that comes to us, a feeling of joy that penetrates us— all these are elements in Mach's sense, just as is a speck of color in the sky or a sound emitted by a piano. Elements of the first kind are distinguished by specific relations which connect each one with others of both groups; changes in the feeling of pain or joy to a certain extent influence *all* other receptions, while the influence of changes in external bodies is more limited. It seems reasonable, and is hardly considered by anyone as an arbitrary act, to collect those distinct elements which concern us more closely and to conceive them as a practical unit which we call our "self." In the same way other receptions are distinguished, which, in view of practical orientation, we summarize as the foreign selves.

But which elements *exactly* in every single case still belong to the denoted unit cannot always be decided. Is it our own or a foreign ego that acts in us while we are in a state of hypnosis? And where is the boundary between medically detectible hypnosis and influence on the will by persuasion or so-called moral constraint? All the elements are connected; everything experienceable forms a common mass which only in certain single places shows stronger and more durable connections. Without any doubt, we are driven by the vast majority of experiences to assume the unity and continuity of consciousness. But that cannot prevent us from noticing that it is an *assumed* point of view and occasionally must be abandoned when one reaches beyond the sphere of everyday experience for purposes of deeper study. In the same way, for the purposes of our everyday life, the earth on which we live is a plane; but as soon as we undertake a world cruise, we *have* to conceive it as a sphere.

*Mach's doctrine of elements, according to which the ego, the individual, is also formed only by a vaguely delineated and partly arbitrary summation of elements, does not mean that such a summary is useless or "false." The concept must only be given up as soon as scientific problems are studied to whose solution it is an impediment.*

7. *Success of Mach's Doctrines.* All of Mach's theories, and particularly the doctrine of elements, have encountered, as we mentioned be-

fore, the most vigorous criticism from philosophers and from many scientists. To what a high degree the later development of physics vindicated Mach and to what a great extent modern physics is indebted to him, we shall see more clearly in the following chapters. Even though the criticism of philosophers has gradually died down, it would be a mistake to think that they in any way have accepted Mach's viewpoint. On the contrary, we know that both school philosophy, by way of its secular oscillations, and public opinion in most countries, have now again reached a phase that is directed toward mysticism and obscurity far more than toward a desire for clarity; and there is almost no word today that has a worse reputation with the public than the word "enlightenment."

But the enlightening insights due to Mach are not among those that have to wait for loud and explicit acceptance or even for recognition by competent scholars. For his ideas gradually and unnoticeably penetrate into the consciousness of the educated and there they find their proper place, not as artificial, lifeless philosophisms, and not as destroyers of useful traditions, but as their natural continuation and completion. In the same way, people gradually, and without explicit renunciation of old beliefs, got used to admitting, after Copernicus, that the earth revolves about the sun, although this idea too aroused objections that seemed, at one time, insurmountable. The history of the origin of the world, about which today there is more or less agreement in principle, and other subjects with which the old mythologies dealt, are other good examples; they show that there is no need for an "official" adoption of enlightening doctrines or for a formal discarding of old antithetical ideas which for some reason had become customarily accepted. The intelligent man who is not concerned with scientific activity in some specialty is often more ready for an expedient change of viewpoint, ideology, and outlook than the scholar.

Philosophers thought that they had found a particularly effective argument against Mach when they claimed that he and his disciples did not act at all according to his doctrine as soon as they worked as physicists or pursued any other activity in life. They preach the dissolution of the world into simple sense elements, but, confronted by an ordinary physical problem or a practical situation, act like any nonpositivist. To this we may answer, that he who believes in the motion of the earth about the sun does not always wear an overcoat for protection from the resulting wind, and he who is firmly convinced that sounds are produced by the vibrations of bodies can still enjoy a violin concert in the same way as the one who is not educated in physics, without continuously analyzing what he hears into simple component oscillations. Not even if one works on the practical construction of musical instruments, need one always refer to the concept of vibration; most of the time it suffices to apply the known practical rules which have been *derived* from the theory of acoustics and made understandable by it.

Thus, it is not Mach's intention that his doctrine be applied to any concrete problem for whose solution the customary means are sufficient. The theory demarcates the boundaries (or investigates them) within which the application of customary conceptual abbreviations is still useful, and it interferes only in more distant areas, e.g., where it is necessary to recognize pseudo problems as such, or in the boundary region between two sciences where from a higher point of view the auxiliary concepts have to be modified; or, finally, when a decisive widening of our sphere of experience makes a change of basic concepts advisable. In each of these respects Mach's theory has already proved its merit. It will surely experience modifications as time goes on, but its essential core will very probably be retained.

*The function of Mach's doctrine of elements is a regulative one; it points out the limits within which the customary auxiliary concepts (like body, substance, mass, individual, etc.) are applicable, by disclosing their origins. All of these concepts are aggregates of elements, formed under the impulse of specific limited needs; they become detrimental to further development if they are retained too far beyond these limits. Notwithstanding the expediency, and even indispensability, of such auxiliary concepts in wide areas of life and science, a critical attitude toward them must, as time goes on, gain more and more ground within the ever-growing realm of human experience.*

### CHAPTER 8

# protocol sentences

1. *Logical Empiricism.* During the last few decades Mach's doctrine of elements has been given a new form, mainly through the valuable activities of the so-called Vienna Circle. In the preceding chapter we pointed out the parallelism between formal and material language. Many statements which apparently refer to the rest of the world of experience really are statements about the language in which we describe the world of experience. In other words: Apparently material assertions, if studied more thoroughly, often prove to be syntactical sentences. Changing the wording of a statement in such a way that its syntactical character becomes clearly recognizable is called, following Carnap, translation from the material into the formal mode (Chapter 7, 2). If we transform in this sense Mach's conception of "elements, of which for us the world is composed," into formal language, we arrive at the concept that is considered the core of *logical empiricism,* as represented mainly by Carnap, Otto Neurath, and Philipp Frank. Mach's "elements" ("sensations," "sense impressions," "receptions") are replaced in the new language by simplest, not further reducible, statements, which are known as "protocol sentences," "element sentences," or "atomic sentences." We saw in the earlier chapters that our point of view of "connectibility," too, leads to the demand for simple and unmistakable basic sentences for every theory and hence for every linguistic structure.

It is true that full agreement has not yet been reached, even among the closest followers of logical empiricism, as to the exact definition of protocol sentences and the questions what concrete sentences belong among them and how they are to be used in detail. The opinion advanced in this book, according to which one is really dealing with Mach's elements—only translated into the formal language—has so far hardly been formulated explicitly. In any case, we agree with Carnap that the question of element sentences is the basic problem of the logic of science (epistemology). Contained in it are problems to which one refers as those of "verification," of "the empirical basis," etc. We also, as Carnap and Neurath do, reject the "absolutism" of element sentences, which would imply the existence of a system of *definitely fixed* basic sentences to which everything else can be reduced by standard rules. Our fundamental conception remains that language, knowledge, and scientific theory grow simultaneously. If, metaphorically speaking, the element sentences are called the foundation on which the structure of science is built, then with the progressive growth of the building the foundations have to be not only completed and widened, but also internally modified (quite apart from the point that the methods of construction, i.e., the syntactical rules, are subject to change). Therefore it is utopic to think that, starting from a given complex of element sentences, one could, by carefully following all syntactical rules, arrive at an "encyclopedia of the sciences" which could command a validity of higher rank than that possessed by any of the existing individual sciences. All we can attempt to do is by analysis and continuous criticism of linguistic usage to further the connectibility; a part of this work is an exploration of the basic sentences of all theories and all communicable knowledge.

*One of the most essential problems of epistemology is the task that has occupied us already in the preceding chapter, namely, to explore that stock of simplest and not further reducible sentences to which the statements of science and of everyday life can be reduced.*

2. *Solution in Principle.* The expression "protocol sentence" is meant to indicate that one is dealing with statements having immediate, present events as their subject and which are instantly written down (or otherwise recorded), as is the case with protocols in the juristic sense. According to the conception of Carnap (1932), one might imagine schematically that all pertinent experiences, sensations, feelings, and thoughts are recorded in the form of a written (or mentally fixed) protocol and then become the basis of further study. In actual scientific work the taking of the protocol and its study (together with that of other protocols) are not distinctly separated from each other, but epistemological examination does well to keep the two acts apart.

Another necessary idealization leading to a useful conception of the protocol sentence is the following. The actual laboratory protocol of a physicist usually contains data about the arrangement of the measuring apparatus, about the electric circuitry, the pointer readings of the different instruments, etc. But this should not be considered as an original protocol, since it still includes sentences in whose construction other protocol sentences were used or—speaking in the material mode—since it contains sentences that do not describe immediately observed facts. Such a real protocol must be further analyzed and resolved until it becomes a sequence of simplest atomic sentences like those considered above. The "original" protocol consists only of very short, very simple expressions corresponding to immediate perceptions, e.g., "here pointer at five," "there red spot of short duration," etc. But even a word like "pointer" already says too much. There should really be only a denotation of a certain movable something which, in connection with other, earlier and later receptions, is recognized as a thing to be called "pointer." The same is true about the word "five," which simply takes the place of a sign for a specific place apprehended by the eye. It is only through the use of many other protocols that we find the name "five" or the idea connected with this name of a number. The correct ideal protocol consists of nothing but single, individual hints to the immediately present.

Of course, one must not believe that such a minutely detailed protocol of any event, not to mention a modern physical experiment, could really be written down from beginning to end. Thousands of years of development of human language and of human intelligence created the innumerable abbreviations and condensations that we use continuously almost without being aware of them. If we did not have these abbreviations at our disposal, we could hardly carry on our lives for a moment in the circumstances determined by the community of civilization in which we exist. Almost every sentence of a civilized language, if resolved into the simplest element sentences or reduced to them, would require entire volumes of written stuff. Only a quite primitive existence, filled with the most elementary reactions to natural stimuli, could actually be described if one were forced to use the form of complete analysis of expression.

But this is not the goal or problem of the epistemologist at all. He is not interested in the actual carrying out of the analysis, but in its possibility in principle and particularly in the fact that a (partial) reduction in specific cases may give valuable insights. In the same way, analytic geometry claims that *any* arbitrary curve could be represented with sufficient accuracy by an equation in Cartesian coördinates. But if one were to try to find the equation of the curve described by the needle of a phonograph while playing a record, one would never arrive at the result. Nevertheless, nobody doubts the validity of the claim of analytic geometry and the immense value of this concept in the sciences and hence in practical life.

*The analysis of a real protocol into elementary protocol sentences which express only the presently apprehended is a postulate whose expediency has to be tested by its use in theory. The practical impossibility of analysis in a concrete case is not a valid objection.*

3. *The Form of the Protocol Sentences.* As compared to the importance of the principle of reduction of everything expressible to elementary sentences, the remaining differences of opinion concerning the exact wording, the linguistic form, and the demarcation of the protocol sentences

seem to be of minor consequence. Carnap asks, for instance, whether expressions like "blue" or "hot" should really be allowed to appear in the protocol, or whether there should only appear such combinations as "blue objects" or "hot body," etc. He thinks that the first alternative would correspond to Mach's doctrine of elements, while the second might be preferred from the point of view of holism. It remains questionable whether the holistic philosophers will be satisfied with this concession; we shall have occasion later (Chapter 22) to return to them. But, anyway, surely this controversy cannot be resolved, since it is not quite clear what in a protocol sentence the words "blue body" precisely mean, or what is supposed to be the difference between this expression and the shorter one, "blue." We must not judge the protocol language, which is formed, so to speak, of crude reactions to simple experiences, by the standard rules for the use of words that hold in a developed scientific language. One will have to modify here even the rules of linquistic grammar (Chapter 6, 1). If we say that protocol sentences are unmisunderstandable statements (Chapter 7, 1), we mean that one disregards here distinctions like those between "hot" and "hot body." The element sentence contains only a *hint,* and its understandability rests upon a very rough agreement in the use of a restricted number of fundamental words.

Otto Neurath has objected to several points in Carnap's position. He contends, and we agree with him here, that it is impossible to construct a scientific language out of "clean atomic sentences," i.e., out of elementary statements that are, in every sense, unassailable and formulated precisely according to fixed rules and of a fixed vocabulary. Neurath, however, destroys the basis of the entire conception as soon as he demands that protocol sentences, as well as all other sentences, must "prove" themselves, and must in cases of failure be discarded. No, the element sentences (or, in the material mode, the elements) are the only objects about which statements can be made that are not themselves element sentences. If John sees a table and, as a joke or a trick, puts down in the protocol that he saw a chair, then the protocol is not discarded, but is considered and used in connection with other protocols which say something about John's behavior in comparison with that of other observers. If somebody reads a pointer position distorted by parallax, then what he saw and recorded in the protocol is not false but has to be used in connection with other receptions about optical phenomena and permits a conclusion which is not in contradiction with the original observation. No statement that contradicts a protocol sentence is right. The protocol sentences themselves never contradict each other; if need be they must be considered together with other sentences which describe the behavior of the individual observers. We shall not go here into questions of detail posed by Neurath and others, concerning the external form of the "protocol" as a whole. We stick to the concept of the protocol *sentences* in which, as we have pointed out, we see the linguistic expression of Mach's "receptions."

Some remarks of Moritz Schlick's are enlightening and only seemingly contrary to Carnap's. Schlick prefers to speak, instead of protocol sentences, of "statements of fact," e.g., "here yellow meets blue now," "here now pain," etc. In such sentences, says Schlick, the act of comprehending (the words) coincides with that of verification; they sound convincing much as tautologies do. This is approximately what we expressed by saying that there exists satisfactory agreement about the correspondence of sounds (words) to certain experiences in very simple cases, to wit, the cases of the element sentences. There seems to be nothing but purely formal difference between Schlick's "statements of fact" and protocol sentences: "On such and such a date at such and such a time, John Smith observed at such and such a place . . ." Perhaps one may consider Schlick's formulation a closer approximation to Mach's doctrine of elements; but it is by no means in contradiction to the basic concept of the protocol sentence.

*Some differences of opinion still existing about the form of the protocol sentences do not touch the core of the matter and can be resolved satisfactorily.*

4. *The Concept of Reduction.* What does it mean to "reduce" statements to protocol sentences? What role do the protocol sentences play in science and everyday conversation? Do they stand at the historical origin of language, or do they form only its logical basis? Such questions occur to everybody who approaches this line of thought for the first time.

In the first place, one cannot deal with a single sentence when the problem of reducibility is posed; one has to take into consideration a whole system of connected statements, e.g., all the propositions of physics or the complete description of some area of practical activity. A part of the system plays the role of linguistic rules, i.e., it fixes the usage of expressions, idioms, etc., or restricts their meaning in a certain way. It is assumed, of course, that these linguistic rules are satisfied by the other statements, or that "connectibility" is secured to this extent. Now imagine the system in question to be supplemented by a further set of connectible statements which were omitted before only because they are considered self-evident, or at least known and familiar to those for whom the communication is intended. The supplementary sentences are such that through them, in principle, everyone who can understand nothing but the simple expressions used in protocol sentences is put in a position to understand the original statements in an unambiguous way. Here "understand " (in both places) means only to know the relations of words to experiences. We imagine individuals who are familiar with these relations as far as the expressions occurring in the element sentences are concerned; only to such persons can a communication be addressed. Now, it is our claim that the supplement added to the given system of statements establishes a relation also between the original statements and experienceable impressions. The simplest, although not always an applicable, form of supplementation would be a successive replacement of single expressions by their definitions. It is the possibility of such or any other supplementation and mediation that we mean when we say in short that the given statements are "reducible" to protocol sentences or, in the material mode of language, to elementary experiences.

In contemporary physics, there is general agreement that reduction of all statements in this sense is feasible in principle. This does not refer to the rather narrow view of some experimental physicists who reject a part of physical theories (mostly those originated in the last twenty years) as nonempirical, and claim for the older theories that they directly reproduce actual experiences. In Part III we shall deal in more detail with the whole structure of theoretical physics.

In the language accompanying the practical actions of everyday life, expressions whose reducibility to elementary experiences in the foregoing sense is not recognized are said to be "unintelligible." The difference between the situation here and the more perfect system of scientific statements is only that in the first case there is often no clear understanding about the linguistic rules to be applied; hence the area of connectibility remains vague and therefore the necessary supplementation is anything but uniquely determined. The smaller the sphere of experience in which we move (in formal language, the more restricted the range of statements in question), the easier is a practically unique reduction.

The situation is different in certain disciplines usually denoted as the "humanistic sciences," including the greater part of the discussions of school philosophy. Here, generally the opinion is still rampant that there exists a "higher kind of understanding" than the reduction of all statements to elementary experiences, mediated by a system of tacitly admitted supplementary sentences. People speak here of "Einfühlung," of "deeper penetration," of "inner insight," or of "recognition of the essence" and contrast this to the "superficial" understanding attained in the natural sciences. In later chapters (Chapters 17 and 18) we shall return to this conception; at this point we only want to make clear what we mean by reducibility.

*If we say that any statement can be reduced to protocol sentences, we mean that the statements can be supplemented by further (explanatory) sentences in such a way that for those who understand the protocol language a correspondence between these statements and experienceable events is established.*

5. *The Postulate of Reducibility.* We have already pointed out that the reducibility of scientific theories to element sentences forms for us a *postulate* which we cannot "prove" by actually carrying out the reduction in every case. The situation has sometimes been regarded as similar to that of the older so-called materialistic philosophy which claimed that all observable phenomena should be reducible to the motion of atoms. This theory is best known in the form given to it by Laplace. He spoke of a superintelligent being who, by solving all the equations of motion, on the basis of the given present conditions, could predict any phenomenon of the future. Laplace's postulate of the reducibility of all of physics to the laws of Newtonian mechanics is no longer regarded as valid.

The opponents of positivism often like to mention this analogy because it suggests that the new idea of "reduction," to protocol sentences or to Mach's elements, will also prove to be useless in time. In so far as this is only a reminder of the fact that no scientific theory, and one of great generality least of all, is safe against a later alteration or even rejection, we accept this warning without objection. Far be it from us to claim that we can present the final norms of all knowledge never to be changed in the future; such claims we leave to those philosophers who stand on other grounds.

But one often finds this criticism presented in a certain form which requires a short reply here. Some people pretend that Laplace's conception —and ours also—is "metaphysical" or contains at least a metaphysical element. (It is nothing rare at all that followers of metaphysics use such an objection in the sense of a reproach.) To that we have to reply that Laplace's theory gave a quite concrete picture of the anticipated further development of physical theories. For a long time, and in certain areas of science even in our day, every possible effort has been made to give physical hypotheses a form corresponding to this picture. Today we are generally of the opinion that this goal is not attainable and in a sense one can now regard Laplace's prediction as disproved. But a proposition that can be tested by observable phenomena (here the development of science) and, as the case may be, can be recognized as false, does not deserve the label "metaphysical." We regard the Laplacean hypothesis, as well as our own of the reducibility of all scientific statements to element sentences, as a normal thesis of positive science, connectible with the linguistic rules in question and hence meaningful. Since, as we shall discuss in more detail later, we consider any *general* statement of a positive science as a hypothesis, it follows without further comment that we have to leave the test of our claim to the future.

*The assumption of the reducibility of all scientific (and of many other) statements to element sentences is a postulate or a hypothesis about*

*whose usefulness the further development of the sciences will have to
decide. Certainly it contains nothing "metaphysical."*

6. *Descartes' Starting Point.* The problem that led us to the theory
of protocol sentences or of elements in the sense of Mach was not unfamiliar to the philosophers of earlier times. Historically, the problem appears as the search for the "philosopher's stone," for the ultimate foundation of knowledge, for a safe basis and starting point of all further investigation. It was perhaps Descartes, among the earlier authors, who most
clearly expressed the aspiration for an absolutely unassailable basis of
thought in his "Discours de la méthode pour bien conduire sa raison et
chercher la vérité dans les sciences," which appeared about 300 years ago.
The well-known result at which Descartes arrived is formulated in the
famous statement:

And noticing how this truth "I think, therefore I am," was so firm and assured
that all the most extravagant propositions of the skeptics could not shake it, I
judged that I could take it without any scruple as the first principle of the
philosophy I sought.

Here, in a certain way, an attempt is made to reduce the whole of science
to one single protocol sentence.

After what we have said, it is obvious that we cannot regard Descartes's
*"cogito ergo sum"* as a self evident or immediately clear statement. At
most one could admit the first part, "I think," as an element sentence; but
then it would be better, as Lichtenberg has pointed out, to say "it thinks."
The second part has the form of a logical inference and hence uses a
complicated relationship whose meaning can be understood only by the
presentation of numerous applications in different fields. Finally, the "I
am" confronts us with the extremely difficult concept of the existential
being, which can hardly be called immediately understandable by anyone. It is doubtful whether such a sentence could have been proposed in
a language that does not allow (as Latin, French, German, English, and
others do) the confusion of the connective "is" with the existential "is."
Incidentally, in all of Descartes' writings that have some problem of the
natural sciences as their subject, one will hardly ever find anything that
could be said to have been based upon the philosophical premise expressed
in *"cogito ergo sum."*

However, though we have to reject the *result* of Descartes' search for
an ultimate or starting point of knowledge, as summarized in his formula,
yet we are highly appreciative of the founder of Western philosophy with
respect to his method and epistemological point of view. The enunciation
of his four maxims of research, obvious though they may seem today, was
in his time a liberating deed, and even today one can only wish that every
scholar would act according to them.

In spite of personal restraint, Descartes was an effective opponent of theology and scholasticism, the ruling powers of his time, and against the belief in revelation as the true source of knowledge. After three centuries of broad and fruitful development of science, for which Descartes paved the way, the situation is different today only in degree. For if one strives today for an unprejudiced and reasoned treatment of basic problems, then one has as opponents first the school philosophers, then some of the specialist scholars, and finally, popular writers who advocate mysticism and myths. In opposition to all these we invoke Descartes' appreciation of clarity:

I judge that I can take it as a general rule that those things which we conceive of most clearly and most distinctly are quite true.

And we find with Descartes that the real problem lies in this:

But there remains the one difficulty of exploring well which things are the ones we conceive of most distinctly.

*Even though we do not accept the formula "cogito ergo sum" as a useful starting point for epistemological research, we regard Descartes, with his pronounced will for clarity, for criticism, and for intellectual responsibility, as one of the decisive founders of the scientific conception of the world.*

7. *The Significance of Analysis.* We have arrived at the end of those discussions which are to paraphrase the concept of analysis as we think of it. The most essential of our results can be summarized in the following statements:

(1) We are not dealing with an analysis of "reason" or of the human "capacity" for knowledge, but we attempt to analyze the expressions of human intelligence.

(2) In order to decide whether a statement, a sequence of sentences, or any communication is "meaningful," we have to find out with what set of linguistic rules it is connectible. Only within such a set, i.e., within a "language," may one ask for the meaning and significance of a communication.

(3) As a basis of all linguistic rules and as a point of departure for all further statements, there appear certain element sentences, or protocol sentences, which express actual present experience by means of a limited number of simple signs, whose immediate intelligibility is assumed.

(4) In the transformation from the formal to the material mode of language, Mach's elements correspond to the protocol sentences.

(5) More complicated assertions are reduced to elementary ones by the addition of a system of supplementary (explanatory) sentences which,

for those who understand the element statements, supply the bridge between those assertions and experienced facts.

(6) An exact, complete, or final system of knowledge cannot be built up from element sentences and linguistic rules, just as it is impossible to give a complete theory of *all* physical phenomena. One has rather to assume that the stock of basic sentences, as well as the methods of derivation, will in time be amplified by essential additions.

These formulations may seem a bit vague and it may perhaps be objected that they contribute too little to the solution of the problem of finding criteria for the evaluation of scientific theories and doctrines of other kinds. With respect to this we may point out the following:

Our results are incompatible with the point of view that we have called "negativistic" (Chapter 5). No theory that sets feeling and instinct against intellect is reconcilable with what we propose as analysis. Moreover, our method allows us to differentiate between metaphysical doctrines and scientific ones in the sense that the ranges of connectibility in the two cases are most unequal (see Chapter 21). Third, we propose for the individual branches of science as well as for science as a whole a definite program: the postulate of the reducibility in principle to immediately intelligible element statements and of the gradual constitution of concepts. Although this principle is recognized today to a certain extent, science is still far from making use of it for the discarding of pseudo problems in *all* cases. Thus, for example, a slogan such as "psychology without a soul" does not pose a problem for us, because we know that "soul" is an abbreviation of the same kind as "thing" or "body," and the soul is no more or less "real" than the body. The following chapters will lead us to an application and therefore an elucidation of these concepts. But the accusation that our results are empty, that they are of no avail and do not lead to any consequences, will even at this point—in spite of the intentionally vague formulations—be recognized as unjustified.

*The point of view of analysis as developed in the preceding chapters, the concepts of connectibility and of reducibility to elements or element sentences, lead to concrete criteria for the study and evaluation of practical and scientific lines of thought.*

# the exact theories

Das Höchste wäre zu begreifen, dass alles Faktische schon Theorie ist.

The highest achievement would be to grasp that whatever we call a "fact" is already theory.

*Goethe*

CHAPTER 9

# axiomatics

1. *High-School Axiomatics.* Early in our high-school education all of us had occasion to learn certain "axioms" of geometry and arithmetic. They were presented as irrefutable truths and soon came to haunt our memories like nightmares. Here are familiar examples of such propositions: every quantity is equal to itself; the whole is bigger than any of its parts; all right angles are equal to each other; and so on. Two things were asserted of these axioms: in the first place, that they are clearly self-evident, and in the second place, that all mathematical theorems follow from them in a strictly logical way.

The student, normally, does not feel any apprehension toward the assertion of obviousness. For how, indeed, could he imagine that a quantity is *not* equal to itself? The situation is not quite the same concerning the claim that all mathematical propositions are derived from the axioms, and exclusively from them. Here, the intelligent student soon senses that in the customary derivations many other "self-evident" concepts besides the explicitly stated axioms have been used. From the modern investigations of the foundations of geometry we know that no geometry can be built up from the few basic propositions that are listed as axioms in the school books. Hilbert's axiomatics, for example, comprises five groups of axioms, among which are propositions such as the so-called axiom of continuity, which is certainly a far cry from the simple statements of the high-school textbook.

Nevertheless, it may be argued that the simple high-school axiomatics is useful for training the student in the method of logical deduction. But this practice has serious deficiencies too. For in such a sentence as: the whole is larger than any of its parts, even the meanings of the words themselves are rather obscure. The statement presupposes that the student to whom it is addressed is, from his everyday language experience, acquainted with the two relations, part to whole and larger to smaller. The axiom asserts that these two relations, in a certain sense, are in each instance simultaneously present or not present, and hence that one can discuss independently the presence of the one as well as of the other in every case. In some examples this is evidently more or less true. For if one says that France is part of Europe, it is generally admitted that France must be smaller than Europe, although, even in this instance, some acquaintance with the concept of area has to be presupposed. However, consider the following: according to common usage it is quite legitimate to say that sound sleep is a part of one's well-being; here, if we really consider it as an independent property and not simply as one aspect of the relation part to whole, the question of bigger and smaller breaks down. One might object that such cases are not meant by the axiom; but this would mean that the given proposition needs a preceding explanation and thus cannot stand at the base of a logically constructed system. From an ambiguous premise one cannot draw unambiguous conclusions. No proposition that presupposes complicated experiences and appeals to a necessarily vague use of colloquial language can be fit to serve as the starting point of a rigorously systematized branch of science.

There have been frequent objections to the so-called axiomatic method of instructing the beginner. However, most of them were made from a point of view quite different from-ours. In general, such a procedure has been criticized as "too formal," appealing too little to intuition and thus "apart from life." These are clearly considerations of a pedagogic nature, with which we need not concern ourselves here. Our critique is directed from the purely logical point of view.

*The formulation of axioms found in high-school textbooks, being based on uncertain and imprecise customs of language and therefore unsuited for drawing unambiguous conclusions, is a failure.*

2. *Classical Axiomatics.* Historically, we find the origin of axiomatics in the tradition of Euclid's *Elements* of geometry. However, the presently existing Greek text begins with a number of definitions, which are followed by five postulates and nine common notions. In the older Latin translations, the latter (among which is, for example, the addition of equals results in equals) are named "communes notiones sive axiomata." According to our contemporary terminology, the "postulates," e.g., the parallel postulate, would also count among the axioms.

The remainder of Euclid's first book consists of theorems and solutions of problems for which the proofs are always explicitly derived from the preceding definitions, postulates, and common notions. The subsequent books contain further definitions (of the circle and the tangent to the circle, etc.), from which additional theorems are derived by means of the original axioms. Here the relation of the various propositions is clear: at first definitions are given, then unproved statements are made about the defined things, and finally other statements are derived from these by ordinary deductive methods.

We find the same schema in the work which about two thousand years later became the foundation of mathematical physics—Newton's mechanics in the *Philosophiae naturalis principia mathematica.* It begins with a series of eight definitions for the concepts of mass, force, and so on. Next, we find the assertion that words such as time, space, location, and motion do not need any definition—only certain refinements. After these follow the "axiomata sive leges motus," while the consequences of the laws of motion form the bulk of the work. We shall not discuss the question here of how far it is really possible to derive rigorously the laws of motion of a rigid body (for example, the physical pendulum) without any premises but those expressed in Newton's three laws of motion.

However, the Newtonian mechanics is above all useful in offering us instructive insight into the construction of an axiomatic system, and the relation of definitions and axioms. Without a doubt the principal part of the Newtonian system is contained in the Second Law of Motion (which includes the first one, the so-called Law of Inertia): "Mutationem motus proportionalem esse vi motrici impressae . . ."; "the change of motion (of momentum, as we should say today) is proportional to the impressed force . . ." Hence, if no impressed force is present, the motion remains unchanged (which is the Law of Inertia). One may compare this with the preceding definition (IV): "Vis impressa est actio in corpus exercita, ad mutandum eius statum vel quiescendi vel movendi uniformiter in directum"; "the impressed force is the action on a body that changes its state of rest or of uniform rectilinear motion." As one can see, the axiom is anticipated by the definition. For, if an impressed force is defined as that which changes the state of motion, it follows that in the absence of impressed forces the uniform rectilinear motion remains unchanged. Thus we see that definitions and axioms are not independent of each other at all, and one recognizes the naïveté of the notion that the axioms by themselves state anything *"about"* the defined concepts. The relation between definitions and postulates in Euclid is quite the same, though not so immediately apparent.

*The classical axiomatics of Euclid and Newton, which for a long time were taken as the model for the construction of every branch of the exact sciences, are characterized by a subtle confusion of apparent definitions and explicit postulates, which in fact cannot be regarded as independent of each other.*

3. *Mach's Reform.* In the area of Newtonian mechanics the confusion arising from an insufficient differentiation between definitions and axioms was remedied by Ernst Mach. It was in Mach's *Mechanics,* pub-

lished in 1883, that for the first time the principle was established which today is so generally accepted and which forms the essence of modern axiomatics. It can be briefly stated by saying that the fundamental concepts are *defined by the axioms,* that is, that, apart from the introduction of new terms, there are no definitions in addition to the axioms at the basis of a deductive science. We shall elucidate this by the example of mechanics.

There are two new basic concepts that enter into the construction of Newtonian mechanics—those of force and of mass. Newton explains mass in his first definition as "quantity of matter." One notices immediately that this definition is completely empty and in no way helps us to gain an understanding of the phenomena of motion. All one has to do is to reflect that it would be possible to substitute the words "quantity of matter" for the word "mass" wherever it appears in a contemporary text, i.e., not to have the sequence of letters m-a-s-s occur at all, and then one would be able to dispense with the first definition completely without anything in mechanics being changed. If we disregard the fact that perhaps in the age of Newton one phrasing was more colloquial than the other, the definition serves, in fact, only as the equation of two expressions, both of which are equally in need of an explanation.

On the other hand, we have already shown that Newton's definition of force largely anticipates the content of the first two laws of motion: the force neither changes the location of a body, nor determines its velocity, but rather *changes its velocity.* Thus force is first defined as something that changes the velocity, and then the law is stated that velocities are changed by forces. This manner of inference has been well put by Molière; the poppy seed is soporiferous; why? because it has the power of soporiferousness.

But scoffing here is ill-advised, for Newton's *Principia* expresses one of the most far-reaching and original discoveries ever made in physics. One can conveniently describe it by two statements: first, the circumstances in which a body is at a given time (its position with respect to other bodies, and other observable properties) determine the instantaneous *change* of velocity (or the acceleration) but not its velocity; and second, for different bodies under the same circumstances the observed accelerations differ by a numerical factor which is proper to the body in question, and hence is a constant for *each body considered.* These are the two discoveries of Newton. Once they are found, it is easy enough to add that the constant associated with each body shall be called "mass" (or if one wishes, "quantity of matter") and the circumstances determining the acceleration, "impressed force."

Thus definitions are reduced to explanations of words, to the (in principle, dispensable) introduction of abbreviations. Everything essential is contained in the axioms themselves. They delineate the concepts, for which verbal denotations can then be chosen as the need arises. We shall return to the contents of the Newtonian propositions in Chapter 12 and shall only summarize briefly here.

*As Mach showed, the Newtonian foundations of mechanics can be remodeled in such a way that one does not begin with definitions, but with assertions (axioms), which also suffice to define the fundamental concepts of force and mass. Then, all one need add to the axioms is explanations of words serving as verbal abbreviations.*

4. *Hilbert's Geometry.* It was David Hilbert who for the first time, in the year 1899, created the new form of axiomatics for geometry. This was the starting point for the extension of the axiomatic method to many branches of the exact sciences. As had become apparent from the works of Euclid and several of Hilbert's predecessors (Pasch, Veronese, and others), geometry is particularly well suited for such a treatment. The properties of space, described by geometry, are the simplest physical phenomena known. They do not refer back to experiences of a different kind as, for instance, mechanics has to refer back to geometry even in its fundamental concepts of motion. Only *one* realm of general experience is used in geometry from the start—that of counting. In the construction of geometry the foundations of arithmetic are taken for granted.

Hilbert's system, as remarked before, differs from Euclid's in that it does not start with definitions of space elements, but considers these as defined by the axioms:

We consider three different systems of things: the things of the first system we call points . . . ; those of the second, straight lines . . . ; those of the third, planes . . . We think of the points, straight lines, planes in certain relations to each other and denote these relations by words as "lying," 'between,' 'parallel,' 'congruent,' 'continuous.' The precise and, for mathematical purposes, complete description of these relations is contained in the *axioms of geometry*.

Hilbert's first group of axioms contains the axioms of connection, examples of which are: two noncoincident points determine a straight line . . . ; there are at least four points that do not lie in one plane. (Notice here that the knowledge of counting is taken for granted.) The second group, the axioms of order, mainly delineate the concept "between"; for instance: among any three points of a straight line there is always one and only one that lies between the other two. These axioms are followed by the third group, the axioms of congruence, which explain the concept of equality. Here is the legitimate place for the proposition, every straight line is equal to itself. For this serves, together with other similar propositions, to determine precisely and completely the way in which the word "congruent" shall be used thereafter.

The main interest of geometric axiomatics is concentrated upon the parallel axiom, which forms Hilbert's fourth group. From the axioms of connection one can conclude only that two straight lines in a plane have either *one* point in common or none. Now the "parallel axiom" is added: through a point outside a given straight line there is at most one straight line that lies in the same plane and does not intersect the first one. It is a result (already found earlier) of far-reaching consequences that such an explicit assumption is necessary in order to draw the conclusions that form the contents of ordinary geometry. If one gives up this assumption, or replaces it by a different one, one can arrive at new geometric theories which contradict certain theorems of Euclidian geometry. Quite apart from the practical importance which these theories have acquired in modern times for the description of certain physical phenomena, they are highly instructive as regards the position of geometry, and hence also of the other exact sciences, in the total realm of our experience. We shall return to the contents of the so-called non-Euclidian geometry in the next section.

The last group of Hilbert's axioms contains the axioms of continuity which are missing in Euclid and whose necessity follows only from a more profound analysis of geometric propositions. Hilbert states the essential hypothesis here in the form of a "completeness" theorem: it is impossible to add to the system of points, straight lines, and planes another system of things such that in the resulting total system all the previously stated axioms are still valid. Hilbert shows how one can construct a manifold of points, straight lines, and planes in which all the remaining axioms are valid, but which does not satisfy the demand of completeness. This manifold does not yield a useful picture of the well-known geometric phenomena.

*Hilbert's axiomatics of geometry rigorously carries through the principle that the elementary concepts are to be defined by the axioms themselves; and, in particular, it demonstrates the role of the parallel axiom and the axiom of continuity.*

5. *Non-Euclidean Geometry.* The best-known and in many respects most important result of axiomatic investigations is the invention of the so called non-Euclidean geometries. We know today that Gauss had much of the essential knowledge (some of it since the year 1792), but refrained from publishing it because he was afraid of the "Geschrei der Böotier." This goes to show how strong the influence of traditional scholastic opinions may become and how necessary an education toward a free outlook and unprejudiced judgment is for the progress of science. The history of non-Euclidean geometry starts with the publication of a work by the Russian mathematician Lobachevski about 1840.

The essential point is to establish the following matter of fact: Dropping Euclid's parallel axiom (previously quoted in Hilbert's form) and substituting for it another suitable hypothesis but retaining all the others, it is possible, by the customary rules of deduction, to derive from this new set of axioms a new geometry. Such a geometric system *does not contain in itself any contradictions,* although it contradicts certain theorems of Euclidean geometry. This fact refutes the allegation that the theorems of geometry taught in our schools are *imposed by the laws of thought,* and absolutely assured truths, independent of all experience. In the philosophical system of Kant's *Critique of Pure Reason* this assertion plays a decisive role. Kant says,

For geometric principles are always apodictic, i.e., united with the consciousness of their necessity . . . ; theorems of this kind cannot be empirical judgments or conclusions from them.

There is no doubt that Kant wanted to establish with these words a fundamental and profound difference between the theorems of geometry and those of other natural sciences, such as optics or mechanics, for instance.

One often tries to make clear how a non-Euclidean geometry is possible by pointing out spatial phenomena that are governed by laws similar in structure to a non-Euclidean geometry. Imagine, for instance, the spatial situation on the surface of a sphere of very large diameter with creatures whose entire existence is limited to this two-dimensional surface. As long as they know only a limited portion of their world, i.e., only a piece of the spherical surface small compared to the diameter, they would have a geometry different in nothing from our Euclidean plane geometry. Their straight lines would be, in fact, arcs of great circles, these being the lines of shortest distance between two points (and the shapes of stretched strings) on the surface of the sphere. As soon, however, as the surface inhabitants extend their experience beyond the immediate neighborhood, they will be forced to change their hypotheses. There are no "parallel" lines on the spherical surface; all great circles intersect each other in two points. Now, it is indeed possible—by means which cannot be explained here in any detail—to describe the situation on the surface of a sphere in such a way that all statements become equivalent to those of a plane geometry in which the parallel axiom does not hold. But the same relation as that between a plane and a very large spherical surface exists also between the three-dimensional space described by Euclidean geometry and a "curved" space not satisfying the parallel postulate. Assume that the space we live in has an extraordinarily large "radius," i.e., an extremely slight "curvature"; then our measuring instruments would not be sufficiently accurate to determine practically whether the Euclidean or a modified geometry is in better agreement with the facts. But the decision would be of no practical interest, anyway, as long as the differences are not noticeable in some way. We may leave open the question whether today there is enough evidence for such a decision. The notion of "apodictic certainty" of the geometric theorems, however, has to be abandoned definitely.

*The study of axiomatics of geometry has proved that a consistent system of geometry not obeying the parallel axiom and hence not agreeing with the Euclidean geometry can be constructed; thus the assertion that the customary geometry is logically inevitable, apodictically certain, and independent of any experience, is disproved.*

6. *Applications of the Axiomatic Method.* Contemporary axiomaticists are mainly concerned with two general problems: the questions of *consistency* and of *independence* of the axioms. By a "consistency proof" is meant the demonstration that from an assumed set of axioms, using the recognized customary rules of inference, one can never deduce both the statements $A$ and non-$A$ (the contradictory opposite). Such a proof has so far, strictly speaking, never been given for any axiomatic system of general interest. All one has succeeded in doing is to reduce the consistency of, e.g., geometry (Euclidean as well as non-Euclidean) to the consistency of arithmetic. In other words, it has been shown that an inconsistency in the set of axioms of the particular geometry would imply an inconsistency in the structure of elementary arithmetic. It is only because one credits arithmetic with consistency that one believes this to be proved in the other cases. We shall return later to the problem in arithmetic itself (Chapter 11).

The question of independence is somehow related to that of consistency. The (consistent) group of axioms $A$ is said to be independent of the (consistent) group of axioms $B$, if the group $B$ can be exchanged for a different group $B'$ such that $A$ and $B'$ together again form a consistent system. It is, for instance, proved that the parallel postulate is independent of the axioms of connection, etc. In each case the consistency is measured by that of arithmetic. If an axiom proves to be dependent upon others, one can try to restrict it in such a way that the remaining weaker axiom becomes independent of them.

The usual theoretical discussion of axiomatic systems suggests a question which belongs to epistemology and which seems of importance to us. Are consistency, we ask, and perhaps independence, *all* one can demand of a set of axioms? Is every system that satisfies these conditions permissible, and are all these systems equally justifiable objects of scientific research? As long as this question is not formulated in another way it cannot be answered reasonably, for the meaning of what is "permissible" or a "justifiable object of scientific research" is not clear. Human activities, of which research is but an example, can only be described, i.e., studied and classified as to their relations to each other and to other facts. A "valuation" would be possible only after an arbitrary standard of values had first been adopted.

If we limit ourselves to an objective description of the situation, we find that there are two extreme cases. On one end we find axiomatic systems more or less similar to the rules of the game of chess. They satisfy all logical postulates but are far from being applicable to more vital phenomena. On the opposite end there are investigations that explicitly aim to influence practical action in certain areas of life, by, e.g., answering directly or indirectly questions arising from technology. All axiomatic systems fall somewhere between these two extremes.

In all cases, however, even in the case of the axioms of chess, there is but one way to establish a connection between the system of axioms and their consequences on the one hand and observable facts on the other: The words and phrases used for the basic or derived concepts of the axiomatic system must be given a more or less definite interpretation by reducing them to *protocol sentences* (Chapter 8, 4). We may agree with Hilbert that the words "point," "straight line," "plane" within the axiomatic system are nothing but arbitrary signs. Yet, if one substitutes for them the words "shoes" and "ships" and "sealing wax," attaching to these words their customary (incidental) meanings, one will find that the relations expressed in the axioms and theorems either are not reducible to protocol sentences or contradict certain protocol sentences. Two points determine a straight line: this is not only an axiom, but with the usual meaning of the words it is also the approximate expression of a matter of fact. That analogy breaks down if one asserts as an axiom that two shoes determine a ship. This situation can be described by saying that the axiomatic system itself remained intact, but it could not be applied. One may also adopt the formulation that an axiomatic system that with no choice of names (i.e., with no coördination of the arbitrary symbols to protocol statements) leads to useful applications in the indicated sense is "worthless." All systems of axioms considered in science are formulated in such a way that they are paralleled by some interpretation in terms of observable facts. As far as the non-Euclidean geometries are concerned, we have mentioned already that their application to observable space phenomena, with the assumption of a slight space curvature, seems possible. In modern relativity theory this is an indispensable tool for the description of physical facts.

*The connection of a system of axioms and their consequent theorems with reality, i.e., the meaning of its statements, has to be determined in the same way as that of all other statements, by coördinating the words and idioms used in them to elementary experiences by means of reduction to protocol statements. On this basis one can differentiate between axiomatic systems for which consistency and independence have already been proved, according to whether or not they can be used for the description of observable facts.*

7. *Axiomatization in General.* The axiomatic method, having had so great a success in geometry, has more recently been extended to various other parts of the natural sciences. We have mentioned previously the clarification of the foundations of mechanics due to Mach, an investigation that must be considered as a forerunner of modern axiomatics. Later, the model of geometry was used in a more formal manner to set up, among others, axioms of mechanics by G. Hamel, axioms of set theory by E. Zermelo, axioms of thermodynamics and axioms of the special theory of relativity by C. Carathéodory, etc. Attempts at extending the axiomatic method to many other branches of the natural sciences are in various stages of development.

The followers of modern axiomatics see in that method the highest form of scientific theory, the form toward which all scientific endeavor strives. Thus Hilbert said,

I think that everything that can be an object of scientific thought at all, as soon as it is ripe for the formation of a theory, falls into the lap of the axiomatic method and thereby indirectly of mathematics. Under the flag of the axiomatic method mathematics seems to be destined for a leading role in science.

If we disregard the reference to the place of mathematics (it is not at all obvious why an axiomatics of biology should subordinate biology to mathematics), there still remains the claim that every theory in a certain stage of its development takes the form of axiomatics. This form was defined by Hermann Weyl as "the complete collection of the basic concepts and facts from which all concepts and theorems of a science can be derived by definitions or deductions." In the last analysis, everybody who wants to exhibit a branch of science systematically intends to proceed according to this scheme, i.e., to collect all the essential facts in the fundamental theorems; it is only the manner in which this is done, its completeness and precision, that will not always be as Hilbert meant it. Nothing can be said against Hilbert's claim as long as the following two points are kept in mind.

In the first place, the axiomatic method is only a *form* of description, hence something that can be taken into consideration only after the essential content of what is to be described is known. It was the discovery of Newton, prepared by Galileo, that external circumstances (to a body) determine its momentary *change* of velocity (acceleration), and not the velocity itself. Once this discovery (or, if one prefers, the "invention") was made, it became another problem to put its content into a set of clean formulas that do not say too much or too little. To take another example, a long time ago it was found that in the mathematical concept of probability one deals with the limit of the relative frequency in an unlimited number of trials, where a certain irregularity in the sequence of the results is essential. Anyone who accepts this basic idea is faced with the problem of expressing the facts in a set of precisely formulated axioms (see Chapter 14). In geometry we find the same situation, only there the essential discoveries date so far back that we are not conscious of them any more. The axiomatization is always a secondary activity which follows the actual discovery of the pertinent relations and puts them in a precise form.

The second reservation one has to keep in mind against the exaggerated claims of the axiomaticists concerns the concept of absolute rigor. All followers of the axiomatic method and most mathematicians think that there is some such thing as an *absolute* "mathematical rigor" which has to be satisfied by any deduction if it is to be valid. The history of mathematics shows that this is not the case, that, on the contrary, every generation is surpassed in rigor again and again by its successors. All classical mathematicians, Gauss included, as any student today can show, have been guilty, on some occasion or other, of a faulty lack of rigor. Certain new developments of mathematics, of which we shall speak in Chapter 11, will show that some things that were taken as quite rigorous thirty or forty years ago have to be doubted today. There is by no means an eternally valid agreement about the admissible methods of logical deduction. Thus we have to regard the task of axiomatization of a science as a relative one, subject to change with time. One tries to give to the basic theorems of a theory such a form that they satisfy all *present* requirements of logical rigor.

*The axiomatic formulation of a discipline may be regarded in each period as the highest level of scientific presentation, if one keeps in mind, first, that it is merely a form, which can be taken into consideration only after the essential relations are known; and second, that the logical requirements which the axioms have to satisfy are themselves subject to evolution.*

### CHAPTER 10

# logistic

1. *Tautologies and Factual Statements.* "Mathematical logic" or "logistic" is a modern name for the fundamental system of logical rules, presented in the form of concise formulas, and the study of them. Before we discuss this matter, we have to find out what is meant here by "logical."

The present stage in the development of positivism is governed by an idea first enunciated by L. Wittgenstein, though in a slightly different form, and advanced with particular emphasis by the so-called Vienna Circle. It is the conception according to which all meaningful statements—or, as we prefer to say, all connectible statements (Chapter 6, 3)—have to be divided into two groups: those expressing a state of fact which can be tested by experience, and those which, independently of all experience, are true or false by virtue of their wording. Statements of the second kind are called "tautological" in the first instance and "contradictory" in the second. Tautological sentences form the content of logic, of pure mathematics, and of all other axiomatically formulated scientific theories.

At first sight it might seem that here Kant's a priori is revived, including the "synthetic judgments a priori" which are supposed to form the content of mathematics. However, the difference is quite considerable. A sentence is tautological if it is true independently of all experience, *because* it does not say anything about reality at all and is nothing but a reformulation or recasting of arbitrarily fixed linguistic rules (definitions). Consider for instance, the statement, the sum of two natural numbers is itself a natural number; everybody can see that this is a statement of a different kind from this: alcohol boils at a temperature of 78°C. For if we try to explain what we mean by the sum of two natural numbers, i.e., if we want to define the word "sum," or to give the rules according to which it is to be used, then necessarily these rules include the result that the sum is itself a natural number. The tautology is a little more difficult to recognize in the statement, the sum of two prime numbers, neither of which is 2, is an even number. Here one needs, in order to demonstrate the tautological and noncontradictory character of the statement, a "proof." But according to our fundamental conception every mathematical proof is the tautological transformation of definitions and other linguistic rules and in any case has nothing to do with observation and experience. Finally, as a third example we might take the assertion, every even number is the sum of two prime numbers. Here we have to remark that no living person today could say whether this is tautological or contradictory (true or false). But we know that this decision does not depend upon some sort of physical experiment or observation of facts, but can be made solely on the grounds of a study of definitions and a carrying out of calculations and similar transformations.

Thus, the theorems of logic and mathematics are in the framework of this conception "tautological," but neither synthetic nor a priori. They are not synthetic, because they say nothing about reality, and not a priori, because they do not come from a superempirical "source" but are the result of arbitrary definitions introduced by us. Furthermore, tautological character is by no means confined to mathematics; it is possessed by any system of sentences that is constructed according to the axiomatic method and that serves as the theoretical exposition of an area of facts, e.g., a chapter of biology.

*Theorems of logic and pure mathematics and of any axiomatically formulated theory are, according to the conception of L. Wittgenstein, "tautological," i.e., they do not say anything about reality and are nothing but transformations of arbitrarily agreed upon linguistic rules. The notion of tautology by no means coincides with that of Kant's a priori synthetic judgments.*

2. *Tautological Systems.* Against the thesis according to which logical, mathematical, and similar theorems are "tautologies," various objections have been raised. Some of them—and these can most easily be settled—originate in the rather unhappy choice of the name "tautology." Obviously Wittgenstein, and the members of the Vienna Circle (who like to call themselves today "logical empiricists"), have created a new concept by making the distinction between two kinds of statements, and for its denotation—even though in analogy with linguistic usage—they arbitrarily drew upon a word belonging to the existing language. But previously the word "tautology" had been used almost entirely in a derogatory sense, to designate empty or superfluous talk; by "tautology" one meant something like a sentence which, without any loss to the reader or listener, could just as well be omitted. The new use of the word is *burdened* with this old meaning and even people who are used to abstract thinking and who are quite familiar with the process of nomenclature in the exact sciences cannot always free themselves from this influence. Thus, a beautiful book

about *Numbers and Figures,* having two well-known contemporary mathematicians as authors, ends with a remark which shows how much the authors feel hurt by the thesis that "mathematics is fundamentally but a chain of tautologies." Having read the previous chapters of our book, the reader does not need any comment upon this psychologically understandable resistance to a new terminology.

It might be suggested that we replace the word "tautological" by "analytic," but that would result in much worse misunderstandings, since it would be reminiscent of Kant's concept of analytic judgments. We have shown above that tautologies in our sense are by no means Kant's a priori synthetic judgments. But neither are they his analytic judgments. According to Kant's theory and that of idealistic philosophy in general, there exist concepts, independently of all human influence and all linguistic conventions, whose delineation we can more or less precisely discover through pure thought. A statement which expresses the result of such acts of thinking is called an analytic judgment. We, however, mean by a tautology a sentence that is derived by *arbitrarily* fixed transformations of *arbitrarily* chosen basic assumptions. In this chapter we shall have to show first of all what such a system of tautological statements looks like and this will bring us back to the discussion of the axiomatic method. On the other hand, since the aim of all language, in everyday life as well as in science, is in our opinion to assert something about observable reality, i.e., to find statements verifiable in experience, we shall have to explain further the role of tautological systems in this respect.

By no means can we accept a view that would assign to tautological sentences something like dogmatic or absolute validity. At most one could call them "apodictic," as long as one keeps in mind the frame of reference that determines their range of validity. The starting theorems (definitions) as well as the rules of transformation (methods of deduction) are, as previously mentioned, to a certain degree arbitrary conventions. Even though at the present time among logicians there is, on most counts, agreement about the basic assumptions, there are still differences of opinion upon certain specific points, e.g., the axiom of the excluded middle (see Chapter 11, 4). A decision about whether one or the other of the logical systems is "right" is impossible. It is only the usefulness of a specific system for the representation of observable phenomena which can prove it to be more or less *expedient.*

*What contemporary logical empiricism calls tautologies must not be confused with the customary meaning of the word in ordinary language, nor with Kant's "analytic judgments." Tautologies have no absolute validity but are valid only within a specific system of basic logical concepts. The application of such a system as a means of representation of a part of reality determines its usefulness.*

3. *Basic Logical Relations.* The system of logistic (or, as it is often called today, of mathematical or theoretical logic) starts with the setting of the basic relations that can exist between statements. These fundamental connectives, of which there are four, are denoted in ordinary language by the expressions "and," "or," "not," "if . . . then." We call them, in this order, conjunction (also logical product), disjunction, negation, and implication (or conditional). The sign "and," for which we write simply a comma in the formulas, means, if put between two statements, that both statements are posited or assumed. The sign "or," whose abbreviation is "v" (*vel*), means that of the two statements between which it stands at least one (but not one and only one) is assumed. In order to indicate negation, i.e., the contradictory opposite, we use the sign "∼" put before or above the statement sign to which it applies. Implication may be expressed by an arrow, "→"; it signifies that if the left-hand statement is posited, the right-hand one is assumed to be posited too: the first one implies the second; the second is implied by the first.

To these basic concepts one can add others, e.g., that of equivalence; but one recognizes at once that this is dispensable, for by the equivalence of two statements one means that the first follows from the second and the second from the first. Hence equivalence is expressible by the two relations of implication and conjunction. If we want to use the formula way of writing, we must say that *"A equ B"* can be replaced by *"A→B, B→A".*

These remarks suggest the question whether all four of these relations are independent of one another or whether some of them can be derived from the others. The latter is, indeed, the case. It suffices, for instance, as one easily sees, to introduce the signs "v" and "∼" as undefinable basic signs, or, as Brentano has shown, only the concepts "and" and "not." We shall show how implication and disjunction can be expressed by the two signs "," and "∼".

That *B* follows from *A* means the same as that *A* and non-*B* cannot exist simultaneously. Hence, in order to express the implication, one has only to signify that the conjunction of *A* and non-*B* is not true. The sign *"A→B"* can therefore be replaced by *"∼[A,∼B]"*, which has to be read: *A* does not exist together with non-*B*. It is equally simple to express disjunction by means of conjunction and negation. That of the two statements *A* and *B* at least one is true can be expressed by stating that the statements non-*A* and non-*B* do not hold simultaneously. The compound of signs *"AvB"* is thus replaceable by *"∼[∼A,∼B]"*, which is to be read: non-*A* and non-*B* do not exist together.

A similar consideration shows that conjunction and implication are reducible to disjunction and negation. On the other hand, it is impossible to construct the other relations by means of negation and conjunction. Of course, it cannot be the purpose of such investigations to express all logical deductions, whenever they occur, by means of the two basic relations previously chosen. On the contrary, once we have seen that signs like "equ", "→", "v" can be replaced by suitable combinations of "," and "∼", we know that the new signs can be used as abbreviations. In the same way one seeks to form larger and more efficient units and by their means to reach more complicated deductive patterns. The whole of mathematics is a construction of this kind.

*The first steps at the basis of mathematical logic consist of showing how the various simplest relations—conjunction, negation, disjunction, and implication—are connected with one another and in a certain way can be reduced to each other.*

4. *Further Formalization.* The foregoing argument can be further formalized and then yields definite rules for the derivation of new tautologies. That is the essential aim of theoretical logic since Leibnitz, who must be considered the founder of the entire discipline. We start with two symbols, "F" and "T" (which stand for the words "false" and "true"), without giving any definition for them. To every statement we assign one of these two letters; that is, only such statements are admitted as premises as are accompanied by one of the symbols "T" or "F". Then one defines operations on statements (truth functions) by directing in what way the assignment of T or F to the objects of the operation transfers to the result.

The only operation acting on a *single* statement is the negation. It is defined by the rule that, if the statement $A$ has the truth value F, $\sim A$ has the truth value T, and if $A$ is assigned T, $\sim A$ is to be assigned F.

For every truth function that connects *two* independent statements, e.g., the implication "$A \rightarrow B$", there are four possible combinations of the assignments of T and F to the two parts. The implication "$A \rightarrow B$" is defined thus: the sign "$A \rightarrow B$" has the truth value F, if $A$ has the value T and $B$ the value F; in the other three cases "$A \rightarrow B$" has the value T. On the other hand, the definition of the disjunction "$A \lor B$" is this: the sign "$A \lor B$" has the value F if F is the value of both $A$ and $B$; otherwise its truth value is T. Once a number of symbols have been defined in this manner, one also knows the distribution of the T and F values in formulas that result from combinations. For instance, the combination "$A \rightarrow \sim B$" has the value F whenever both $A$ and $B$ have the value T; in all other cases, its value is T.

Of special interest are those formulas which have under all circumstances the value T. These are the actual propositions of mathematical logic. For example, according to the above conventions about the operations "∼" and "v" (negation and disjunction), the combination "$A \lor \sim A$" has always the value T. For $A$ and $\sim A$ cannot, according to the definition of "∼", both have the value F, and according to the definition of "v" the combination could have the value F only if both parts, the one before as well as the one after the sign "v", have the value F. The formula "$Av\sim A$" can be called the "theorem of the excluded middle" (in the simplest case). Other "always true" formulas or theorems in truth-function theory (propositional calculus) are: "$[(A{\to}B), (B{\to}C)]{\to}(A{\to}C)$" and "$(A{\to}\sim A){\to}\sim A$". The first one is, in words, the fact that $A$ implies $C$, or more briefly (but not exactly correctly), if $B$ follows from $A$ and $C$ follows from $B$, then it follows that $C$ follows from $A$. The second formula is the basis of the so-called indirect proof; for it says in words (approximately), if a statement implies its own contradiction, it follows that the statement is false.

If one writes down any formula consisting of complexes of the four signs we have introduced above and any letters $A,B,C, \ldots$ , then one can determine purely mechanically the truth conditions of the formula, and in this fashion it is possible to derive theorems. Further pursuit along these lines forms the first chapter of any textbook of mathematical logic, the so-called truth-function theory or propositional calculus, which has a certain analogy to elementary algebra.

*As in algebra, where according to fixed rules algebraic formulas and theorems are derived, truth-function theory arrives at formal laws determining the connection between the basic operations.*

5. *Difficulty of Deduction*. From the foregoing examples of theorems of truth-function theory, which of course can only give a faint idea of the first beginnings of mathematical logic, there are many interesting things to be learned. In the first place, they show how vague and unreliable ordinary linguistic usage is in such simple cases. For the sign "v", introduced above, corresponds to the English word "or" only when the latter is used in the sense of the Latin "vel", but not in the case of the *exclusive* "or" (aut). If "or" in this latter sense is to be expressed one has to write "$(AvB),\sim(A,B)$", i.e., "$A$ or $B$ and not at the same time $A$ and $B$". The sign "$\to$" of implication, too, does not always coincide with that which is customarily expressed by the words "it follows". According to our definition, "$A{\to}B$" is always true when $A$ is false, whatever $B$ may be, i.e., a false statement implies any arbitrary true or false statement. If, e.g., to the correct theorems of arithmetic the theorem "$2 \times 2 = 5$" is added, then any true or false result can be derived from the premises, in particular, of course, the theorem "$2 \times 2 = 4$". In the customary way of speaking it is not so; there the conception—which is not exactly definable —is used that from false antecedents only some conclusions, namely false ones, can be drawn.

On the other hand, our examples show how logical theorems can be constructed by applying arbitrarily adopted rules, as in a game. Such theorems represent "eternal truths" only as long as one takes the rules for granted. They do not become statements about reality, verifiable in experience, before the language of formulas is translated by a more or less vague correspondence into the language of everyday life. Analogously, in chess it is "unshakably true" that a player has lost the game when his king is open and without defense against the attack of his opponent. If one takes this theorem and gives the word "player," "king," "attack," "opponent," etc. the meanings customary in everyday language, it becomes vague and doubtful. There is here another analogy with the relation between logic and reality in that the theorem does not become meaningless, but must be considered false or true, according to experiential circumstances. We shall later return to this point (Chapter 10, 7).

The comparison with the game of chess can also serve to illustrate another important point. Thinking of certain situations in practical life where decisions are to be made, one might be inclined to believe that the difficulties arising here are due exclusively to vagueness, indefinite and flexible conditions, and the impossibility of exact description by language. If everything were as clear and unambiguous as in logic, one may think, then decisions would be easy, and almost obvious. The chess-game analogy refutes this idea. Taking, say, an advanced point in the development of the game as a start, in which, say, black has the next move, the set of all possible continuations of the game is completely given by the rules of chess. Thus it is uniquely "determined" which next moves of black will lead to certain loss, which will lead to certain victory, and finally, which leave open both possibilities. (Incidentally, one or another of these three classes of next moves may be empty; also, certain well-defined assumptions about the manner of playing of the opponent may be included in the premises.) But something that is determined theoretically or in principle is by no means actually *known*. The complete enumeration of all possible continuations of the game goes beyond our capabilities. Under certain conditions such an enumeration could be replaced by "theorems," i.e., by tautological transformations of the chess rules, perhaps of this form: For certain starting positions $(x)$ and next moves $(y)$, only a checkmate of black can result. To find such theorems, i.e., to derive them from the original rules, seems in the case of the chess game extraordinarily difficult. A type of game in which the players have too much knowledge of this kind at their disposal is of no interest for them; the game of nim is appreciated only by children.

Theoretical logic, including mathematics, is based upon a system of rules which is immensely more abundant, diversified, and complicated than that of chess; moreover, it is subject to change in time. Of all the theorems derivable in the system of rules, only an extremely small part has been found so far and further progress often presents extraordinary difficulty. However highly one may rate the difficulties of *practical* decisions that cannot be reduced to theoretical questions, there is no reason to underestimate the intricacies of decisions in logic and mathematics.

*The theorems of truth-function theory are additions to language indispensable for the purpose of higher precision. They do not contain anything that is not implied somehow in the basic assumptions (the rules of the game). Nevertheless, it remains a very hard problem, and one that can never be exhausted, to find explicitly all theorems that can be produced in this way.*

6. *Russell's Theory of Types.* We want to mention here another important chapter of logistic which shows more clearly than truth-function theory how much present-day logistic theory differs from the classical logic, of which Kant said that since Aristotle it had made neither a step forward nor a step back. We mean the so-called theory of types of B. Russell, which proved to be indispensable in getting rid of certain otherwise unsolvable contradictions.

In introducing the concept of connectibility we spoke in Chapter 6, 2 about what is meant by a sentential function or propositional function. An important part of all linguistic rules has the purpose of delineating the area of applicability of predicates. When we say "*x* bears green fruit," this sentence is meaningful only if we put for "*x*" the name of a plant, but not if we put for it, e.g., "subway" or "circle sector." The totality of the objects *x* for which the individual statement is meaningful—no matter whether it is true or false—forms a "class," namely, the class belonging to the particular predicate. In our example, the class belonging to the predicate "bears green fruit" consists of the totality of plants, at least as long as one gives the words only their customary, nonsymbolic meaning, corresponding to usual parlance. Each single plant is then called an individual member of the class.

Now, undoubtedly statements can be made whose subjects are classes themselves; or better, that which appears as a class in one case may in another case be an individual of another class. When we say, e.g., "*x* possesses 23 vertebrae," this is a sentential function defined for a vertebrate, i.e., the corresponding class is formed by the totality of vertebrates. But this totality is an individual member of the class "classes of animals," of which one could, for example, make the statement "*x* contains more than 200 species." Russell was the first to point out clearly that the two classes, "classes of animals" and "vertebrates" stand in a certain relation of subordination; they belong to different types or ranks. No statement can be meaningful for classes of different types at the same time.

This concept of types must not be confused with a distinction of smaller and larger classes. The sentential function "*x* has four legs" is defined for a bigger class of animals than that of the vertebrates, perhaps for the totality of all animals. But this totality is not of a higher type than that of the vertebrates; it is only bigger, more comprehensive, the vertebrates being a subset of the set of all animals. On the other hand, the concept of the class of animals, i.e., the class of which one could say "$x$ contains many species," is from the point of view of the theory of types a higher concept than that of a vertebrate, an insect, or any individual animal, etc.

The theory of types, or the doctrine of the "hierarchy of types," served originally to resolve certain contradictions that appeared in the theory of sets, a branch of pure mathematics. No satisfactory solution had existed previously. In a work of great scope, *Principia Mathematica,* Whitehead and Russell showed how to reduce all mathematical concepts to the simplest logical operations. But far beyond its original purpose, the theory of types serves as an important reference for the constitution of a general conceptual system and for the logical construction of a scientific language comprehending broad areas of experience. Today we are still a long way from being able to show decisive practical results. But considering that for centuries philosophical discussions were governed by the controversy between so-called universalists and nominalists, i.e., the question whether classes are as real as individuals or, on the contrary, of higher reality, or are merely abstract names (Chapter 21, 5), one may harbor a faint hope that today's mathematical logic, one of whose pillars is Russell's theory of types, constitutes the first step toward a useful conceptual structure which does not admit of such absurd questions.

*Russell's theory of types forms an important part of theoretical logic which increases its efficiency as compared to classical forms of logic. It constitutes the first step toward a general rational conceptual structure and discards old pseudo problems, like the controversy between the universalists and the nominalists.*

7. *Universal Physics.* In the framework of the present efforts, going on in different countries along different paths, to arrive at a "philosophie scientifique," at a conception of the world free of metaphysics, theoretical logic certainly plays an important role. But we cannot object too strenuously to the opinion occasionally voiced by representatives of the Viennese and the Polish schools (Łukasiewicz, Ajdukiewicz, Kotarbinski, Tarski, etc.) that *all* one need do is to develop mathematical logic further.

Certainly mathematical logic, i.e., the formal construction of symbolic systems and their tautological transformations, is an indispensable means for a useful description of reality, at least as indispensable as elementary and nonelementary mathematics is for the correct presentation of physical phenomena, say the propagation of light. Occasionally one finds also mathematicians who are of the opinion that physics is reducible to mathematics; they hold, for instance, that electrodynamics has become a "part of geometry" through the theory of relativity. Such utterances are logical misconceptions and go ill with the critical subtlety which the mathematician otherwise often exhibits.

By the mere manipulation of signs according to chosen rules one can indeed learn nothing about the external world. All the knowledge we gain through mathematics about reality depends upon the fact that the signs as well as the rules of transformation are in some wise made to correspond to certain observable phenomena. This correspondence is *not a part of logic* or mathematics and has no place within its tautological construction. To explore how the correspondence works is a big problem. For in order to describe it in any concrete case, one cannot use the filtered, sharp, and more or less formularized language of logistic; rather one has to resort to ordinary speech which is imperfectly built up and not sufficiently reducible to element statements. Between the exact theories and reality there lies an area of vagueness and "unspeakability" in the literal sense.

The question whether logic rests upon experience or originates in the human mind independently of all experience is wrongly posed. We observe that there are things which are black and things which are not black. But this distinction is not strict, the disjunction is incomplete, and we cannot even circumscribe precisely the range of objects to which it applies. But it is this observation, duplicated again and again, that led us to create the logical relation of $A$ to non-$A$, which after suitable agreement about the use of the signs is free from uncertainty and vagueness. The same is true for the other relations of logic—the disjunction, conjunction, etc. They are abstracted from experiences in which they are realized only *approximately*. The beginning of this schematization (using a more general but not very expedient expression, one could say rationalization) goes back, as we saw in the first chapter, to the creation of ordinary language, hence to the distant past of the origins of human history. Its latest stage is the systematic synthesis of a logical language of formulas. Of course, one may ask the question, which qualities enable man—man alone or also some higher animals—to carry on such intelligent activity. But even this question would not lead us out of the domain of experience and into the realm of the transcendental or of metaphysics; it merely opens up another discipline of (biological) research, which is to be attacked by the usual means of empirical science.

However, it is not this historical question of the genesis of the basic logical concepts that is essential for us here; rather it is the present relation between logical insights and reality. Logic does not float freely in midair, without connection to the world of observation. What we have said above about axiomatics (Chapter 10, 6) also holds for logistic. The words and idioms appearing in it—that they are presented in other forms than by customary letters does not make any difference in this respect—correspond in an unexact and never precisely determinable way to elements of observable matters of fact. It is only because logical formulas, after having been interpreted in ordinary language, according to this correspondence, yield a useful description of experienceable relations, that the study of theoretical logic is regarded as a part of scientific activity. We agree with the mathematician F. Gonseth—in a certain deviation from the "logical empiricism" of the Vienna Circle—who in a theory which he calls "idoneism" conceives of logic as of a "physique de l'objet quelconque" (physics of all things) and says that

the intuitive rules of logic and common sense are nothing else than an abstract schema drawn from the world of concrete objects.

Remembering the explanation of the concept of axiomatization given in the previous section, we may say that theoretical logic is in axiomatic form the doctrine of the most general and the simplest *typical relations* that are observed among objects of any kind.

*Theoretical logic—like the axiomatic of a specific discipline—is a tautological symbolic system developed according to accepted rules; its importance for science lies merely in the fact that if the single signs and basic formulas are made to correspond to certain very general factual situations, any derived formulas correspond to certain observable matters of fact. It is, therefore, just as false to say that the logical inferences rest upon experience, as that logic has nothing whatever to do with experience.*

CHAPTER 11

# the foundations of mathematics

1. *Tautological Part.* When anyone, on any occasion, wants to give an example of an absolutely certain and indubitable truth, he does not hesitate to cite some mathematical theorem known to him, perhaps the Pythagorean theorem or even the formula of multiplication, "2 times 2 equals 4." If thus the *results* of mathematical rules are taken as completely and unshakably true, one should think that this is even more the case with the general foundations from which such results are derived. Nothing is more astonishing for the layman than to hear that among mathematicians there are differences of opinion as to the basic principles of mathematics— their meaning, their applicability, and their content. If, moreover, an eminent contemporary mathematician declares that the present uncertainties by no means concern merely questions on the frontier of mathematical knowledge but go directly to its core, then the general naïve faith in the "most absolute" of all sciences must be completely shaken.

After all that has been said in the previous chapters it is not difficult for us to understand what one has to think of the certainty or uncertainty of mathematical theories. "Pure" mathematics in the sense of customary parlance is only a system of tautologies, i.e., of conventions about signs and transformations according to accepted rules, or, we could say, a system of deductions. From the point of view of the extreme formalists (which we do not share), all assumptions about symbols and rules are *completely* arbitrary, such that without any further justification one may construct different mathematical systems which are not in agreement with one another. From our point of view this is true only with the essential reservation that all tautological systems that play any role within science rest in the last analysis upon a certain coördination of the symbols with other observable experiences. Only if one disregards these coördinations completely, which is, e.g., possible by excluding all use of colloquial expressions, can one regard different systems that are complete and consistent within themselves as equivalent to each other. This relation of mathematics to reality, which is so often neglected, is particularly well pointed out by F. Gonseth in his interesting book *Les Mathématiques et la Réalité*.

After all, it is not a factual question but rather one of nomenclature whether one wants to define the concept "pure mathematics" in such a way that it is sharply distinguished from all other natural sciences. We know from Chapter 9, and shall see again in the next chapter, that the theory of each domain of experience has its tautological part which appears in its most complete form as an axiomatic structure. Now, one may single out a specific realm of experience and call its treatment "mathematics"; then mathematics is in principle not different from other areas of knowledge and consists of a tautological and a nontautological part. This point of view was taken by M. Pasch, who for half a century tried to clarify the basic concepts of mathematics in a number of valuable works. However, it corresponds better to present usage to reserve the name "mathematics" for the purely tautological parts within the different branches. As far as geometry, which is usually considered as a part of mathematics, is concerned, the interplay of tautological and empirical questions was clearly described earlier by various scholars like Helmholtz and Mach, and was discussed above in Chapter 9. It would be a grave error to think that the situation in arithmetic is fundamentally different. If we say that the number 17 is a prime number (which is a tautological proposition) we have also in mind a simple empirical fact, which can be observed with 17 apples or coins, that a division into "equal" groups is impossible. A result which is not so trivial, e.g., that the number 681,199 does not admit of any factorization but $727 \times 937$ can be verified by trying to divide a corresponding number of objects into equal parts. A shepherd who has to care for 30 sheep can check experimentally that $\frac{1}{3}$ plus $\frac{1}{5}$ is more than a half. All these examples belong to the domain of experience the theory of which has arithmetic as its tautological part. It is only because the transition between the facts and the axiomatic concepts seems so extremely simple, familiar, and clear here that one usually pays no attention to it and forms from the tautological considerations alone the concept of a science called arithmetic. As far as geometry is concerned, the customary linguistic usage is a little vague in this respect. In mechanics or other parts of physics, it occurs to nobody any more to call their theorems, as far as they refer to real facts, independent of experience and absolutely certain truths, i.e., to confuse the empirical and the tautological aspects.

*There is no difference in principle between the disciplines of arithmetic, geometry, mechanics, thermodynamics, optics, electricity, etc. It is merely a habit (suggested by the actual situation) in arithmetic, and sometimes in geometry, to reserve the name "arithmetic," or "geometry," for the purely tautological part of the studies. Thus the foundations and basic assumptions of arithmetic are debatable in the same sense as those*

*of any part of physics, i.e., on the one hand, as to the internal questions of
tautological structure, and on the other hand, as to the relations with the
world of experience.*

2. *Mathematical Evidence.* In all discussions of the foundations of
mathematics, without distinction between tautological and factual questions, the word "evidence" appears at an early stage. The simplest mathematical statements, so it is asserted, are "self-evident" (manifest) and their
absolute certainty is derived from the evidence for them. In fact, even the
contemporary controversy between the so-called formalists (Hilbert) and
the so-called intuitionists (Brouwer) is for a large part based upon questions of "mathematical evidence."

We can assume that everybody, or at least everybody beyond a certain stage of education, is familiar with an experience for which he uses
the word "evidence" or "self-evident truth." If anyone claims that to him
the truth of a statement is evident or immediately apparent, he is hardly
inclined to resolve this impression of his into simpler parts, i.e., to analyze
it and to exhibit its components. This could lead us to accept the words
"This is evident to me" as a kind of element statement or protocol sentence (Chapter 8). As in the case of the statement "This is red," or "Here
I have the sensation red," the words should, then, not be analyzed further,
but should be regarded as a piece of raw material that has to be used along
with other material of the same kind.

But physical optics, whose significance is derived from the fact that
there are primitive impressions like red and blue, light and dark, or element statements of the form "Here I see red," by no means is as a scientific
theory *based* upon such concepts as blue and red, or light and dark. Surely
no course in optics starts with an attempt to make clear what the meanings
of blue and red are, or derives anything from the assumption that these
meanings are a priori known. The connection between the simple protocol
sentences and the physical theory is not so immediate and in any case not
so simple.

For the moment we do not have to go deeper into the question what is
the connection in other areas between element statements and the theories.
The point here is that, even granted the existence of a not further analyzable elementary experience of "evidence," it does not follow that mathematics (or any theory) should be built upon the assumption of evidence
as a self-explanatory and obvious basic concept. For this to be possible,
one condition above all would have to be satisfied: there must be a certain
agreement about what knowledge is evident, that is, not only among the
mathematicians themselves, but also among those who are only starting to
study mathematics and who therefore do not yet draw conclusions from
the theory.

It does not require much speculation to convince oneself of how divided, in all domains, the opinions are as to which statements have the property of evidence. We may even exclude such matters as the spherical shape of the earth, the existence of antipodes, or the rotation of the earth about its axis. Let us limit ourselves to purely mathematical concepts. To almost everybody the properties of the positive integers, as they are taught in school, are evident. Most educated people claim, moreover, that the so-called existence of an infinite series of numbers is evident to them. More serious discussions arise if one asks whether the continuum of points on a line segment or the continuum of numbers between 0 and 1 is immediately evident or not. Some people even assert that it is immediately evident that all properties of geometric figures remain unaltered if one changes the dimensions of the figure. The latter lend to Euclidean geometry the character of evidence, while the former, who take the continuum for granted, jump over a wide area of mathematical difficulties. There is no doubt about the lack of agreement as to what is evident "to us." For each person it seems to depend upon education and incidental experience what appears evident to him, not to speak of the vagueness of linguistic formulation of allegedly "evident" propositions. The famous dictum of the mathematician C. G. J. Jacobi, "Mathematics is the science of what is clear by itself" can in no way be maintained today.

*It is impossible to accept as the basis of mathematics merely statements that seem self-evident, if only because there is no agreement as to what statements actually belong to this class.*

3. *Intuitionism.* Among the various controversial schools of thought in the field of the foundations of mathematics, it is the intuitionists who— as their name indicates—place the greatest emphasis upon intuition, evidence, and immediate apprehension or immediate insight. According to L. E. J. Brouwer, the founder of the intuitionist school, the simplest mathematical ideas are implied in the customary lines of thought of everyday life and all sciences make use of them; the mathematician is distinguished by the fact that he is conscious of these ideas, points them out clearly, and completes them. The only source of mathematical knowledge is, in Brouwer's opinion, the intuition that makes us recognize certain concepts and conclusions as absolutely evident, clear, and indubitable. However, he does not assume that it is possible to list in a precise and complete way all basic fundamental concepts and elementary methods of deduction, which in this sense are to serve as a basis of mathematical derivations. It should always be possible to supplement the once fixed set of assumptions by accepting new ones, if a further intuition leads that way. A first intuition yields us the concept of "two" from which the concept of multiplicity is inferred. Originally Brouwer regarded the continuum too as immediately

given by intuition; later he tried to comprehend it by a new concept, the "sequences of free formation," i.e., to reduce the continuum in some way, after all, to a sequence of numbers.

Disregarding certain rather mystic formulations that Brouwer gave to his doctrine, one recognizes his point of view as very close to a radical empiricism. The thesis that the fundamental assumptions of mathematics cannot be formulated in a definitely fixed and complete form, but are subject to continued examination and possible supplementation by intuition (we should prefer to say, by experience which changes the stock of what appears as "evident"), corresponds exactly to our conception. The opposite point of view is that of Kantian a-priorism, according to which the basic mathematical concepts are once and for all impressed upon the human race by the properties of its reasoning power. Such a prediction that a specific chapter of science will never change—and the "a priori" means just that (see Chapter 22)—has no place in the concept of science that this book represents.

On the other hand, we see no reason why at any point of time the set of assumptions momentarily appearing as necessary should not be assembled and, in the form of axioms and fundamental rules, be made the basis of the derivations. *Today's* mathematics, as we know, can be derived only to a small extent from assumptions regarded as intuitive or evident by Brouwer. There is nothing to do but consider the remaining premises for the time being as further hypotheses which perhaps later will prove to be dispensable or replaceable by "intuitive" ones. This is without importance for the inner working of mathematics; witness the fact that the content of the textbooks in the various mathematical fields did not change appreciably in recent years, in spite of the immense influence intuitionism exerted, and justifiably so, upon mathematical thinking.

*In agreement with the empiristic conception of science, intuitionism holds that the source of mathematics is the insight which we intuitively comprehend from experience of the external world, but which cannot once and for all be collected in a closed system of axioms.*

4. *The Excluded Middle.* Not only did intuitionism bring new life into the discussions on the foundations of mathematics, which seemed to have reached somehow a dead end, but it also, for the first time in centuries, opened up again problems in elementary logic. Some rumors have spread to nonmathematicians—and were accepted with justified suspicion —that the intuitionists deny the validity of the simple rule of the excluded middle. That is, besides the two statements "today is Tuesday" and "today is not Tuesday" this revolutionary theory is supposed to admit a *tertium quid*. The situation here is as follows.

In no case of extramathematical application is the validity of the "tertium exclusum" questioned. Within mathematics, too, it remains absolutely unshaken as long as one deals with *finite* sets. If, for example, "*A*" signifies any precisely defined property of a natural number such that it is possible to determine unambiguously whether a given natural number possesses property *A* or not, then the following alternative holds: among the natural numbers from 1 to ten million there exists a number which has the property *A*, or there is no such number (but there is no third possibility).

Brouwer, however, noticed that the problem is not so simple once one treats an "infinite" sequence of numbers (such as all even numbers) instead of a finite set (such as the numbers between 1 and ten million). The proposition, "there is a number with the property *A*" still signifies in this case the same as before, namely, running through the sequence of even numbers, one will find a number possessing the property *A*. But if we say there is no such number, that does not mean that running through the sequence of all even numbers we never hit upon a number of the property *A*, because it makes no sense to speak of an examination of infinitely many numbers. The negative statement is rather an abbreviation for the following much more complicated assertion: by means of the axioms and deductive methods of mathematics it can be *proved* that between the property of being an even number and the property *A* there is a *contradiction*. This is, we think, the only meaning one can reasonably assign to the statement that there is no number having the property *A* in the infinite set.

After this explanation it should be clear that between the assertions, there is a number . . . , and, there is no number . . . , in the case of an infinite set of numbers, the relation of contradictory opposites no longer exists. There is no difficulty in imagining that besides the finding of a number and the provability of a contradiction there is still a third possibility, namely, that neither does one find, on running through the numbers, one that has the property *A*, nor is a contradiction between the definition of the numbers and the property *A* derivable by means of mathematics. It is only when one makes the additional *assumption* that every mathematical problem is solvable that the extension of the theorem of the excluded middle to all problems dealing with infinite sets becomes justified. The nonmathematician will hardly be inclined to regard such an assumption as "logically necessary" and thus all that seems so objectionable in the intuitionist thesis disappears.

  *Brouwer, the founder of intuitionist mathematics, has shown that in certain mathematical problems dealing with infinite sets of numbers the elementary rule of the excluded middle is not admissible, without an additional arbitrary assumption. Statements like: there is a number . . . and: there is no number . . . , in this case only seemingly, by virtue of their abbreviated linguistic formulations, have the form of contradictory opposites.*

5. *New Logic.* We saw in Chapter 10 that the theorem of the tertium exclusum is an immediate consequence of the basic formulas of logic if one assumes these according to the conception of classical logic. Therefore, if one wants to have a logic that satisfies the requirements of intuitionist mathematics and that does not break down on application to infinite sets, it is advisable, instead of admitting "exceptions," to formulate the basic axioms a little differently. This problem was solved for the first time by A. Heyting, but we shall follow the later exposition by A. Kolmogoroff, which points out more clearly the fundamental idea.

Let the letters $A, B, C$ . . . signify, instead of statements, as before, *problems* to be solved. We may think of mathematical problems, e.g., to construct a triangle under given stipulations, or to calculate a number defined in a particular way, say the root of an equation. We shall use the sign for negation in order to signify that the solution of a problem is impossible, i.e., leads to a contradiction. Letters connected by means of a comma—"$A,B$"—will be taken to mean both problems; those connected by "$v$"—"$AvB$"—to mean at least one of the two problems $A,B$. Finally, the sign for implication, "$\rightarrow$", will be used in the sense that "$A \rightarrow B$" means to reduce the solution of $B$ to that of $A$. Now, for the use of the four signs "$v$", "$\sim$", "$\rightarrow$", "$,$" one can prescribe those and only those rules which correspond to the situations in solving problems. For example, the formula "$[A,(A \rightarrow B)] \rightarrow B$" is always true; in words it means that the solution of the problem $B$ is reducible to the solution of the two problems, $A$ and the reduction of $B$ to $A$. Similarly "$[(A \rightarrow B),(B \rightarrow C)] \rightarrow (A \rightarrow C)$"; in words, if $B$ is reducible to $A$, and $C$ to $B$, then the reduction of $C$ to $A$ is reducible to these two problems, namely, to the carrying out of the two reductions. In the ordinary propositional calculus (Chapter 10, 3), the first of these two formulas would state that if $A$ holds and $B$ follows from $A$, then $B$ also holds; and the second, if $B$ follows from $A$, and $C$ from $B$, then it follows that $C$ follows from $A$.

Thus in these two examples there is no essential difference between the propositional calculus and the new problem calculus. But while in the former the formula "$\sim AvA$" is valid, i.e., always, either non-$A$ or $A$ holds, we have no reason to admit the generality of the theorem: one of the two properties of problem $A$ must be true, either $A$ is solvable or $A$ is recognizable as contradictory. One can see here that with a suitable agreement about symbols there will result an algorithm that agrees on the whole with ordinary truth-function theory, but that does not contain the formula which expresses the theorem of the excluded middle. This argument has the same significance as the acceptance of the logical independence of

Euclid's parallel axiom, which led to the construction of the non-Euclidean geometries (Chapter 9, 5). We have arrived here at a special form of "non-Aristotelian logic," a form which is also called by the misleading name (since it is reminiscent of "intuitive") "intuitionist logic."

The main application of the intuitionist contribution consists in supplying us with a method of rejecting from all previous mathematical results those in whose derivation the tertium exclusum was used, including, in particular, all those theorems which rest upon so-called "indirect proofs." If, for instance, we are looking for an unknown quantity $x$ and we can prove that the assumption that there is no such $x$ leads to a contradiction, then, according to the new conception, the existence of $x$ is not proved. Brouwer demands a "constructive" proof, i.e., the establishing of a method of calculating the number $x$. This way of looking at things proves to be fruitful in the study of the basic elements of mathematics, even though it leaves the actual work of mathematicians in most special branches almost unchanged. Mathematicians usually were satisfied with an indirect proof only if a constructive one could not be found. It makes no sense to argue about whether a quantity "really exists" if only an indirect proof can be given for its existence; the word "exist" cannot be defined independently of what one wants to admit as proofs.

*The construction of a "problem calculus" in the sense of Heyting and Kolmogoroff yields a model of logic in which the theorem of the excluded middle does not appear among the basic formulas. The study of such a logic widens our insight into the basic elements of mathematics and, in particular, points out the special position of the so-called indirect proofs within mathematics.*

6. *Formalism.* It is mainly Hilbert and his followers who have objected to the thesis of the intuitionists since it first became known. According to the ideas of Hilbert and the "formalistic" school led by him, mathematics in the narrower sense is replaceable by a purely mechanical method for deriving formulas, a method which has nothing to do with the meaning or interpretation of the symbols used. Certain aggregates of symbols are assumed as premises; these are the axioms, and from them further groups of signs are derived according to fixed rules and in a purely mechanical manner, i.e., without the use of conclusions drawn from their interpretation; the new groups are then the provable theorems. Thus, the entire content of mathematics is, according to Hilbert, transformable, in principle, into a system of symbolic formulas.

Besides this formal system, however, there is, as Hilbert states, still something else which serves as justification of the system of formulas and is called "metamathematics." It is not clearly stated whether the rules that govern the use of signs in the formal system and describe the methods of deriving new formulas are also considered as part of metamathematics. At any rate, it comprises all arguments that are supposed to lead to the proof of the consistency of the formal system. By a consistency proof is meant the proof that a certain "false" formula, e.g., the formula "1 = 2," cannot be derived; for, on the one hand, the appearance of this formula would make the system useless, and on the other hand, from any other "false" formula existing in the system the proposition "1 = 2" would follow.

Everything then depends upon how and with what means metamathematics works. It uses meaningful deductions, i.e., it operates with words and idioms whose meaning is somehow abstracted from linguistic usage. According to Hilbert's original thesis, metamathematics should apply only the most elementary and immediately evident logical premises and deductive methods, at any rate only the simplest inferences appearing in the formal system of symbols under consideration, and should use those only in a finite number of repetitions. Therefore, the theorem of the excluded middle too can only be applied to a finite set. The essential idea was that metamathematics, by using only finite means of elementary logic, should be in a position to construct and support the structure of formal mathematics, which deals with infinite sets. That is exactly the point where the questions posed by intuitionism start infiltrating into metamathematics.

One cannot say that the end which Hilbert posited for metamathematics has been attained even in a single partial area or that there is any hope of reaching it in the near future. On the contrary, the mathematician Gödel recently showed that, in principle, in order to furnish a consistency proof of a formal system one needs means that go beyond what is formalized in the system. That does not necessarily mean a failure of Hilbert's efforts, but it shows that metamathematics does not get around the questions thrown into the discussion by the intuitionists. The opposition between the formalists and the intuitionists, which was originally so violent and apparently irreconcilable, seems gradually to reduce to this: on the one hand, Hilbert's formal mathematics comprises more than a formalization of Brouwer's mathematics could yield, but on the other hand, the metamathematics, which is indispensable in Hilbert's total structure, has to incorporate essential ideas of Brouwer's intuitionism.

There is one point in which the opponents still seem irreconcilable. While the formalists—in this they follow mainly Poincaré—regard a consistency proof, once it is given, as a complete and total justification of a deductive system, the intuitionists, according to their rejection of the general principle of the excluded middle, do not consider consistency as something positive. According to our repeatedly stated view, formal (tautological) systems appear in science only because they can be coördinated with certain sets of experiences or groups of phenomena, and from this coördination they derive, in the last analysis, their "justification." Inner consistency is certainly a necessary criterion of the usefulness of a system, but for its applicability, i.e., for the possibility of coördination with the world of experience, a sufficient "scientific proof" cannot be given at all (see Chapter 12).

*Dividing mathematics into a formal system, which progresses according to mechanical rules, and a metamathematics, which is supposed to lead to the justification of the formal system, does not exclude the difficulties that intuitionism has pointed out. The coördination between mathematics (its tautological side) and reality cannot be reached by a mathematicized doctrine and certainly cannot be settled by a consistency proof.*

7. *Logicism.* With the formalists and the intuitionists one frequently mentions the "logicists" as the third party in the controversy about the foundations of mathematics. Bertrand Russell (see Chapter 10, 6) attempted in his book *Principia Mathematica* (together with A. N. Whitehead), based upon essential preliminary studies by Frege and Peano, to construct completely the basic concepts used in mathematics, starting from their simplest and most plausible elements. The solution of this logical problem, to which the authors apply admirable ingenuity, will never be able to command universal acceptance. For it remains undecided, and depends on each individual, whether such concepts as sequence of numbers, cardinal numbers, etc., are less simple and immediate than successor, one-to-one coördination of elements, etc. The choice of the preferred starting point will always depend upon the experience of the individual. But about the relation to reality, to the world of experience, logicists do not *want* to say anything; they see their goal in the complete exhibition of the tautological relations, i.e., relations that are fixed by definitions and other linguistic rules. In this respect, their merits are indisputable; we mention here only one example.

In almost all branches of mathematics there appears a type of argument that always has been regarded as a "principle," characteristic of mathematics, and at times considered an inscrutable mystery: the process of so-called *complete induction.* If we divide 7 by 3, then the first digit after the decimal point of the quotient is a 3, and the remainder is 1. Furthermore it is easy to prove that in division by 3 a decimal which yields the remainder 1 must always be followed by another 3 with the remainder 1. From this one customarily "concludes" that all the "infinitely many" decimal digits of the quotient are 3's. This is the method of mathematical induction, and with respect to it the question was raised (e.g., by H. Poincaré), how is it possible to draw from such a small and in any case finite number of inferences an infinite number of conclusions (namely about all infinitely many decimals). The fact is that nothing at all is concluded here. The sentence "All decimal digits are 3's" is only a different linguistic expression for

"The first decimal digit is 3, and as often as there appears a 3, it is followed by another 3." The word "all," in this context, i.e., applied to the infinite sequence of digits in the decimal fraction, has no other meaning than that determined by the concept of succession (by which the sequence of natural numbers is defined). There are other problems in mathematics in which the word "all," referring to infinite sets of a different kind, has another meaning and where the method of induction is not applicable at all. This situation is fully cleared up in Whitehead and Russell's foundation of mathematics. While the ordinary textbooks of mathematics have the purpose of developing chains of mathematical deductions ascending from simpler to more and more complicated forms, Russell drives the examination of the tautologies in the opposite direction, toward the origin.

We return now to what was said at the start of this chapter, that mathematics as a whole, like any other science, has a tautological and an empirical side; it differs from other sciences in that here the formal side is much more essential and decisive than anywhere else. Thus it becomes understandable that mathematics has often been identified completely with its tautological part, as witnessed by Goethe's well-known utterance,

Mathematics has the completely false reputation of yielding infallible conclusions. Its infallibility is nothing but identity. Two times two is not four, but it is just two times two, and that is what we call four for short. But four is nothing new at all. And thus it goes on and on in its conclusions, except that in the higher formulas the identity fades out of sight.

To this we have to say that four is not only two times two, but also three plus one, and fifteen minus eleven, and the cube root of 64, and so on. It is the task of mathematics in the narrower sense to describe the relations of these various "identities." But there is also an empirical side to mathematical doctrines, where there is no more talk about the "infallibility of conclusions," and which must not be neglected in an epistemological investigation.

The logicistic foundation of mathematics deals with an analysis of its tautological or deductive part, by attempting to reduce the basic mathematical concepts and methods to the simplest and most plausible elements. There is no reference to the relation with reality; the connection with the world of experience is hidden in the choice of the basic elements. Our final conclusion is this:

*None of the three forms of the foundation of mathematics, the intuitionist, the formalistic, or the logicistic, is capable of completely rationalizing the relation between tautological systems and (extramathematical) experiences, which is its very purpose, i.e., to make this relation a part of the mathematical system itself.*

### CHAPTER 12

# the structure of physical theories

1. *Physicalism*. Radical representatives of the empiricist conception of science usually point to physics as the model science and actually demand that anything called a science should lend itself to incorporation in a sufficiently wide system of physics. This conception is known as physicalism; in the same sense one also talks of a "physical or physicalistic language" which should be capable of expressing every factual experience. It makes little difference if instead of "general physics" the name "unified science" is used, and instead of "physical language," the word "unified language." In so far as this is meant merely to secure "connectibility" among the different fields, we refer to what we have said in Chapter 6, 3. Here, we want to discuss to what extent the conception of unified science might be useful beyond the idea of providing connectibility.

In the first place, the various sciences, if we neglect details and accept the customary boundaries between them, are distinguished by the *objects* they deal with. The physicist treats light and heat; the economist, ground rent and interest; the linguist, word and sentence forms. If we examine a little more closely what the individual scientists make concrete statements about, we find that the objects of the various sciences can be summarized under a common expression: every proposition of a positive science refers to actions of men and observed by men (Bridgman). The physicist and the physiologist predict the course and the results of experiments or technical processes; the economist deals with an extremely complicated complex of occurrences which result from the coöperation of a large group of men; the linguist is interested in spoken or written expressions which are the result of a long development of human linguistic activity. The purely descriptive natural sciences do not constitute an exception; they are only marginal cases with respect to this point of view, as even the geologist can only say what happens if one examines rocks by means of hammer and drill.

This way of looking at the subject matter of the sciences leads also to a suitable characterization of their differences. We find that physics (in which we include geometry and the nontautological part of the rest of mathematics) deals primarily with the *simplest* relations observable within the range of human activity. The word "simple" here has the following meaning. While pursuing physical research one can neglect entirely the vast majority of relations that are possibly observable in connection with the experiment. Very little or nothing depends upon the personal situation and qualities of the experimenter, least of all upon his relations to society; but even of the physical object one is hardly interested in its past or future, and at most in a particular aspect of its origin. Only a very specific part of the total occurrence, a part that is comparatively easy to separate, is the actual aim of the experimentation. One may compare this to a statement in which the word "ground rent" occurs. This phrase refers to a manifold of interconnected activities of whole societies, to an entanglement of relations and cross relations which cover long stretches of time and can scarcely be analyzed with present knowledge. The problems of other sciences, compared to those of physics, are closer to life, less abstract, and hence more difficult and complicated. One may, of course, pose the problem of reducing the complicated to the simple. But it would contradict all we learn in the history of science if one believed that the concepts used in one limited field must be sufficient to cover every other. Later (Chapter 19, 3 and 5) we shall return to this point, particularly in discussing the relation between biology and physics, which is analogous to the relation between the whole of physics and mechanics. It certainly is not a demand of positivism or the positivistic conception of science to interpret all physical phenomena in a mechanistic way. Why then should we demand that everything treated in other fields of science be reduced to physics? In so far as physicalism means this, we have to reject it (see Chapter 19, 3).

*In studying the methodology of the other sciences, one may start from ideas and procedures tested and used in physics; but it must not be supposed that what is sufficient for a limited discipline is necessarily adequate for a more general one.*

2. *Description and Explanation.* When Kirchhoff in 1876, in the introduction to his lectures on theoretical physics, said that the aim of mechanics is "to describe completely and in the simplest manner the motions that occur in nature," his utterance found the sharpest opposition from the physicists. Four years earlier Mach had developed in an extremely enlightening paper, "The history and the roots of the principle of conservation of energy," more radical opinions, which, however, remained for the time being unnoticed. Today few physicists object to Kirchhoff's formulation. The language used by physicists has approached to some extent the language of positivism.

Why, we ask, were the physicists so indignant, and why are representatives of other sciences still today (see Chapter 17) indignant when the task of science is called "description"? What is the background of this apparent resentment? By "description" one usually means the manner in which the illiterate or the layman depicts a matter of fact. The scholar wants to feel superior to that sort of thing and claims that "explanation," as he offers it, should be regarded as a fundamentally different, and higher, form of presentation. But what Kirchhoff meant and Mach expounded in detail is exactly that there is no fundamental difference and that explanation is but a special form of description, namely, a description that is systematic, unified and, as far as possible, complete. We do not draw the conclusion from this that the word "explain" should not be used any more. Still less do we intend to depreciate the value of scientific explanation by subordinating it to the general idea of "description."

The motion of a single falling body may be described at first in a primitive way, by recording the location and the velocity it has at different times. But if one wants to "describe" *all* motions of falling bodies collectively, one can point out as their common feature only that they are characterized by a constant acceleration in the downward direction (Galileo). Going a step further and attempting to subsume the phenomenon of free fall under a general description of motions of solids (Newton), one has to say that all bodies located in the vicinity of the earth's surface have a component acceleration directed vertically downward, of constant magnitude, which possibly is combined with other component accelerations (due to resistances, impulses, etc.). It is only a matter of taste whether one finds in the Galilean or the Newtonian point of view the first transition from description to explanation. The advance in any case lies in the fact that each time, relative to the range of phenomena covered, the description as a whole has become simpler, shorter, and more comprehensive. One may also put it roughly this way: explanation is a description of relations, of interconnections between phenomena. This seems to correspond to the point of view presented in great detail by Karl Pearson in his *Grammar of Science.*

According to linguistic usage, "explanation" is, as a rule, associated with the concept of "cause and effect." Thus it is often asserted that a description presents only the superficial appearance of an experience, while an explanation discloses its true inner essence. We shall discuss the meaning of such expressions, which refer to the idea of causality, in the fourth part of this book. In so far as, in using the word "explanation," one thinks of elucidation, familiarization with and clarification of a matter of fact, one touches upon a partly psychological, partly pedagogical problem with which the actual theoretical structure of physics is not concerned.

*Today it is no longer controversial that the aim of physics is the description of phenomena. A systematic description that is oriented toward the relations and interconnections within a class of phenomena is called an explanation.*

3. *Economy of Thought.* The notion that physical theorems or formulas, e.g., Fourier's differential equation of heat transfer, are primarily descriptions of observable occurrences was supplemented by Mach in a decisive way when he pointed out a characteristic feature common to all scientific descriptions. We stressed previously the systematization and unification inherent in a scientific description. Mach observed—and traces of this idea can be found already in the work of Auguste Comte—that the progress from the prescientific state to the scientific and then the steady advances within the evolution of science consist mainly in an increase in the economy of thought. That is to say, compared to the primitive manner of describing separately each of the various forms of motion of a heavy body (freely falling body, body thrown with an upward or downward thrust, or at an angle, etc.) it is shorter, more efficient, or, briefly, more economical, to stress in all these cases the common element, namely, the constant acceleration in the downward direction. Then, it is a further immense gain from the point of view of economy of thought to have for all motions of any kind of body, in whatever circumstance it may be, a single differential equation from which all properties of its motion can be derived. A still more economical, or, if one wishes, even higher, form of natural law is given in the principle of conservation of energy, which by the greatest sort of condensation describes a common feature of a vast number of different phenomena. As a most conspicuous example in modern physics we must mention the theory of relativity; it achieves a transformation of all physical problems by a single well-formulated idea that has proved efficient in a hundred places. Every formula, every equation compares to the explicit listing of all numerical relations contained in it, as the work of an automatic machine to the corresponding manual work. The theoretical comprehension of greater areas of experience is possible only by the development of means which allow a summarization in thought over great complexes of phenomena. Any scientific concept is such a tool. The simpler ones are concepts such as velocity, acceleration, temperature, etc. From here to more complicated concepts, such as a nonholonomic mechanical system, or a reversible thermal process, or the "wave packet" in modern quantum mechanics, there leads a progressive adaptation of thought to facts in the sense of Mach's notion of economy.

Simple and obvious as Mach's remarks about the role of the economy of thought in science may be, they found strong opposition in the ranks of physicists and philosophers, which still today has hardly faded. It seems that primarily the choice of the word "economy" is responsible for this. The predominant use of this word in other areas of practical life lent to it an aura pointing toward business and profit, and the prejudice of scholars causes resentment of such implications. Had Mach described the same observation but chosen for its name, say, "concentration of thought" (which by no means is recommended here), its reception would have been much more favorable.

Into what devious paths philosophical misunderstanding of a simple idea of natural science can lead may be seen here in an instructive example. E. Husserl, the distinguished creator of phenomenology, who otherwise treats Mach's idea with understanding, says in his *"Logische Untersuchungen,"*

This principle [namely, the principle of economy of thought] is hence by no means a principle in the sense of a rational theory, an exact law which would be capable of functioning as the basis of rational explanation (as the purely mathematical or mathematical-physical laws can), but one of those valuable teleological points of view . . .

In this context one of Mach's particularly persistent critics (H. Buzello in *Kantstudien*) declares,

The only "formal principle" which Mach incorporates into his epistemology is the principle of economy . . . hence it is a regulative principle serving for the classification of knowledge . . . Then Mach considers the principle of economy as a constitutive one, necessary to constitute the object of experience.

To all this one can simply reply that Mach has nothing teleological in mind, nor a formal or regulative or constitutive principle, nor a "principle" in the sense of philosophy at all. He indicates an essential feature of the evolution of science which he observed and described in simple words. That in this field (the science of science, i.e., the systematic description of the observable behavior of scientists) statements in the form of mathematical laws cannot be made is evident; but Mach by no means deserts with his assertion of the "economic nature of scientific research" (he preferred this phrase) the solid ground of description of observable phenomena.

*As Mach showed, a characteristic feature in the development of scientific descriptions of observable facts is the increasing "economy of thought"; that theory appears as the superior one which allows us to survey a wider area by a single idea, a formula, or a law.*

4. *Induction and Deduction.* A phrase of Newton's, often quoted particularly by experimental physicists—"Hypotheses non fingo" (I do not frame hypotheses)—is sometimes regarded as the supreme principle of the empiricist conception of science. There is no justification for this at all; one could much better assert that, according to the conception of the positivists, science consists entirely of hypotheses. For we consider any nontautological proposition to be subject to continually renewed examination by observation.

But it is hardly possible to say anything precise in the face of such a general problem, particularly since the meaning of the various expressions used is so highly undertermined. It is not so much the word "hypothesis" itself that seems uncertain to us (although there is also a parlance in which "hypothesis" means something by its very nature nonverifiable) as expressions like "Science consists of . . ." It makes a big difference whether one thinks of the entire *activity* of scientists, or the *result* of such activity incorporated in a definite theory, or the totality of ideas occurring in its historical *development*. Let us then omit formulations of too great generality and consider more closely the structure of a physical theory and the elements of which it consists. For the sake of readier understanding we shall return for this purpose to the case of Newtonian mechanics mentioned already in Chapter 9, 3, which in a certain sense represents the basic type of classical physical theory.

"There is no doubt that all our knowledge starts with experience," said even Kant, and, whatever may be the meaning of the reservation he added, we have to state here that at the basis of mechanics, as the (historical and logical) starting point of all mechanical research, stands the observation of phenomena of motion. Newton had primarily at his disposal the recorded experimental results of Galileo, the results of astronomical observations which Kepler had collected in formulas, and finally his own experiences. Then he sought in this totality of phenomena for a common feature and, perhaps after several unsuccessful attempts, he was struck by an idea which might first have occurred to him as a guess: that bodies mutually determine their accelerations (not velocities), or more precisely, components of their accelerations, and that under otherwise equal circumstances for every body the component-acceleration impressed upon it is inversely proportional to a constant which is a property of that body. At the moment it is not important for us that the original form of Newton's idea was much less concise than this modern version of it (only sketchily referred to here) and was mixed up with much that can be explained only historically and has to be rejected today. The following also should be understood in the sense of such a retrospective construction but not of a historical account. The language in which first conjectures are formulated and then further developed is the inexact language roughly reducible to protocol sentences (Chapter 8).

The original conjecture is first of all tested with the phenomena out of which it evolved. If it not only passes these tests but also holds good in other cases, of which the discoverer did not think originally, faith in it grows. At a certain stage of the process of testing, the guess becomes a physical theorem, a law. By collecting a suitable group of such laws, and perhaps supplementing them by propositions that have the purpose of regulating the unambiguous use of the expressions that occur, an axiomatic system is created. This entire procedure, here only sketchily described, is known as the method of *induction* (Chapter 12, 6).

Once a system of axioms, however deficient it may be, is established, deductive treatment, or as one prefers to put it today, the process of tautological transformations, may begin. In mechanics and most other parts of physics one has to use essentially mathematical analysis; differential equations are integrated, their possible solutions are investigated, and so on. But it would be wrong to suppose that in the two steps, namely, induction, which leads to general axioms, and succeeding deduction, which leads to the derivation of concrete conclusions, the play of physical theory is exhausted. Immediately below we shall turn to the discussion of further structural elements, which once more relate the theory to the world of experience. Let us only insert one remark here.

The process of induction just sketched has two sides: it is to a certain extent determined by observations, but it also leaves a certain measure of freedom of decision to the scientist. The classical conception of the formation of theories directed its attention only to the first point. It was Henri Poincaré who in a series of well-known popular writings emphasized for the first time the other aspect, the freedom left to the scientist in establishing the basic laws. According to Poincaré, the content of the fundamental premises of a physical theory consists of mere *conventions*. In the course of many generations, he states, by a process of intellectual selection, people came to agree with these assumptions, e.g., to regard Euclidean geometry as the simplest, most convenient, and most useful basis for the description of spatial phenomena. This convention may in the course of time be altered or even entirely replaced by another one; and the situation is similar in all other fields of physical research. Occasionally the name "conventionalism" has been suggested for Poincaré's conception of science. One can see that conventionalism comprehends correctly one aspect of the process of induction, an aspect that is significant also from our point of view. We may for the time being summarize the whole situation in the following manner:

*Every physical theory begins with observations and conjectures derived from them, which in the course of the process of testing grow into physical laws and—after the possible addition of suitable propositions regulating linguistic usage—become an axiomatic system (induction). From a sufficiently complete axiomatic system one can draw conclusions by tautological transformations (deduction).*

5. *Supplementary Axioms.* There is a very common opinion, even among the followers of the empiricist conception of science, that after establishing a sufficiently general system of axioms the further task of the physicist is limited to purely deductive considerations. However, if physi-

cal assertions are supposed to state anything about reality, at least the special data of every problem must be incorporated as empirical elements in the solution of the differential equations that express the axioms. The range of what is called here special empirical data must not be underestimated; they are often statements which are hardly less general or less important than the basic axioms themselves.

In the case of mechanics one usually does not overlook the fact that the initial coördinates and velocities of moving bodies are used in the solutions, but this is not the essential point. The Newtonian equations, which are supposed to determine the motions of particles, contain, in addition to quantities that can be considered as known, the incidental "impressed forces," and hence quantities that may depend in a complicated manner upon time, location, velocity, and even upon one another. Later we shall return (Chapter 15, 2) to the point that the most decisive accomplishment of Newton in the field of celestial mechanics was that in addition to the axioms of motion he also gave the unique law of force that rules astronomical phenomena. But to find in every special case of terrestial motion the corresponding force functions (and the definition of the mechanical system in question) is a difficult problem which is frequently not solvable at all and is certainly a process that does not fall within the framework of tautological transformations in any way. From an epistemological point of view one may say that what one needs in such cases is additional axioms; but then, of course, the system of axioms necessary for the solution of everyday mechanical problems is still for a large part unknown. At any rate, in the solution of special problems of mechanics one still has to do a job that has the nature of the above-described process of induction, i.e., a process that leads from observations to guesses and later to exact formulations of "laws."

Many a physicist might object that it is only the primitive particle mechanics (mechanics of small, rigid bodies), representing a kind of limiting case in the general physics of continuous media, which shows this character, i.e., which in its application still depends upon the additional determination of various force functions. However, there is no fundamental difference if one envisages the area of mechanics of continua or other similarly constructed physical theories. It may not be superfluous to point out that among the most common mechanical phenomena there is a vast number of problems which are, at least for the time being, insolvable, not because of mathematical difficulties, but because one does not know the additional axioms, i.e., because one has not yet "abstracted" from observations the general "laws" that would be suitable to serve as a basis for an exact description of the class of motions in question. We master at present the mechanics of continuous media only in so far as we have to deal with purely elastic bodies or so-called perfect fluids; in all other cases, for example, those of plastic materials, or of the soil, or of flexible fabrics, etc., reliable data are missing, and it is not at all certain that they will be found within the framework of Newtonian mechanics. Very similar is the situation in thermodynamics, whose classical differential equations presuppose the knowledge of thermal conductivities and thermal capacities, and their dependence upon all other variables; or in electrodynamics, in whose equations dielectric and permeability coefficients are used, etc. This shows incidentally how unjustified is the widespread opinion that all we need to solve any physical problem is large-scale computing machines or other kinds of "robots."

Once all necessary data—whether one calls them additional axioms or not—are found for a specific problem and the required mathematical deductions are carried out, one may reach results which can be tested by observation. For this purpose a translation from the exact language of the axioms and their transforms into the inexact language built up from protocol sentences is necessary. Exact formal language plays its role only in the transition from the precise basic propositions (axioms) to the precise conclusions (deductions). The transition to reality is possible on both ends only by means of the natural language which is reducible to protocol sentences.

*Even after one knows the general axioms of a field one needs for the solution of any problem or any group of problems a process of the type of induction (which develops from observations via conjectures to exact formulations), and it very often remains uncertain whether this prerequisite, the establishing of the necessary additional axioms, can be fulfilled in every case. Conclusions drawn from the thus completed axiomatic system may be tested by observation, as soon as the results are retranslated from the exact language, used in the deductive part of the theory, into ordinary language.*

6. *The "Inductive Inference."* We have already discussed in detail what is meant by a deduction or tautological transformation. It still remains for us to say something about the process of induction, in so far as this is possible without reference to the concept of causality, which will be taken up in the next chapter.

The earlier logicians, beginning with Aristotle, saw the problem of induction as a problem of logic: as there is a deductive inference from the general to the particular, there is analogously an "inductive inference" from the particular to the general. Francis Bacon in his *Novum Organon* (1620) and later John Stuart Mill (1843) constructed a whole system of "inductive logic." David Hume (1748) took a freer point of view, and a progressive logician of more recent times, C. Sigwart (1873) recognizes that induction . . . is a generally used process subject to psychological laws, but that its logical justification cannot be given a foundation from any point of view in the sense that . . . induction is a kind of rigorous proof of general propositions by single facts.

Nevertheless, even Sigwart seeks to "solve the problem of induction" within the framework of logic.

From the use that we made above of the word "induction" it should be clear that from our point of view, in agreement with the quoted remark of Sigwart, the inductive process is not logical conclusion or inference and induction is not a logical problem. However, this statement by itself says very little, since one may disagree to a large extent about the delineation of the concepts "conclusion," "proof," and "logic." It will be more useful if we point out precisely what, according to our thesis, is the actual situation in this respect. Single observations provide, at first, the basis of *guesses* as to the occurrence of further, analogous cases not yet observed. If a guess seems to prove its worth, it is pronounced a general "law" ("the inductive generalization"), and is first stated in words of ordinary language which have only a vaguely defined coördination with reality. Another creative step, which is by no means uniquely determined by observations, transforms the individual "laws" referring to some area of experience into an axiomatic system, which at the same time serves as a definition of the expressions used in the laws, and from which one can later draw precise conclusions. This entire process we call induction; its core is the transition from statements on observations to a tautological system.

Here is an example: Kepler found that the paths of several planets are ellipses, and he guessed that this might be true for all of them; in other cases it was found to be true, and then the conjecture was stated as a law. Combined with the laws of free fall, which Galileo found in an analogous way, Kepler's laws yielded the basis for Newton's axiomatic system of celestial mechanics (which includes the law of gravitation).

The question that presents difficulties to the philosophers, logicians, and metaphysicians here is this: How do we *know,* where does our conviction come from, that the results found by induction are *true?* This question does not exist for us, since we do not claim to have such knowledge or such certainty. An axiomatic system is never true or false, but only more or less useful (Chapter 9). Newton's system of celestial mechanics, after two centuries of unopposed acceptance, had to undergo an essential alteration by Einstein's theories, and we do not know what further evolution it is still going to experience in the future. The change was made necessary by the fact that in a specific situation, namely, the variation of the perihelion of the planet Mercury, one could not succeed in finding suitable additional axioms (about the presence of perturbing masses, or similar things) which would have left the Newtonian system unaltered. As long as there are men who make observations and collect experiences, no inductive "conclusion" is safe from change.

*What we call induction is a construction, based upon observation, but not uniquely determined by it. We do not know of a "proof" of the "truth" of an inductive "conclusion"; any inductive step in a theory is subject to continual testing by new observation (see also Chapter 13, 5 and Chapter 14, 6).*

7. *Methodology.* Everything we have said in the foregoing about the construction of physical theories, about their relations to other branches of science, about the relation between explanation and description, about the economical nature of science, and finally about the interaction of deduction and induction, is certainly in need of many and detailed additions for the purpose of clarification, justification, and factual completion. If we omit these amplifications—and that holds analogously for all parts of this book—it is not in the naïve belief that any problems are "settled" by our brief remarks, but because, in a volume of moderate size, we wish at least to touch upon a certain broad complex of questions. Thus, we shall not add here any more details, however desirable it may seem (the problem of induction in relation to causality will be taken up in Chapter 13, 5 and Chapter 14, 6), but we shall raise only one more question which, so to speak, stands above what we have discussed so far, namely, what is the position within the general framework of science as a whole of the methodological statements pronounced here (and partly also in other chapters)?

According to what has been said in connection with Mach's notion of the economical nature of science, we restate that we are dealing primarily with a description of the characteristic features of scientific activity. This is particularly true of our discussion of induction and deduction. We seek to describe certain elements in the behavior of scientists in their scientific work and the content of science resulting from this work. In a book by Karl Popper, mentioned before (Chapter 6, 5), whose position is often close to our "moderate" positivism, this view toward methodology is called "naturalistic" and is opposed by a different one. Popper holds that in this field one is concerned less with knowledge than with conventions, i.e., with the construction of interconnected rules, and hence he recommends that one speak of a "logic of research" in the sense in which one could design a "logic of chess," for example. But the systematic exposition of the rules of chess is also nothing but a description of the behavior of chess players, with the strict addition that he who behaves differently from these rules is no longer playing "chess." Such rigor and strict closure of the rules is not attainable for the game called "science." The situation is here rather analogous to the rules for the use of a living language, where one is confronted with a wide range of prescriptions, from the strictest grammatical laws to stylistic finesses which can hardly be formulated explicitly. A controversy over the question whether a statement about the stylistic properties of a language is cognitive or normative seems rather superfluous to us.

On the whole, Popper's book contains many details that can serve as supplements to what we have said here, e.g., about the "testing" of a theory, which may be accomplished by an unsuccessful attempt at falsification (see Chapter 6, 5); about the concept of the "simplicity" of a theory; and about the concept of "validity." In the last analysis, serious differences of opinion concerning methodological questions cannot occur once the phantom of absolute cognition and absolutely certain knowledge is abandoned. We summarize the main results of this chapter in the following manner:

*All exact science starts with observations, which at the outset are formulated in ordinary language; then these inexact formulations are made more and more precise and are finally replaced by axiomatic assumptions, which at the same time yield definitions of the basic concepts; tautological transformations are then the means of deducing from the axioms conclusions, which after retranslation into common language are tested by new observations. Of no scientific statement or basic concept do we know what changes it will experience in the future.—All of these propositions are supposed to be merely descriptions of the hitherto observed ways of research.*

## PART IV

# causality and probability

Der denkende Mensch irrt besonders, wenn er sich nach Ursach und Wirkung erkundigt; sie beide zusammen machen das unteilbare Phänomen.

The thinking man errs particularly when he asks for cause and effect; both together are the indivisible phenomenon.

Goethe

# causal propositions

1. *Isolated Occurrences.* Among the relations which our everyday language has expressed in various ways ever since very early times, the most interesting one, from the epistemological point of view, is that of cause and effect. Historically it can be stated that originally there was no clear distinction between the causal and the purely temporal relation. The prepositions "weil" and "da" in German, "cum" in Latin, "puisque" in French, "since" in English, and many others indicate this; and the change of usage which the German "nachdem" is undergoing in our own time also belongs to these examples. Today every educated man "knows" that there must be something of "necessity" in the cause-and-effect relation over and above the purely temporal succession in order that a causal chain be determined. But as soon as one tries to describe what the "necessity" consists of, great difficulties arise.

Let us look at some quite simple examples of customary causal turns of phrase: The stone fell to the ground, *because* the support on which it lay was removed; I did not make the train, *since* I left home too late. The first of these sentences undoubtedly contains more than the statement, the stone fell *when* its support was taken away. The additional idea is: Whenever under otherwise equal circumstances the support of the stone is taken away, the stone falls; if the support is not taken away, the stone does not fall. In the second case, the addition to the statement of the individual occurrence is analogous: Every time one leaves home, under otherwise constant circumstances, too late, one misses the train; if it is not too late, one does not. In this example, the additional statement can be regarded as a tautology which defines the concept "too late"; in the first case it is certainly a statement about reality. As a third example let us take a linguistic formulation which is slightly different in form: The court rules that the shot which hit the victim was the *cause* of his death. This means, in addition to the temporal succession of shot and death, that there is the claim that such a shot every time it occurs under congruent circumstances will be accompanied by the succeeding death of the victim, and the victim will not die when the shot does not occur.

It is immediately apparent that the discussion has only slightly shifted the problem, namely, toward the question what is to be understood by "equal circumstances." We will not make any attempt now to go into this further, but we shall make it our first point to state that linguistic causal expressions are based upon the assumption that certain single events or occurrences can be completely isolated and are repeatable. The causal expressions originated under the influence of a primitive world picture; in this picture there exist occurrences that can happen or not happen independently of all other events in the world, so that one may imagine that everything is present again, except for the one fact thought of as isolated. If $A$ is such an isolated fact (e.g., the taking away of the support of the stone), then there may be another isolated event $B$ coördinated with it (the falling of the stone) which follows $A$ every time $A$ happens under the prescribed circumstances, but does not occur when $A$ is not realized in these circumstances.

Many examples from everyday life show that such a world picture, however primitive it may seem from the point of view of contemporary science, is extremely useful and even indispensable for practical life. A quite different question is, what is the meaning of those causal sentences if one is forced, as scientific thinking requires, to give up the simple idea of completely isolated and freely repeatable single events? We shall go into this in a little more detail in what follows.

*The customary causal expressions ("because" sentences, words such as cause and effect, etc.) correspond originally to the primitive idea that there exist isolated single events* A, B, . . . *which can occur independently of all other happenings. If in a certain constant set of circumstances* B *always follows when* A *has happened, and never occurs without* A, *then one applies to the couple* "A,B" *the various causal phrases.*

*2. The Problem of Causality.* We do not mean to assert that in today's intellectual language the causal relation is used *only* in the original primitive sense. It is also customary to say that the stone falls because it is attracted by the earth, or because it is subject to gravitation. The totally uneducated person does not understand what this means, since for him the presence of the earth does not belong to the "interchangeable" parts of the world; the idea that the stone would not fall were the earth not present, requires a capacity of abstraction that one acquires only as a result of education, schooling, and living experience. On the other hand, the foregoing sentence does not satisfy the criterion that the cause of an event precedes its effect.

A further advance from the primitive notion of causality is reached as soon as it is realized that the requirement of "equal circumstances" does not imply the constancy of the *entire* rest of the world, but that in every case, according to experience, independence of far-removed influences can be taken for granted. When, for example, one considers the correlation between the turning over of a glass and the flowing out of the water, one disregards in the naïve conception of causality whether the observations occur under different constellations of the stars. Here again the—insuperable—difficulty appears, of indicating exactly *what* is supposed to remain constant. Another step in the elaboration of the idea of causality is achieved if, in generalizing, one passes to *classes* of events. What is observed of one stone and its support is transferred to every other stone and its support, which may be quite different from that of the first one. At this point the relation to the concept of induction comes into the picture (see Section 5).

A particularly rich source of confusion consists in the fact that certain causal expressions—in a historically quite understandable way—are used linguistically in another and quite different sense, namely, for the denotation of *logical* relations. If $A$ is the cause of $B$, one also says: "From $A$ follows $B$" or "$B$ is the consequence of $A$." Exactly the same words are used when $A$ and $B$ are not events but propositions and $B$ is derived from $A$ by logical deductions or tautological transformations. The similarity is particularly pronounced in German, and has probably influenced the philosophical theory of causality to a great extent. In French it is a little easier to distinguish between "il suit" and "il s'ensuit," and between "succession" and "conséquence," but that does not preclude all confusion.

The growing child who learns a language and at the same time becomes acquainted with the world of experience grows into the linguistic habits of its environment. A certain area of application of the causal expressions not exactly delineated is fixed within any linguistic community by general (not specialized scientific) literature. Noticeable differences, however, will be found once the range of civilized nations who live in a community of culture is transgressed. At any rate, a complete description, specified according to regions and periods, levels of education and age, of what is expressed by the various customary causal idioms, would be a worthwhile task for a special investigation and not easy to carry out. A suitable treatment of these questions, which belong to the study known as semantics, would in our opinion be more important than the discussions, so much favored by many philosophical writers, about when the words "cause," or "reason," and "effect," or "consequence," *should* be used, and so on.

In fact, philosophers of all times have dealt at length with questions grouped around the word "causality" and related expressions; many of them have claimed that they "solved definitively the problem of causality," others have declared it to be unsolvable. We can only describe the task posed by these authors for themselves, either explicitly or implicitly, as an attempt to reconcile the entirely primitive ideas on which causal expressions are based with the improved insight into the world of experience that is available to us today. Since linguistic usage itself is, in addition to any present uncertainty, changing continually and partly adapting itself to the altered state of our knowledge, we should be inclined to agree with those who think the problem unsolvable. But this does not mean that we are pessimists or that we advocate intellectual resignation. For we also know that the "problem of motion" which since the Greek skeptic Zeno has bothered generations of philosophers, has remained "unsolved." We do not mind that a bit—because we have a science of mechanics which gives us the answers to all reasonable questions about motion. In our opinion, the problem of causality will experience a similar development. The only difference here is that, instead of a single discipline, the whole of all science, accompanied by a sober critique of language, will play the essential role in directing scientific curiosity toward questions that can be stated clearly and therefore answered.

*The so-called problem of causality arises from the fact that the primitive ideas to which the causal expressions originally corresponded proved with the advance of knowledge to be untenable, while language can adapt itself only incompletely to the changed situation. The problem of causality can be "solved" as little as the "problem of motion"; all we can expect is that, in a manner analogous to the one in which mechanics answers all specific questions concerning motion, all concrete questions about causal relations will in time be answered.*

3. *Some Historical Remarks.* We cannot mention here, even in the briefest form, all directions in which philosophers of ancient and of recent times have tried to investigate the concept of causality and questions related to it. We may only point out in a very few words some typical examples. Let us quickly pass over some quotations whose discussion does not seem very fruitful to us. Heidegger, the leader of the "existentialist" school, arrives in a recent book at the result that

the essence of cause is the transcendental trichotomy of causation into world design, preoccupation in being, and ontological justification of being.

Hegel had given the following definition earlier:

Cause is the unity of identity and diversity, the truth of that which diversity and identity turn out to be—which is reflection in itself and at the same time reflection in others, and vice versa. It is the essence posited as totality.

A famous treatise by Schopenhauer, his first work, *Of the Fourfold Root of the Theorem of Sufficient Cause,* gives a careful analysis of the different ways in which causal expressions are used in the language of literature. In the first place, there are causes which are assigned to changes in the external world (the stick expands, because the room was heated); in the second place, cognitive causes (the temperature increased, because the thermometer shows . . .); in the third place, existential causes, which supposedly are apprehended by immediate insight (the external angle of a triangle is greater than either of the two opposite internal ones, because it is evident that . . .), and finally, motivations (I do that, because it is my will to do it). There is nothing to say against this enumeration, except that when we speak of causation in the scientific sense, we mean only the first of the four cases. In his explanations Schopenhauer applies mainly the concepts of Kant's epistemology. He considers the law of inertia in the form that only the *change* of a state of motion, but not the motion itself, needs a cause, as "knowledge a priori and above all possible doubt." Galileo, however, hardly 200 years earlier encountered the greatest difficulties in trying to convince the believers in the "eternal law of causality," when he was led by *observation* to the assumption that a constant change of location of a body is possible without a lasting cause.

Going back in the history of philosophy to the period before Kant, we find in David Hume a climax of enlightenment that has never been reached again. Hume broke with the dogmatism which, in a way, up to then had made it impossible even to discuss the relation between cause and effect. He noticed that without observation and experience we cannot know anything of cause and effect. He pronounced in simple words that all we know of what is often called "necessary effect" is that we find sometimes a correlation between two things that are, according to our observations, temporally (and to a certain extent locally) connected. The habit of observing this fact can in certain cases become so deeply rooted that at the occurrence of the one event we think automatically of the second; thus we have the impression that we are dealing with something similar to the connection between a premise and conclusion:

> The efficacy or energy of causes is neither placed in the causes themselves, nor in the deity, nor in the concurrence of these two principles; but belongs entirely to the soul which considers the union of two or more objects in all past instances. It is there that the real power of causes is placed, along with their connection and necessity.

According to Hume, the relations of our will to the actions that result from it are familiar to us only through experience. He also arrived at an unprejudiced comprehension of the stories and claims about miracles which seem to contradict causality (see Chapter 16). Kant, who had been "awakened from dogmatic slumber," as he said, by Hume, later sought to restore to the causal connection the "logical necessity" that belongs to logical deductions.

The earliest stage in the treatment of causality is characterized by the formulation of an axiom called the "general law of causality" without any attempt at linguistic criticism. Thus Leibniz says in his *Monadology,* confusing real and cognitive cause,

By virtue of the principle of sufficient reason we consider that no fact could be found true or existing and no proposition valid, without a sufficient reason why this should be so and not otherwise.

We shall discuss later the idea of a law of causality as such (Section 6).

*Among the earlier treatments of the problem of causality Hume seems to represent the culminating point. Hume did not, as is often claimed, consider causal and temporal succession as equivalent, but he recognized that the impression of "necessary connection" is inferred merely from the experiential temporal connection between certain phenomena. In contrast to Hume, Kant returned to the older, "deeper," conception, according to which causal connections possess something of the necessity (and "dignity") of logical conclusions.*

4. *Further Amplification.* In order to reduce Hume's positivistic conception of causal connection *ad absurdum,* the following objection was made. If somebody every day for a long time makes the observation that each time his watch shows four o'clock a train rolls by, he will nevertheless not believe that the movement of his watch is the *cause* of the appearance of the train, or think of a necessary connection between the two events in the sense of a causal relation. If he did believe this, he obviously would be wrong. To this we reply that in this example the prerequisites for even the most primitive causal judgment, which we have mentioned above, are not present, unless the man in question is blind to all other happenings in the world. For a man in his right senses cannot possibly regard the position of the hands of his watch as an independent and isolated event which could, under otherwise essentially unchanged circumstances in the environment, happen or not happen. He sees that, e.g., the sun never stands very high in the sky when his watch shows four o'clock, and that there are infinitely many other things which accompany regularly the change in the position of the hands of his watch. Possibly he could (and he would not be so very wrong with this assumption) regard the totality of these events as the cause of the appearance of the train—but he could do this only if he lacked any experience of the social relations between the activities of men and the motion of vehicles. The assumption of a causal connection in this case seems so strange to us only because the idea of the existence of a man with a thus limited and one-sided range of experience is rather absurd. Anyway, it has to be taken into account that the amount of observation that forms the basis of our causal judgments is,

as a rule, of much greater order of magnitude. In most cases it comprises not only personal experiences, but also the results of observations that have come down to us for generations by word of mouth or in written form.

The fact that there is a "causal connection" between sexual intercourse and the pregnancy of women did not occur to men until a certain, rather late, stage of civilization was reached, and there are still today uncivilized primitive tribes who do not know that connection. In this case the comparatively long intervening time and the irregularity of the occurrence of the effect make observations more difficult. The word "irregularity" merely indicates that a full insight into the working of causality in the primitive sense has not yet been gained in this domain.

Mach noticed that in certain cases of measurable phenomena the causal concept is replaceable by that of the mathematical *function*. For example, the volume $v$ of a gas is a function of its pressure $p$; in signs, $v = f(p)$. This expresses, according to Mach, the fact that changes of pressure "cause" changes of volume. However, E. Zilsel showed in an interesting study that this idea is in need of supplementation and alteration in several respects. We agree with Philipp Frank's point of view according to which the mathematical expression of a causal relation (where mathematical formulation is in order) is a differential equation with time as the independent variable. In fact, pressure and volume of an ideal gas at constant temperature are functionally related in such a way that the product of the two numbers $p$ (pressure) and $v$ (volume) is, in a state of equilibrium, equal to a constant $c$; thus $v = f(p) = c/p$. But the causal connection is not completely expressed in the functional relation $pv = c$, in which both $p$ and $v$ play the same role. One has to consider the more comprehensive equation which states that the rate of change of volume (in mathematical symbols, the differential quotient, $dv/dt$) is determined by the difference between the actual pressure $p$ and the equilibrium value $c/v$. If this difference is zero, $v$ remains constant; if $p$ is greater than $c/v$, then $v$ decreases, and vice versa. Hence we say: changes of volume are caused by the pressure and not the other way around. The primitive causal concept has experienced here an essential modification, concerning the temporal relation between cause and effect. In our example it can hardly be said that the effect temporally *succeeds* the cause (that the change of volume occurs *after* the deviation of the pressure from the neutral value has taken place); rather it would be more correct to state that the change of $v$ and its cause, the difference $p - cv$, are observed simultaneously. But this is simply an indication of the typical difficulties that occur whenever one attempts to use an expression of ordinary language in the area of exact science (see Chapter 15, 1).

One often relates to the causal concept the distinction, which we mentioned in Chapter 12, 2, between the words "explain" and "describe." A phenomenon, it is said, is not "explained" until one knows its cause. But since, as we have noticed, the indication of cause is nothing but the account of a complex of observations of a specific kind, it is apparent that even from this side a clear demarcation of the boundary between "descriptions" and "explanations" cannot be reached. The differential equation of a phenomenon of motion or of any other physical process can be taken as a description as well as an explanation.

*The empiricist conception of causality, established by Hume, cannot be shaken by simple counterexamples; it holds its own even in the face of the higher requirements of science. In the cases of measurable phenomena, we regard—somewhat differently from Mach—as the mathematical expression of the causal relation not the functional relation between two variables but a differential equation with time as the independent variable.*

5. *The Inductive Inference.* It was mentioned in Chapter 12, 7 that in connection with the problem of causality we would have to take up again the concept of induction. The problem of induction, as we saw, originates in the attempt to find for the transition from manifestly unprecise observational sentences to a tautological (and hence "rigorously valid") system of propositions a theory of similar structure to that of logic and thereby to give this transition the character of rigor. This purpose can easily be achieved by the insertion of a causal statement—if one conceives of causality in Kant's sense as an absolute, a priori valid category. A simple schematized example will make this clear.

An observational sentence, let us call it *S,* states: A body cools off if its environment has a lower temperature. Starting from this and similar more detailed observations—which is the method of inductive physics—we pass to a tautological system whose basis is the differential equation *D* of heat conduction. Now the causal statement *C* is intercalated: The temperature difference between the body and its environment is the *cause* of its cooling off, i.e., it effects the cooling off. He who conceives of causality in an absolute way, i.e., who sees in the connection between cause and effect a kind of logical necessity, has achieved with the enunciation of sentence *C* what is for him the aim of inductive inference: an assertion about the temperature change under certain circumstances which is strictly valid for all future cases. The experiential statement *S,* with hardly a change in its wording, has thus become a "law of nature." Then the transformation of the natural law into the formula *D* seems of little, rather formal import.

Within the framework of the empiricist conception of science the interpolation just described is superfluous. Our knowledge about the external world cannot be increased by the introduction of new expressions and new ways of speaking. If statement *S* is verified by sufficiently many and careful observations and is tested in the light of all our general experience, it can be given the form of the causal sentence *C;* but that does not improve its validity. We do not possess any guarantee that the behavior described in $S$ will be observed in all future times; and the transition from $S$ to $D$, whether direct or by means of $C$, cannot change anything in this respect.

With or without the insertion of causal expressions, the fact remains that general statements found by induction, which stand at the basis of a deductive theory, are neither "absolute," nor "eternal," nor "strictly valid truths." They are, if we interpret the words occurring in them in the customary inexact language, assertions about reality which are subject to continual (inexact) testing. If one regards the basic propositions as part of an axiomatic system in which all expressions find their definition, they become precise statements, which do not say anything about the world of experience and only serve, by means of tautological transformations, to yield further precise statements; the latter, when interpreted in ordinary language, supply inexact assertions about reality which can be tested by new observation. In all this nothing is changed by the use of a language in which the fundamentals of the theory are said to express the "real causes" of phenomena, or their "actual reasons," etc.

*In order to justify the inductive inference, i.e., the transition from specific observations to general statements, one often inserts causal statements as connecting links. It is easy to see that nothing is gained thereby, and in particular the validity of the general statements is neither increased nor widened in range.*

6. *The Law of Causality.* So far we have hardly touched upon that point which takes the largest space in the philosophical treatment of the problem of causality, namely, the so called general "law of causality." In Section 3 we quoted a formulation due to Leibniz. Kant says in the first edition of the *Critique of Pure Reason,*

Everything that happens (begins to be) presupposes something which it follows according to a rule.

And in the second edition at the same place,

All changes take place according to the law of connection of cause and effect.

Schopenhauer chooses as the most general formula the one due to Christian Wolff (1679–1754): "Nihil est sine ratione cur potius sit quam non sit" (Nothing happens without a reason why it should happen rather than not happen). The number of examples of different formulations could be increased at will. We may only add that almost all philosophers regard the law of causality as the most important, the most far-reaching, and the most firmly founded of all principles of epistemology. Philipp Frank has recently discussed in his excellent book *Das Kausalgesetz und seine Gren-*

*zen* all pertinent questions in a detailed manner offering many clarifications, particularly of physical problems.

We have seen how a single primitive causal statement, *"B* follows from *A,"* originates in certain not very precisely describable observations about the connection between two phenomena *A* and *B*. Now, the law of causality claims that for *every* observable phenomenon (let us call it *B*) there exists a second phenomenon *A,* such that the sentence *"B* follows from *A"* is true. This assertion may be taken as an inductive generalization of the observable fact that one can, in many cases, formulate causal statements. A proposition found by induction is never "provable"; nor can it be verified in experience, but at the most, falsified (Chapter 6, 5). There can be no doubt that the law of causality in the formulation just stated is in agreement with all our own experiences and with those which come to our knowledge in one way or another. It would be hopeless to look for an example to the contrary, for an event to which no other could be correlated as its cause. Considering the great indeterminacy of the content of primitive causal statements, there remains at least the possibility of regarding the cause of an event as "not yet" precisely known. Beyond that, in a certain agreement with the quoted point of view of the philosophers, we can also state that in practical life there is hardly a more useful and more reliable rule of behavior than to *assume* of any occurrence that we come to know that some other one preceded it as its cause.

But all of these assertions depend upon the presupposition that one remains within the most primitive and naïve sphere of thought in which, as we have pointed out, the customary causal expressions of language originated, and where there are single isolated "events" which may or may not occur without any change in the rest of the world, etc. If we give up this prescientific point of view, which is adapted to and derived from everyday experience, we lose all possibility even of formulating in a useful way the law of causality as a statement about reality. Kant's first formulation becomes immediately invalid as soon as we cease to think of the entire world as consisting of separated, discrete occurrences, and that was probably the reason why Kant replaced it by a new one. The second of Kant's formulas avoids the fault of the first; but since now the wording of the law of causality itself contains the term "law of connection between cause and effect," there remains here nothing but a vicious circle or at best an element of a tautological system, which, however, is by no means worked out by Kant in that context. Very similar is the situation concerning other attempts, suggested so far, to formulate a law of causality. Either they use the naïve, though practically useful idea of isolated "events," or they become more or less empty.

In the special case in which one deals with changes of measurable quantities, the causal relation can be reduced to the exact form of differential equations; that, of course, implies giving up the conception of single successive "events." If one wanted to establish a law of causality on this basis, it would have to read: All happenings of the world can be described by differential equations with time as the independent variable. That is indeed the claim of physical determinism, to which we shall return in Chapter 15.

*The law of causality is the inductive generalization of the experience that, as a rule, one can find for any event B another event A such that the statement "B follows from A" (or an equivalent one) is possible in the sense of Chapter 13, 1. If one abandons the naïve but, for practical life and most scientific problems, entirely satisfactory point of view of dissecting the world into single isolated "events" which are repeatable under constant conditions, the primitive causal statements and hence the law of causality lose their meaning.*

7. . . . *And Its Limitations.* All philosophical endeavors concerning the law of causality can be characterized as the attempts to find a way out of the following dilemma: An even half-way clear formulation of such a law is possible only if we accept an extremely simplified picture of world happenings; on the other hand, any closer observation contradicts this picture most decidedly. The situation here is in the last analysis the same as the one in the formation of concepts (body, individual, ego, etc.), which we dealt with in Chapter 7. These concepts, as well as that of causality, are *constructs* that grew out of the practical demand for orientation in our environment, and have an evolution of thousands of years behind them. Their practical value, approaching even indispensability, not only for everyday life, but also in wide ranges of scientific activity, remains undisputed. We regard it as quite natural and expedient behavior to try to extend as far as possible the means of thought, which have been acquired through generations, to new situations. But the point of view which holds that this is the only possible way, and that whatever situation occurs one *must* not dispense with these means, seems detrimental to the advancement of science.

The inadequacy of the customary causal concept forces itself upon everyone who tries to use a language that is to hold its own against more serious criticisms. We have already pointed out the situation in the mathematical-physical sciences and we shall return to it in Chapter 15. But even the critically minded historian, for instance, avoids as far as possible statements such as: The moral disintegration of the upper classes was the cause (or one of the causes) of the decline of the Roman Empire. For if in this sentence one replaces the causal expression by its meaning in ordinary language (i.e., by the explicit description of the experience to which it is correlated), it would read: We imagine the entire history of the Roman Empire repeated several times, in some cases only with the exception that the moral disintegration is missing (and whatever else may be regarded as a cause), and we claim that decline would not occur if and only if these exceptions take place. Even without such an exact analysis one senses the inadequacy in this use of the word "cause." The historian who is careful about his words will prefer to describe the development and the succession of situations, without using the summarizing and abbreviating causal expression. (To what extent every historical description implies the presupposition of repeatability will be considered later, in Chapter 18.)

This situation, this intellectual uneasiness at the use of causal expressions, was undoubtedly the reason for the many endeavors of philosophers in the field of causality. School philosophy attacked the problem with a preconceived idea: to an expression that is customary in all languages and whose practical expediency is beyond any doubt, there *must* correspond a specific, clear "idea," which has only to be "discovered" or unveiled. Some day the history of idealistic philosophy will be written from the psychological point of view, and it will then become clearer what motivated men to such overrating of their linguistic creations. We do not feel guilty of undervaluing the results of historical evolution and we are far from underestimating the wealth of thought accumulated in the traditional stock of language. But we do not think that the insights that determined the linguistic forms are the most profound; they are but the oldest, most immediate, simplest, and least precise. No essential progress in the understanding of "causality" can, in our opinion, be gained by collecting and comparing all ideas that can be associated with the *words* "cause and effect," and then abstracting from this collection the "pure idea of causality." What has to be done is to examine thoroughly in every single area of science the process of transition from observations to the formation of theories. One may not find in this way a uniform idea of causality but one will find in every area an "improvement of language" suitable for it. Faced with the question what the common element of causality in the various areas might be, we reply: The common element is merely the indeterminate, vague, and preliminary concept, that does not stand up against a serious critique, and that has its legitimate place in everyday language.

*Like such words as "body," "substance," "individual," "soul" (Chapter 7), the various causal expresions are an expedient of communication of limited utility. They denote an important specific relation between observed phenomena which is only vaguely delineated and not exactly definable. The great value of these expressions for practical purposes, and their usefulness in wide areas of scientific thought, are beyond all possible doubt. But the expressions are based upon a primitive and incomplete world picture and it is impossible to make them compatible with a critical conception of our environment or to replace them generally by a precise formulation.*

CHAPTER 14

# probability

1. *Frequency.* Among the various alternate forms in which language expresses the causal connection between two events $A$, $B$ is the following. Equivalent to *"A is the cause of B"* or *"B follows from A"* one finds the proposition: "From the occurrence of $A$ the occurrence of $B$ can be predicted." Lending to the causal connection, as is customary, the character of "necessity," one may add: "with certainty," or "for sure." This is the point where another parlance branches off and gradually leads out of the area of causality: one may speak of uncertain, or more or less certain, or of only "probable" predictions.

The most important difference between probability and the causal relation is that the former is graduated. One speaks of higher or lower probability and thus one can correlate these attenuated causal judgments to measure, and hence to arithmetic. Another less striking characteristic is that if one deals with predictions (primarily with uncertain ones), one often pays more attention to the effect $B$ than to the cause $A$ and the latter is often not even mentioned explicitly. Thus it is predicted that the event $B$ will occur with this or that probability, without indicating any specific premise $A$; the implication is then that the totality of all present circumstances is assumed as the cause of the future event. But there is, of course, in the area of "uncertain" causal statements also the complete form: If this die is handled in such and such a manner, it is very probable that. . . .

When one studies the meaning of probability judgments, i.e., attempts to describe experiences to which such a statement points, one will certainly find that they consist of connections which at times take place and at other times do not. At the basis there is, just as in the case of the causal judgment, the primitive idea of "repeatability under the same circumstances." But while the causal statement assumes a succession of $B$ upon $A$ without exception, the probability statement is the indication of a state in which $B$ in some cases follows the occurrence of $A$, and in other cases does not. This shows clearly that here—as opposed to the strict causal judgment—a certain graduation is possible corresponding to the higher or lower frequency of cases of one kind or the other. Aristotle understood this and explained: "The probable is that which happens frequently" (where "probable" is used in the sense of "highly probable").

In many popular explanations of the concept of probability it is not the number of observed verifications that is given as a measure of the probability, but rather the number of *reasons,* of motives, which are favorable to the assumption in question. The prediction that it will rain tomorrow is indeed made more probable if not only the barometer at the place in question has dropped, but also the distribution of air pressure in a wider vicinity and, further, the over-all weather situation indicate rain; hence there are three reasons for it. But these single "reasons" are themselves not causes in the sense of exceptionless correlation, as the causal judgment requires (otherwise their number would make no difference); between them and the occurrence of rain there also is only a probability relation. In this manner, therefore, one probability judgment is merely reduced to the concurrence of several probability relations, and the question still remains to what degree each of the latter is to be taken into account. Thus one cannot avoid evaluating the probability of a statement (in so far as a measure can be assigned to it at all), in the last analysis, by the frequency of cases in which the assertion in question holds true.

*The observation of couples of events,* A, B, *which are loosely connected with each other in such a way that* B *follows* A *in some cases and in others does not, leads to the probability concept. The frequency of the occurrence of the successor* B *to* A *provides an estimate for the probability. On the whole, the prerequisites for the concept of probability, its imperfections, and its practical usefulness are subject to the same considerations as those advanced in Chapter 13 about the causality concept.*

2. *Subjective Probability.* In philosophical literature one will often find vigorous objections to the above-outlined reduction of probability measure to the frequency of events, and even to the principle of relating the probability concept to observable events at all. The point of view of Sigwart's *Logic* may be taken as representative of the whole of school philosophy. According to him, probability theory deals with the study of certain *forms of inferences,* and hence is a part of logic. His line of thought is about as follows.

In some problems a discussion following the customary rules of logic arrives in the first place at a so-called disjunctive judgment, i.e., to a sentence of the form: *"A is either b or c"* (A is the subject; b and c are predicates). Then, he says, "on the grounds of the ratio of the amount of knowing to the amount of not-knowing on which the disjunctive judgment is based," one can derive a "measure of subjective expectation" and that is the probability of *b* or *c,* respectively. For example, about a person *P* it can logically be asserted that within the next year he will or will not die. One of the two alternatives is certainly true and each of them has a certain probability. The knowing or not-knowing on which the disjunctive judgment is based—at least so one would think—consists of the experience that all men eventually die; but from that one can surely not derive a "measure of expectation" for the case of *P.* Hence it is apparent that Sigwart must have in mind a different kind of knowledge; this can only be knowledge of the age, the state of health, the occupation, etc., of *P* and on the other hand the collected experience about the length of life of other men with the same characteristic properties. From the totality of *this* knowledge one may, perhaps, derive a statement such as the following: The probability of *P*'s death in the next year is very small. The mere fact of replacing "probability" by "measure of subjective expectation" offers no advantage. If somebody is asked in what way the probability judgment enunciated is related to the knowledge it is based on, he can hardly reply anything else than this: Among a great number of persons of the category in question only a small number die within a year.

Terming the judgment a "subjective" one can only mean that somebody else called upon to judge has at his disposal more or less knowledge about *P* and the life span of the corresponding group and will therefore pass a different judgment. If, e.g., it is known that *P* comes from a sick family, and if something about the rate at which the sickness is hereditary is known, this may change the probability judgment. In no case, however, can there be a connection between the experiential knowledge and the probability statement other than that given by the frequency relation.

Often the "subjective" or "logical" theory of probability is supplemented by theorems that are supposed to tell when the alternatives of a disjunction are equally probable (or are called that way). Thus C. Stumpf says,

> Those cases are equally possible about which we are in equal ignorance. And since ignorance can be set equal in its measure only if we know absolutely nothing about which alternative will happen, we can more specifically substitute this explanation for it.

In brief this means: The alternatives of a disjunction are equally probable if we know absolutely nothing about the possibility of their occurrence. But what sort of ignorance is meant here? In the case of a correct die, as well as in the case of one whose center of gravity is displaced in a known way, we certainly know "absolutely nothing" about what the next throw will show. If the ignorance refers to a specific single trial, then with *every* die the six possibilities should be equally probable. But if it means that one must not know anything that distinguishes the six faces of the die, this is never true, since we know at least that the six faces bear different numbers. Hence nothing is left but to demand that nothing should be known that would lead to the conclusion that one face will fall more frequently than another—which leads us back to the frequency concept.

*The "subjective" or "logical" theory of probability, preferred by school philosophy, seeks in vain for a basis of probability measurement that would be different from the frequency of the occurrence of the event in question. Even the explanation of equal probability of alternative cases is not possible without reference to the frequency.*

3. *Probability Calculus.* When in the framework of the positivistic conception of science we deal with a general concept such as that of probability, we see two possible approaches. In the first place, we may examine what it is that is referred to by the word "probable" and similar expressions in everyday language, including nonspecialized scientific literature. On the other hand, we may try to construct an exact theory serving for the description of an area of facts to which the linguistic expressions in question point. The problem, however, that school philosophy regards as the only important one does not concern us, namely, to find the "true and real essence" of probability, to expose its "pure idea," which is supposed to exist somewhere and to be hidden somehow in the imperfect expressions of everyday language.

In the discussion of causality we had to limit ourselves to the first of these two approaches. For we know of no special discipline in which the general concept of causality plays a special role—unless one counts as such the whole of physics (whose relation to the idea of causality and probability will be discussed in the next chapter).

The situation is a little different concerning the various applications of the probability concept. Surely there is no sphere of human life in which expressions such as "presumable," "probable," "easily possible," or "hardly possible" are not customarily used. One even speaks of the probability of a past occurrence, whereby one thinks vaguely of the frequency with which such an event would happen as a consequence of known premises in case these premises should be realized repeatedly. But it is a fruitless endeavor to try to account for such ways of speaking in the form of an exact theory. Everyday language is simply not precise; it does not contain rigorous conventions of correlation (Chapter 3) and it is vain to search for the *exact* meaning of a sentence (which may be quite connectible with the rules of ordinary language) such as: It is less probable that we shall have war next year than that there will be an earthquake in the same space of time.

But there exists a special area of experience in which all ideas connected with frequency and similar concepts, and hence also with probability, are quite easily susceptible of a treatment of higher precision. That is the sphere of mass phenomena and repetitive events. Among these a simple, repeatable game of chance, such as the dice game, is the best-known type. If one says that the six faces of a certain die fall with equal probability, this has a comparatively precise meaning; it means that on continual throwing, each of the six sides falls equally often, on the average. From the mathematical point of view the expression "on the average" is still in need of a more precise definition. But it is apparent that in occurrences of this kind the main source of indeterminacy and lack of precision, otherwise a property of the probability parlance, does not exist. In the first place, one can pretty easily state here what events must precede the observed effect: the putting of the die into the cup; the shaking of the cup; the throwing of the die. In the second place, the procedure can without difficulty be repeated at will as often as one wishes and almost without alteration; and in the third place, the effect of each trial (appearance of a specific face) is unambiguously determinable. These circumstances form the basis of an exact theory of probability, usually called the *calculus of probability*.

Clearly such a theory can cover only a small part of those occurrences to which, in ordinary language, the word "probable" is applied. It is the theory of a specific class of observable phenomena, namely, the class of mass phenomena and repeatable events, in the same sense in which thermodynamics is the theory of the phenomena of heat. The whole thing has nothing to do with a search for the "true meaning" of the word "probability."

*Out of all the cases in which the various probability expressions of everyday laguage are used, one special group may be singled out in which the probability concept can be given a precise meaning. This is the starting point of the so-called calculus of probability, which then becomes the exact theory of mass phenomena and repetitive events, in the same sense in which mechanics is the theory of the phenomena of motion, or geometry, the theory of the phenomena of space.*

4. *The Limiting Value of Frequency.* It will be useful for us to go into a few more details concerning the transition from the vague probability concept of ordinary language to the exact theory of repeatable events, and thence to the calculus of probability.

The first difficulty is to give a precise meaning to the words "frequency" or "average frequency" of the occurrence of an event. For this we have certain analogies in other areas of exact science, e.g., in the way the concepts of velocity and of specific weight are defined in mechanics. Velocity we call—imprecisely—the ratio of the displacement of a particle to the time used for it. But what displacement and what time are to be taken if one wants to specify the velocity with which a falling body arrives on the ground? Analogously, specific weight (or density) is—roughly speaking—

defined as the ratio of the weight (or mass) to the volume of a body; but if we say that the density of the earth increases steadily with depth or with the distance from the surface, to what ratios do we refer?

All such questions have been solved completely for physics since the days of Leibniz and Newton. The infinitesimal calculus represents a closed, consistent system of tautological constructions which lead, among other things, to the concept of the differential quotient. It can be used to provide a refined picture of many situations given in experience. We imagine that the path traversed by a moving particle is representable by a mathematical function of time and that this function belongs to those which are "differentiable." Then the velocity at a specific moment may be defined as the differential quotient, i.e., as the limiting value which the ratio of displacement to time approaches as both the numerator and denominator of the quotient tend to zero. Analogously, the density at a point of an arbitrary medium is defined in the following way. One takes a small piece of the body around the point in question, and lets its dimensions diminish successively more and more; in every phase of this process one forms for the piece under consideration the ratio of mass to volume and one assumes that in the "transition to zero," i.e., as both numerator and denominator of the quotient approach zero, the ratio becomes equal to a certain limiting value. This value is then called the density of the body at the point under consideration.

The problem of making the concept of "frequency" mathematically precise is solved in a similar fashion. If among $n$ observations the event considered happens $m$ times, the quotient $m/n$ is called the (relative) frequency within the trial sequence of length $n$. If, then, one wants to speak of frequency as such, without specification of the length of sequence of trials, one must imagine that the trials can be continued ad libitum. Furthermore, it is assumed that when the numerator and denominator of the fraction $m/n$ become bigger and bigger, the quotient approaches a certain limiting value. We then consider this limiting value as the measure of the frequency of the whole sequence and, according to what was said above, as the measure of the probability. S. D. Poisson recognized that this assumption is an appropriate picture of reality, at least in very many applications. He wrote in the introduction to his work of 1837, *Sur la probabilité des jugements,* one of the standard works of classical probability theory:

> All things in nature are subject to a universal law . . . This consists of the fact that if one observes very considerable numbers of events of the same kind . . . one will find among those numbers very nearly constant ratios. For every class of observations these ratios have a special value from which they deviate less and less as the series of observed events grows in length, and they would attain this value rigorously if it were possible to extend the series to infinity.

The present author (1919) made the definition of probability as the limiting value of the relative frequency the basis of a rational calculus of probability, which follows methodically the same lines as geometry or mechanics or similar branches of science.

We need not stress here once more explicitly that such a mathematical definition of probability will never be able to do justice to all customary applications of the word "probability." Expressions such as "force" or "work" in mechanics also denote concepts that correspond only in comparatively rare cases to what is denoted by these words in ordinary language.

*As a basis of an exact theory of repeated events and mass phenomena one may choose a probability concept defined as the limiting value of the relative frequency of an event in a sequence of trials continued indefinitely.*

5. *The Complete Theory.* Our definition of mathematical probability has the immediate advantage that it yields a reasonable addition theorem for the probability calculus. If one calls an infinite sequence of trials in which several different results (events) may occur (e.g., an ideal game with dice that do not wear out) a *collective,* it follows from the definition that the probability for the assumption that *within one* collective one of several mutually exclusive results occurs is equal to the sum of the probabilities of the individual results. For example, the probability of throwing an even number with a single die is equal to the sum of the probabilities of the occurrence of a 2, a 4, and a 6. A theory that does not use the concept of the collective and of the frequency within a collective cannot even state correctly the addition theorem. For the probabilities of *arbitrary* "mutually exclusive" events can have any sum, even bigger than 1.

Perhaps the most important insight supplied by the derivation of the probability concept from the frequency within a collective is the following. One may ask the question: Is there a definite, measurable probability for the assumption that a certain specified individual, John Smith, of New York, is going to die within a year? From the point of view of our theory the answer is a clear-cut "no." Only within a class, within a precisely defined group of persons, which can be considered as unlimited, does there exist a frequency of deaths; and we can speak of a limiting value only if we think of an indefinite continuation of observations within the group. But the individual, John Smith, is a member of many different classes, e.g., of the class of "men and women in New York 40 years of age" or of the class of "men in the United States in normal jobs, not over 40 years of age, and insured for 5 years." The probability of death in these two classes will, in general, be different and each of the two numbers (and many others) can be taken as John Smith's probability of death. If one thinks that a "true," and hence uniquely determined, number can be found by including in the definition of the class as many properties of John Smith as possible one does not get any result. For by *all* his properties only the one individual and no other one is determined, and thus any possibility of computing a frequency vanishes.

Besides the addition theorem for probabilities of mutually exclusive events within a collective, there is a need in probability calculus for a "multiplication rule." This rule states, e.g., that the probability of throwing a 5 and a 6 in succession is equal to the product of the probabilities of 5 and of 6. In order to derive the multiplicative law, which expresses a well-known empirical fact, in a sufficiently general form, one has to subject the collective to another axiom besides the one that requires the existence of a limiting value of the relative frequency. The second axiom demands that the succesion of the various labels or trial results within a collective is in a specific sense "random." This requirement can be brought into a precise form by asking that in a subsequence of all trials, selected without knowledge of the trial results, the limiting values of the frequencies of the various possible results are the same as those in the total sequence forming the collective. The empirical fact expressed by the "axiom of randomness" in an idealized form is that it is practically impossible in· a continued game of chance, e.g., roulette, to change one's chances of winning for an unlimited duration of the game by a calculated selection of parties (or of stakes), i.e., by a so-called gambling system. Originally objections were raised to this formulation of the axiom of randomness within the framework of the mathematical (tautological) theory. Later, however, owing to the work of A. Wald, A. H. Copeland, and W. Feller, a consistency proof for the probability calculus as based upon the two axioms, existence of a limited frequency and randomness of succession, was successfully carried out.

Finally, our conception bears out the analogy between the probability calculus and the rational theories of other areas as far as the nature of its problems is concerned. According to the classical point of view represented by Laplace, which in more recent times was adopted without reservation, even by H. Poincaré (1912), it is the outright task of probability theory to compute the probability of any describable event. But nobody claims today that it is the task of geometry to determine the distance of two well-described points on the surface of the earth. One realizes rather that geometry deals only with *relations* among spatial quantities and shows how to compute the length of the side of a triangle only if other lengths, etc., are given beforehand. Thus a rational theory of probability enables us to calculate unknown probabilities only from given probabilities. The general problem can be formulated in this manner: In every single case the probabilities within certain initial collectives are taken for granted, and then, by means of theorems derived tautologically from the axioms, the probabilities within specific, derived collectives can be computed. In the foregoing example for the addition theorem, the initial collective consisted of the gambling results of a die, hence of a sequence formed by the numbers 1 to 6; the end collective, of a sequence of "even" and "odd." Once the six probabilities $p_1$ to $p_6$ of the first-mentioned collective are given, the latter ones are found as the two partial sums $p_1 + p_3 + p_5$ for the odd, and $p_2 + p_4 + p_6$ for the even results.

*Based upon the concept of the collective and the two axioms, existence of a limiting frequency and randomness of the succession of results, a consistent mathematical probability theory can be constructed, which—in analogy to geometry, mechanics, etc.—forms an exact rational theory of the mass phenomena and repetitive events.*

6. *Transgression of the Borderline.* It is a well-known phenomenon that people often try to apply a theory, once it has found a certain recognition and proved its usefulness, far beyond its range of validity. In so far as this attempt belongs to what we have called (Chapter 1, 3) "change of usage," it is a regular procedure and may work out to the advantage of the evolution of science. But this endeavor often overshoots its mark, as many examples show. The usefulness of the energy principle in wide areas of physics and chemistry led the chemist Wilhelm Ostwald to the idea of making energetics a *Weltanschauung,* i.e., of extending its application to all possible observable phenomena. He went so far as to suggest a measure for the subjective feeling of happiness of men in a formula containing certain quantities of energy (see Chapter 26, 7).

In the calculus of probability there has always been a strong tendency to transgress boundaries and this trend has received a new impetus since the frequency conception has become more and more prevalent. Among older instances we mention that Laplace tried to compute the advantages and disadvantages of monarchistic and republican rule; the mathematician A. A. Markoff, the credibility of the Bible; the philosopher E. Hartmann, the answer to the question whether there are spiritual causes of natural phenomena; and for all this the formulas of probability calculus ought to serve! One may perhaps in those cases use the probability expressions of everyday language, just as one may colloquially speak of an energy of the feeling of happiness, but the prerequisites for the application of the exact probability concept are in no way satisfied.

We are primarily interested here in the repeated attempts at using the probability calculus for the so-called solution of the problem of induction. E. Zilsel made such an attempt on the basis of the classical conception of probability, and H. Reichenbach, on the basis of the frequency theory.

We know (Chapter 12, 7, Chapter 13, 5) that the cardinal problem in any treatment of induction is to discuss how the transition from accumulated unprecise and even partly inconsistent observations to a specific exact theory of the domain in question can be performed. Reichenbach starts by formulating a rule which he calls the fundamental rule of induction and in which only a single collective or mass phenomenon is taken into consideration. It runs as follows: If in a finite sequence of $n$ observations an event occurs $m$ times, hence with a frequence $m/n = p$, and if otherwise nothing is known, then we "posit" that the limiting value of the frequency (as $m$ and $n$ tend to infinity) is equal to $p \pm \epsilon$, where $\epsilon$ is a small unknown positive quantity. Analogously one could say: If the measurement of the side of a triangle yields the value $l$, we "posit" that its length is $l \pm \epsilon$. There is nothing much to say against such propositions, except that they are obvious. More correctly and more generally, one might state that for the data going into a problem within an exact theory one chooses values which are based upon necessarily imperfect measurement and that one has to take that lack of precision into account in retransforming the theoretical results to statements about reality.

But Reichenbach gives his induction rule—and here lies the transgression of the limits of the theory—a much more general interpretation. In the first place, it is supposed to be applicable to happenings of everyday life, e.g., when one wants to judge whether on a certain day a train is going to leave on time. In our opinion there is in such a case no possibility of computing in a reasonable manner the number $n$ of observations and the number $m$ of events, from which $p = m/n$ results, however rough the approximation. For even on the first day of the introduction of the time-table, or even on the day the railroad starts operating, one forms a "probability judgment," which is based upon various considerations, e.g., upon one's opinion about the possibility of a strike, or of an accident, and upon experiences of a more general kind about the reliability of people throughout the country, etc. Each of these considerations is very vaguely connected, in the manner mentioned in Section 1, with some frequency of experiences. And after all, what can the traveler do with the information that the probability of a train leaving on time is between 0.374 and 0.376? Is there any sense in thinking of a several-hundredfold repetition of exactly the same situation where in 37 per cent of the cases the train leaves on time? Obviously, this represents an example in which, although customary parlance allows the use of the word "probability" on the grounds of a vague and unclear idea of the countability of cases, the application of elementary or higher mathematics, the formation of a quotient and its limiting value, and the introduction of accuracy limits $\pm \epsilon$, etc., are completely out of place.

Even more striking is the attempted application of the "rule of induction" to the problem of induction itself. Reichenbach defends seriously the view that the number of successful and unsuccessful instances of testing of a physical theory, such as the theory of relativity, can be counted, and each one of them can be given a definite "weight," e.g., the red shift counts + 3, the deviation of a light ray by the sun, + ½, the motion of the perihelion of Mercury, + 5, etc. Here the most elementary prerequisites of counting are not satisfied, for 1 thought plus 1 thought by no means always equals 2 thoughts. Calculations that operate with "numbers" of thoughts, of successful instances of testing, etc., are model examples of nonconnectibility with the most elementary rules of language—not to mention the fact that a theory which definitely breaks down in the case of one single phenomenon must be rejected, and not be given the probability 0.99 if one can quote 99 instances in which it holds true. At any rate, in this way, one is not capable of reducing the question of the usefulness of a theoretical idea in any physical area to a question of probability calculus. It must be noticed that even in unprecise colloquial talk physicists hardly ever use the expression that a *theory* has a greater or smaller numerical probability. The physicist judges the usefulness, the possible acceptance or rejection of a theory by various criteria quite different from the ones above—to mention but one example: by the point of view of economy of thought (Chapter 12, 3). It is only within the framework of *one* theory which is taken for granted, and when all that remains to do is determine the value of a constant factor, that one can apply the concepts of the probability calculus to a sequence of uniform trials and then compute the probability for different possible values of the constant (so-called error theory).

It has been pointed out above that we consider as the legitimate domain of the calculus of probability the problems concerning mass phenomena and repetitive events. In other words, we hold that any statement of the probability calculus is nothing else than a proposition on certain infinite sequences of numbers or signs which stand for well-defined events or occurrences. There is no doubt that one may try to build up another theory, also connected with the colloquial usage of the term "probability," which concerns itself with the psychological problem of *plausibility* or *degree of confirmation* of a single statement or of entire systems. The mathematician G. Pólya has given some fundamentals of such a theory whose main characteristic is that no numerical value can be ascribed to the plausibility of a statement. In contrast to this, R. Carnap, once a follower of logical empiricism, thinks that he can apply not only numerical values, but even rules of classical probability calculus to degrees of confirmation. This means, essentially, that he *counts* statements, judgments, confirmations, as Reichenbach does (see above). The ultimate goal of the confirmation calculus is again to give a mathematical foundation to the procedure of induction (inductive logic, see Chapter 13, 5). Our point of view may be summarized as follows.

*The calculus of probability, which, like geometry, mechanics, etc., is the exact theory of a specific area of phenomena and which is itself derived from an empirical basis by means of induction, cannot serve to justify or rationalize the alleged inductive "inference" within the range of other areas of facts. The transition from observations to general theoretical statements cannot be mathematicized at all; it is not a logical conclusion, but a choice of that precise description of observed facts which one believes will stand up in the face of future observations, but which can be altered at any time for various reasons.*

7. *Different Points of View.* Many mathematicians who are under the influence of school philosophy reject the conception of a probability calculus based upon the concept of the collective as a "purely empirical" point of view. Others object that the collective as an infinite sequence of observations does not exist in reality, and hence that the theory is too abstract and could not be used for the description of real phenomena. To answer both of these objections one need only point to the repeatedly mentioned analogy with all other branches of exact science. There exists no infinitely long straight line of infinitely small cross-sectional area; nevertheless, geometry, which works with this and similar concepts, is useful for the explanation of phenomena of space—and is on the other hand not a "purely empirical" science.

Of course, one cannot say anything against someone's treating the tautological part of the theory of any area of experience in such a way that he gives a comprehensive exposition without referring back to the empirical starting point. But then he must not enunciate the results of his calculations in a form which gives the impression that these considerations represent statements about certain real phenomena. The typical flaw in the thinking of the older presentation of the calculus of probability may be illustrated by the following example.

Forming with the signs "0" and "1" (or any other two signs) all those combinations which consist of a total of $n$ signs, one gets a group of $2^n$ different combinations. It is found that, if one takes $n$ as a very large number, the great majority of combinations belonging to the group consists of approximately $n/2$ zeros and $n/2$ ones. More precisely, Jacob Bernoulli (1713) derived the following theorem: The larger $n$ is, the larger is the fraction of those combinations in which the number of zeros or of ones deviates from $n/2$ by less than, say, 0.1 per cent. Obviously, this is a purely arithmetic property of numbers and it is connected with reality only in so far as is any arithmetic theorem (Chapter 11, 1). But

Bernoulli himself and most textbooks state the result in such a way that it says: if one throws a "true" coin for heads and tails and carries out a long enough sequence of trials, it is almost certain that the number of heads will deviate by less than 0.1 per cent from half the number of trials. All we have to remark here is: The transition from the arithmetic theorem to this statement about reality can be justified only by defining a "true" coin as one for which the probabilities of the two alternatives are ½ each, hereby using the probability concept suggested by us, which establishes a connection with the frequency of occurrence of an event. A special variety of the confusion here is the idea that the derivation of the arithmetic theorem actually "mathematically *proves*" the fact that an event possessing the probability ½ will in a long sequence of trials almost certainly occur with a frequency approximately equal to ½, even if one did not previously define the probability by means of the frequency in a sequence of trials.

The calculus of probability is particularly interesting, from the point of view of the general topics treated in this book, because in this special discipline almost all fundamental questions that have played a role in the history of the inductive sciences are still under discussion. From the naïve empiricist on the one hand, who does not admit any exact concepts but accepts only the conceptual spheres vaguely delineated by the words of everyday language, up to the no less naïve "pure theoreticians," in whose mind all of science dissolves into separate systems of tautological transformations, every point of view is still represented today. There still are, e.g., the followers of the classical theory according to which everything depends upon the a priori recognition of equally possible cases, and they speak of "free formation of expectation," of "indifferent ranges," and of "compulsory, nonarbitrary construction of assumptions of equal right." Others again find that with the use of exact concepts "probability can no longer be a guide in practical life," or they predict the near approach of the breakdown of the whole of science if it continues to prove to be so unrealistic.

More recently the view has been defended that for the treatment of the problems of probability theory customary logic that knows only true and false judgments is not sufficient and that one has to create a special "logic of probability." To each judgment, according to this, there should be correlated a number between zero and one as its "probability value." It is not stated what value the correlation of the value number itself has. There is little doubt that it is possible to give to a part of the tautological considerations within the calculus of probability the external form of a "multivalued logic"; but that cannot have any essential influence upon the meaning and the results of the theory.

*In the contemporary discussion of the foundation of probability theory all the various points of view are represented that have played a role in the evolution of the inductive sciences: a-priorism, pure empiricism, the idea that statements about phenomena which are not taken into consideration in the definition of the basic concepts can be "proved mathematically," and finally the tendency to transgress all limits of validity of the theory by giving to the names of the basic concepts retroactively the widest interpretation. It may be expected that for this sector of the world of experience (the area of mass phenomena and repetitive events) also clarification will be reached gradually, which in other fields such as those of spatial phenomena, the phenomena of motion, heat processes, etc., has either already been reached or is actually in progress.*

### CHAPTER 15

# deterministic and statistical physics

1. *Differential Equations.* We mentioned in Chapter 13, 4 that the precise form of causal statements in physics is that of a differential equation with the time $t$ as the independent variable. If, for instance, one attempts to solve a problem of heat conduction in which the temperature $\theta$ appears as the unknown, the theory yields an equation in which essentially the differential quotient $d\theta/dt$, i.e., the rate of change of temperature, occurs as a function of time, location, and possibly temperature itself. Such an equation allows the computation of the temperature in its dependence upon time, if the initial temperature is given, i.e., if the value of $\theta$ is known at any one moment. Hence one can say that the differential equation together with an initial condition yields a prediction of the course of events. In other cases one may have to handle several differential equations simultaneously and with complicated initial conditions; but the general schema of the computation which results in a prediction of future values from present ones remains the same in principle.

The physical statement has primarily one thing in common with the original naïve form of causal assertion "from $A$ follows $B$," namely, that it presupposes the isolation and repeatability of single phenomena. Every time certain variables take on specific values and satisfy specific prerequisites, the same occurrence is repeated; the fact that the rest of the world has changed in the meantime is neglected. It is, however, here no longer assumed that one is dealing with loosely succeeding events $A$, $B$ as cause and effect. Rather, the "cause" is continuously at work, while the change of the variable considered (e.g., the temperature) occurs simultaneously. The increase (or decrease) of its value, observed after a certain length of time, is considered the "effect."

According to the conception of classical physics, which was absolutely predominant from the end of the seventeenth century to the middle of the nineteenth, all observable phenomena are describable in principle in this fashion. This fundamental idea of *determinism* or of deterministic physics is a precise expression of the so-called law of causality. The efforts of most philosophers of the eighteenth and nineteenth centuries toward securing for the law of causality a dogmatic validity were founded to a large part, though perhaps unconsciously, upon the impressive success of classical physics (Chapter 13, 6).

A theory based upon differential equations in the way just described can be modified in two respects without leaving the sphere of deterministic physics. One may on the one hand, as Vito Volterra showed for the first time (1887), consider the momentary rate of change of a variable as depending upon *all* the values that it took on during the preceding time. Thus the future is not predicted from the knowledge of the present alone, but from the knowledge of the present and the past; this is sometimes called "physics with a memory." The mathematical form of such a theory is that of a so-called integrodifferential equation. The second modification, which so far has not played any role, but possibly may yet gain great importance, would be to consider instead of continuous changes with time, discontinuous jumps following one another after very small time intervals. The differential equations would then be replaced by difference equations in which the future values of the unknown could be calculated for specific discrete instances of time.

*In any case, with or without such modifications, it is a precise schema of calculation which classical deterministic physics substituted for the vague ideas indicated by the causal expressions of language. Only this schema, its applicability or rejection, and not the vague idea of causality as used in everyday life (and by the philosophers) is meant if the general possibility of deterministic physics is questioned.*

2. *Additional Axioms.* Laplace (1814) gave expression to his unlimited confidence in deterministic physics when he created the fiction of the "mathematical ghost" which from the present values of all state variables could compute the future course of all events (Chapter 8, 5). He made this remark, however, in his *Essai philosophique sur les probabilités,* which assigns to the calculus of probability a very wide, and, in our opinion, unjustifiably wide, range of application.

We may ask the question to what extent Laplace's optimistic idea was justified and to what extent it was confirmed by the later development of physics. For it is obvious that at the beginning of the nineteenth century, when Fourier had just started to develop the theory of heat conduction and there was not yet even the slightest trace of the fundamental electromagnetic equations, no one could have provided Laplace's ghost with the necessary data for his calculation.

For a first survey, it will suffice if we take the oldest and best known of the deterministic theories, namely, the Newtonian mechanics of rigid bodies, as an example. Undoubtedly it was the tremendous success of this theory in the prediction of the motions of celestial bodies that caused such high confidence in the physics of differential equations. As we know (see Chapter 9, 3), Newton's axiom of motion can be stated in the form that for any single body at any time the product of mass and acceleration is equal to the sum of the forces acting upon it. The acceleration being the differential quotient of velocity with respect to time, it follows that the course of the motion can be calculated as soon as the initial position and velocity of every body are given—provided one knows the forces or the laws that determine the forces. That is where the difficulty comes in. The great and decisive accomplishment of Newtonian celestial mechanics consisted in the fact that for all motions of celestial bodies there was found to hold a single simple law of force: Any two celestial bodies attract each other according to the law of gravitation, i.e., with a force which is inversely proportional to the square of their instantaneous distance. If one combines these two laws—the differential equation (axiom of motion) and the law of gravitation—a complete description of the motions of celestial bodies is indeed possible; and one is justified in calling that, in close relation to customary linguistic usage, a causal explanation.

But if we now transfer the Newtonian axiom of motion to the motion of an arbitrary rigid body in our environment, we lack (Chapter 12, 5) the knowledge of the acting forces (except the force of gravity) and their laws. He who regards Newton's mechanics as a sufficient basis for the prediction of all motions from initial conditions must tacitly assume that a previous determination of all force laws is possible. And he who thinks that mechanics can give a "causal explanation" of motions must also assume that these laws of force are sufficiently uniform and simple. For, in the extreme case, if every phenomenon of motion were to require the construction of a separate and complicated law of force, the theory would lose its meaning. It is only because large groups of motions that are very different in appearance are governed by one clear and simple formula of force that one gets the impression which is paraphrased by the statement that the differential equation supplies a "causal explanation" of the phenomenon.

Now it is true that in many terrestial phenomena of motion interesting to the physicist it has been possible to formulate more or less simple laws of force which correspond pretty well to observation. The problem changes somewhat if, instead of single rigid bodies (or particles), one deals with continuously distributed masses; however, fundamentally it remains the same. As we mentioned in Chapter 12, 5, some "additional axioms" which, essentially, have the form of laws of force, are *always* necessary for the utilization of the axiomatic system of Newtonian mechanics. But it can by no means be claimed that at present the task has been accomplished of finding the additional axioms for all of the types of motion that are accessible to observation. For example, there is so far no satisfactory description, based upon Newtonian concepts, of the phenomena of water flow, as in rivers, channels, wide pipes, etc. In this area particularly, refuge has been taken in purely statistical theories (turbulence theories). In other parts of physics, outside of mechanics, the situation is quite similar: despite the great and indubitable success of the deterministic theories, there remain gaps, whose bridging one may perhaps expect in the future, but which certainly do not permit the claim that in our day the high aim of deterministic physics has been reached even approximately. Here, we have limited ourselves to the immediately observable, so called macroscopic phenomena, and have not even mentioned the range of atomic physics.

*Deterministic physics, despite the great range of areas in which it has been successful so far, has by no means reached a state of perfection which would justify the notion that it can describe all the observable phenomena of the macrocosm.*

3. *Intervention of Statistics.* The place in which the deterministic description of physical occurrences was replaced for the first time by statistical ideas was in the theory of games of chance. Let us imagine, for the sake of having a concrete example at hand, a kind of roulette such as is used in many gambling casinos. A little ball is set into rapid motion along a circular horizontal path; at first, owing to centrifugal force, it is pressed against the outer rim, but after a few revolutions its speed decreases and it falls toward the middle, rolls over several rows of symmetrically arranged faces, and finally comes to rest on one of them. The number or color of the section in which the ball lies is the result of the game; in order to start the next one, the croupier takes the ball back to its initial position and puts it into new motion. It is easy to imagine an added mechanical gadget, operated by an electric current, that could eliminate the human intervention, returning the ball to its initial position and giving to it an impulse for the motion. Then we are faced with a closed physical process and the question arises what the differential equations of physics can accomplish for its description, whether, in particular, they are capable of predicting from the once given initial conditions the course of the whole event, i.e., the succession of all gambling results.

We know that the last question has to be answered in the negative. There is no doubt in our minds that the ball at every moment follows the Newtonian laws of motion and all the laws derived from them. But we do not know the forces that affect the single game results. For the arrangement is such that the final decision as to where the ball will come to rest depends upon very small and insignificant influences which are not practically accessible to control, such as dust or other particles on the surfaces, vibrations of the building, drafts in the air, variations of the electric impulses, etc. If one really wanted to try to take all of this into account, one would soon reach the limits of existing mechanical theory, of which we spoke above. For example, for the air vibrations we do not have any sufficient theory of a nonstatistical character. Therefore, one must conclude that at the present stage of our knowledge a prediction of the course of the game by means of the physics of differential equations is in principle, and not only because of mathematical difficulties, impossible.

On the other hand, we have the methods of probability calculus, which allow certain predictions, though different from the deterministic ones, to be made. Not only can we say that, assuming certain conditions, each color in a long sequence of trials will appear equally often, but we also will remain in agreement with the observations if we predict the frequency of, say, an uninterrupted sequence of 10 or 20 "reds" in a sufficiently long game. Here we may leave open the question whether the data used in the calculation came directly from a frequency observation on the moving ball or were derived more indirectly from probability assumptions (e.g., about the variability of the initial impulses) by means of calculations applying theorems of Newtonian mechanics. So much, at any rate, is clear, that within the framework of the theory in question, first, only results can be arrived at which are verifiable but after a long—strictly speaking, infinite—sequence of observations; and second, that in the calculation, data are used which are based upon statistical observations or statistical assumptions (i.e., again, assumptions concerning the frequency in a very long sequence of trials).

*In the treatment of mechanical processes which form the basis of certain games of chance, deterministic physics breaks down in the sense that its equations in connection with the actually accessible data of the problem do not suffice for the prediction of results of the game. On the other hand, the calculus of probability yields certain statistical predictions which are in good agreement with experience, i.e., predictions which can be verified approximately after a very long series of games.*

4. *Classical Statistics.* In very early stages of the history of physics there originated the idea of explaining various physical phenomena by the assumption that the bodies in our environment, particularly gases, are nothing but a conglomeration of very many, invisibly small, not further dissectible "atoms." Since the middle of the nineteenth century, this hypothesis has gradually become the starting point of a specific part of physics that was originally called the "kinetic theory of gases," and later, "statistical mechanics." The decisive tool of this theory is the probability calculus. The area of science at present frequently called "classical physical

statistics," has never been given a logically correct and consistent exposition that made a clear distinction between premises and conclusions, between deterministic and statistical statements, between probability methods and others.

The best-known result in this branch of research is the formulation which, about 1870, L. Boltzmann gave to the second law of thermodynamics, i.e., the theorem of the increase of entropy in every closed process. A theorem that up to then was taken as a quite unambiguously determined statement, of the same kind as the first law of themodynamics (the energy principle) suddenly became the statement of a highly probable, but by no means certain, expectation. The situation, whose explanation from the logical point of view was given much later, is the following.

If one considers a gas as an accumulation of a very large number of particles (molecules) whirling about in space, one can characterize its state at any moment by the ratios in which the various possible velocity values are represented in the aggregate, i.e., by the so-called velocity distribution. From certain plausible assumptions, one can derive, by means of the probability calculus, the result that there is one special velocity distribution which, together with those very close to it, has an overwhelming probability compared to the whole of all other velocity distributions. Various considerations suggest that the probability value of the velocity distribution at any time be taken as a measure of the entropy of the gas (more precisely, that the entropy be set proportional to the logarithm of the probability). If the successive states of a gas behaved like the sequence of results in a dice game or any other collective, one could conclude that the gas in the course of time would almost always be found in a state of maximum or almost maximum entropy and that any state is almost always followed by a state of higher entropy. The latter is a consequence of the randomness of the collective; for if one considers instead of all games only the subset of those which follow a specific result, then, according to the axiom of randomness, within this subset the same frequency distribution must obtain; hence those results must be predominant which correspond to the predominant probability in the collective. This is equivalent to saying that, starting from a given state, the entropy *almost always* increases.

But it is not possible, and also does not correspond to Boltzmann's conception, to assume that the successive states of a gas are of the same type as the mutually independent results of a trial sequence of dice throws. Boltzmann tried to calculate in a deterministic way, by the use of theorems of Newtonian mechanics, the changes that the velocity distribution would undergo owing to collisions of molecules. In a consistent statistical theory, however, the change of velocity distributions should be regarded as regulated by a system of transition probabilities. Plausible assumptions about such a system were indeed found and led to the desired result: It can be derived that the sequence of successive states of the gas—which is not to be expected with certainty but nevertheless with a very high probability— is such that almost always any state is followed by one of higher entropy. We may remark here that, quantitatively, the repeatedly used expression "almost always" refers to figures which do not customarily occur in everyday arithmetic, e.g., to probability values that deviate from 1 only from the 100th or 1000th decimal place on; therefore "almost always" means, for all practical purposes, nothing but "always."

Besides the sphere of the more or less hypothetical atoms and molecules, physical statistics were successfully applied to the so-called Brownian motion. In this case we have a mass phenomenon immediately accessible to observation. Brownian motion is a random motion of minute particles (colloids) suspended in a fluid or gas and visible under the microscope. Following a line of thought similar to the one described above, one finds here excellent agreement between experiment and probability theory.

*In classical physical statistics one starts by making certain plausible assumptions, according to the methods of probability calculus, about initial probabilities as well as transition probabilities, and derives from them statements about the course of events to be expected with very high probability. The value of this "high" probability is so near to 1 that the statements are practically indistinguishable from those which are called "deterministic." In all cases that can be checked the agreement between observation and calculation proves to be excellent.*

5. *Atomism.* The parallelism of deterministic and statistical theories in physics has its counterpart in another couple of opposite concepts: the atomistic and the continuity concepts. As a rule, it is the statistical theory that is connected with atomistic ideas, while the continuity assumption and determinism go hand in hand; but in principle the points of view are independent of each other.

In the classical mechanics of nonrigid bodies one deals from the start with concepts like density, specific weight, etc., which presuppose that space is continuously filled with matter; opposed to this is the above-mentioned assumption that matter consists of not further dissectible units (atoms, molecules, or their constituents). In the field of electrical phenomena it was Faraday (1837) and Maxwell (1871) who founded the continuity theory; but since the time of H. A. Lorentz (1895) it is commonly recognized that a large part of the phenomena cannot be explained save by the hypothesis of a fixed elementary unit of charge that is contained in the electron. A further decisive step was taken by Planck (1899), who derived radiation laws from the assumption that the energy of particles that are the mediators of heat oscillations can change only in jumps, by an integral multiple of the product of frequency and a universal constant. Since then this constant, Planck's so-called elementary quantum of action, has proved to be a fundamental quantity ruling the whole of physics. In particular, the atomistic theory of light, founded by Einstein, assigns to the photon or light quantum a value of energy which is derived from Planck's quantum of action.

Each of these theories, which treat as discontinuous a process that under superficial observation seems continuous, implies a certain limitation of precision for the conclusions drawn from continuity theories. According to the original naïve notion of determinism, there should correspond to every numerical result derived from the differential equations with arbitrary accuracy (with arbitrarily many decimal places), a specific "reality." In other words, it was assumed that with a sufficient increase in the accuracy of observation the calculated numerical value should appear as the result of the observation. But an observational result is always an integer, namely, the number of the smallest recognizable units of measurement, and there is always the following dilemma: either the unit of measurement is chosen big enough that one gets the same result in repeated observations (as when one measures the length of a table in inches); or a much finer instrument is used with a much smaller unit of measurement (say a thousandth of an inch), so that the successive results of repeated observations behave similarly to the results of a dice game, i.e., they form a collective. In the latter case one has to depend upon taking as the "true value" of the measurement a suitably calculated mean value, and in addition one must determine the "deviations" of the single results, for which one can easily give a suitable definition. If every trial yields the same value, which is the case with a sufficiently large unit, that value is at the same time the mean value, and the deviation is zero. It is apparent from this discussion that the precision of a measurement is only determined by *two* values—the unit of measurement and the deviation of the results from each other.

A consistent determinism must assume that in a correct experimental setup the deviation zero can be reached, however small the unit of measurement is. But if matter is composed of corpuscles, the unit cannot be pushed below the dimensions of these elementary particles. For not only the object of measurement but also the instrument itself consists of macroscopic bodies, hence of a very large number of corpuscles. It was not until recently that experiments whose objects of measurement are the smallest elements of matter were discussed rigorously (by Heisenberg). We shall return to that later. In any case, there can be no question of reaching an arbitrarily high precision of measurement for quantities that are defined only as average values within a large number of corpuscles, like the temperature, the velocity of an extended body, etc.

*Physical observations on macroscopic phenomena have a limit of precision in the dimension of the smallest particles which, either for matter or for energy or for charge, are assumed in the various atomic theories. Hence, if for no other reason, it is meaningless to speak of a "mathematically exact" validity of deterministic statements.*

6. *The Indeterminacy Relation.* The recent development of physics has given much occasion for discussion of the fundamental questions in which we are interested here. The reason is twofold. On the one hand there is the completely new conception of matter as a kind of "wave" and of light as a kind of matter. On the other hand, the role that the probability concept plays in all parts of physics has become much more extensive.

It is difficult to give even a superficial notion of wave mechanics in the framework of this book. But we cannot quite get around the subject, because a large part of the present-day argument between positivistic and antipositivistic conceptions is based upon it. A few brief remarks will have to do.

A simple (sinusoidal) wave, extended to infinity, represents a uniformly distributed density in the whole of space. If many waves of different amplitudes and different wavelengths (or frequencies) are superimposed upon each other, very irregular distributions may result; e.g., in this manner one can effect by a "wave packet" a concentration in one point. Now atomic phenomena satisfy certain equations that describe the relations among various wave phenomena. In order to remain in agreement with observations, one has to assign to the appearance of corpuscles concentrated wave packets. The rectilinear motion of a particle is, then, analogous to the rectilinear propagation of light, which in the classical wave theory of optics is interpreted as the result of a wave phenomenon. These ideas were first enunciated by Louis de Broglie (1924) and were given the form of a concrete mathematical theory by E. Schrödinger. But the difficulty in principle does not begin until one asks: What is it that oscillates, that performs the wave motion? In the old optics one resorted to the conception of the ether, an expedient that gave excellent heuristic service. Thus the physicist could escape the ultimate consequences of his theory and did not have to stick only to the relations between the measurable quantities occurring in the equations. Today this is no longer possible. One does not find an agent of the wave motion that would more or less correspond to macroscopic conceptions. The only interpretation one can give to the wave intensities occurring in the equations is that they are probabilities. In other words, one is faced with a statistical theory that establishes relations between probability values, in such a way that the mathematical form of these relations is that of the wave equation.

A new and popular interpretation of the unsurmountable limit of precision in certain kinds of observations is based upon the wave conception. A single wave of a certain amplitude and frequency possesses a precisely defined velocity of propagation, but no precise location; it is distributed over the entire space. On the other hand, a "wave packet," suitably constituted of waves of different amplitudes and frequencies, has a precisely determined location (the point of concentration), but its velocity is entirely undetermined, since to every frequency of one of the wave components belongs a different value of the propagation velocity. The greater the concentration, the more exact is the localization and the less exact is the velocity determination. The quantitative expression of this relation is known by the name "Heisenberg's indeterminacy relation."

The most important consequence of the wave conception of matter, however, was its influence upon the theory of light. Since the time when the argument between Newton and Huygens was decided in favor of the latter and of a wave theory of light, light propagation and corpuscular motion were regarded as basically different phenomena. But the photoelectric effect in Einstein's interpretation and other similar phenomena pointed toward the recognition that light also has typical characteristics of corpuscular motion. When it was observed then that radioactive radiation, previously regarded as a corpuscular effect, also shows the interference phenomenon, and hence the typical characteristics of waves, it became clearer that what we have here is not an antithesis, but rather two different aspects of a unique phenomenon. The full clarification and further development of these ideas will remain the task of physicists for a long time. To what extent and in what sense their fundamental ideas will be able to modify our physical world picture in its general outlines can hardly be guessed at yet. Most of the critical views thus far expressed, especially those of school philosophy, seem very rash and will have to be drastically revised.

*Wave mechanics represents a new and far-reaching physical theory which allows the uniform description of a wide range of phenomena. The theory has essentially a statistical character: it expresses relations between probability values. It seems too early to appraise the full effect of the theory upon the epistemological conceptions of physics in general.*

7. *Intuitiveness. Decline of Causality.* In connection with the modern physical theories, particularly the theory of relativity and quantum theory (including wave mechanics), it has become customary to discuss again and again the question of *intuitiveness*. Newtonian mechanics with its action at a distance, Maxwell's field theory of electricity, the explanation of light by ether vibrations, all of these are today regarded as intuitive ideas which are accessible to the imagination of a normal intellect. But the "space curvature" of non-Euclidean geometry occurring in the theory

of relativity, the discontinuous change of energy values in the atom and, above all, matter waves, are supposed to be quite "nonintuitive." This classification, of course, is intended to depreciate the new "nonintuitive" theories as compared to the older ones.

Now it is certainly much more "intuitive" to imagine that the earth is a plane surface and not a sphere, that the earth is at rest and the sun really "rises" in the morning and "sets" in the evening, etc. Nevertheless, one does not return to these conceptions which once commanded unlimited recognition, because they do not lead us very far. Thus, many adherents of the principle of intuitiveness are compelled today to admit that the conception of the spherical shape of the earth and the Copernican system are sufficiently intuitive. This implies the admission that intuitiveness is primarily the result of habit. Any new theory that seeks to describe a widened range of phenomena by modifying the basic concepts must by its nature seem nonintuitive at the beginning. In the course of time it becomes intuitive to those who get sufficiently acquainted with it. The subjective differences in judging what is intuitive are obvious. To many a mathematician analytical symbols are more intuitive than any illustrative geometric drawing. It is also a well-known pedagogic fact that students can be *trained* to improve their faculty of spatial imagination. Hence the now favored absoluteness of the concept of "intuitiveness" must be rejected and, at any rate, cannot be regarded as a criterion for the acceptance or rejection of modern physical theories.

But the most fashionable slogan which spices discussions about modern physics is that of the "destruction of causality." All true natural science, it is said, consists in the search for causes and reasons, for complete causal chains, etc. Seen in this light, the introduction of probability considerations seems a destructive, disintegrating element. In this context one may also hear the words "positivistic suppression of thought." That is supposed to mean that the positivist prohibits the search for the *true* causes of the individual occurrences in nature in all fields where a statistical theory is proposed.

The previous considerations of this chapter should make it quite clear that there is nothing prohibited here, and least of all, thinking. Further, we do not present an opinion of the kind expressed in the metaphysical statement "probability is an objective feature of natural occurrences" (Reichenbach). We describe the present (and partly the past) state of physical theories, i.e., the endeavors "to classify perceptions systematically, and from given perceptions to draw conclusions for expected ones" (Carnap). We have seen that theories that are in this sense successful use, in part, the classical methods of differential equations with time as the independent variable, and in part, the methods of probability calculus developed in the nineteenth century.

Whether one of the two methods, and which one of them, will prevail at some future time, nobody would want to predict who has studied the past evolution of the physical world picture and who does not indulge in the childish thought that we today, in the middle of the twentieth century, have arrived at the end or near the end of the evolution of science. One could at most draw the conclusion from a study of the history of physics that theories which once have served to represent some wide area of facts in accordance with observations, will in an altered framework be retained in some form or other. The claim of discovering and propagating eternal truths is entirely foreign to us. But we think a once useful picture of a section of reality will retain a certain applicability, even beyond the so-called decline of civilizations which changes more or less permanently the conditions of life for people.

The causal concept of everyday life, or better, the causal expressions of everyday language, have not been banished from contemporary physics (they have always played a much less important role in the theoretical structure than one is inclined to think). Only the precise form of deterministic physics (of differential equations) has proved to be too narrow, and a supplementation by other means has become necessary. It is quite possible and even likely that linguistic usage will gradually adapt itself to the new theories and that the subjective "demand for causality" will be satisfied in this way. Thus people during the last century got used to the law of inertia, which at the time of its first appearance was taken as a strict contradiction to causality. In the same way, we think, people will gradually come to be satisfied by causal statements of this kind: It is *because* the die was loaded that the "six" shows more frequently (but we do not know what the next number will be); or: *Because* the vacuum was heightened and the voltage increased, the radiation became more intense (but we do not know the precise number of scintillations that will occur in the next minute). In no case, however, can the vague and changeable causality concept of everyday life be binding upon the formation of exact scientific theories.

*The parallelisms of deterministic and statistical lines of thought in contemporary physics will possibly in the future be replaced by a uniform description. But the development of the theory is not determined by the demands suggested by the vague causal expressions of everyday language; on the contrary, linguistic usage gradually adapts itself to the general results of science. Objections against modern physics originating in the popular concept of intuitivity are also temporary and cannot influence the evolution of science which has to meet the challenge of an ever-growing range of experience.*

### CHAPTER 16

# miracles

1. *Disruption of Causality*. David Hume, to whom, as we mentioned, the first decisive elucidation of the causality concept is due, found it appropriate to include in his *Inquiry Concerning Human Understanding* a chapter on miracles. In this respect he followed the example of, among others, Spinoza, who had treated almost a hundred years earlier, in the sixth chapter of the *Tractatus Theologico-Politicus,* the belief in miracles as professed by the church authorities. Since then such discussions have disappeared more and more from philosophical writings, and this book will not return to the old questions about the "credibility" of traditional miracle stories either. But the present time, with its various forms of negativism (Chapter 5), has opened to the human want for miracles new areas which lie on the borderline of science. As we do not concede to the idea of causality the rank of an infallible dogma regulating all scientific theories, we cannot omit to take a look at those modern or old doctrines which play with the causality concept in a more or less loose fashion. We refer to the various "occult" sciences, primarily to the again fashionable astrology, all sorts of meta- and parapsychology, and similar surrogates of science, which drift into the realm of the most confused superstition, but sometimes have a basis in still unexplored physiological and psychological facts. No doubt there are also new results of psychic research which are dismissed as superstition only by those who under the influence of school philosophy distrust everything radically new. With such topics we shall deal also. But our main point is the logical position of the miracle concept.

Linguistic usage labels as a "miracle" a phenomenon in which the causal law is violated, i.e., where an otherwise valid causal statement suffers a nonexplainable exception. Now the causal concept, as we have seen (Chapter 13), rests upon the idea of repeatability and isolation of single occurrences. Only if it is at least *imaginable* that the event $A$ "under otherwise equal circumstances" may occur or not occur, can we assert that $A$ is the cause of $B$. It is the claim of the causal statement that $B$ then follows upon $A$ without exception. If one wants to call an occurrence, or more precisely a relation between two possible occurrences, a "miracle" to signify that it stands outside the causality law, one must assume that the premise $A$ is repeatable, that it is followed as a rule by $B$, but in the exceptional case, by non-$B$. This unique case would then be a miracle. But since in the repeatability the "ceteris paribus" plays an essential role, the miracle claim is very difficult to formulate precisely, perhaps even more so than a causal statement.

For example, it is reported that the founder of a religion, in order to give comfort to his thirsty people in the desert, hit a stick upon a rock, whereupon water appeared from it. In order for this to be a miracle one must assume that if "under otherwise equal circumstances" again a stick is hit upon a rock water never appears. But if this "never" were meant quite seriously, the entire story would lose its significance. In fact, the tale, viewed in a wider frame, indicates a model-like connection, namely, this: if in the case of some specific moral behavior (to be understood in the most general sense) of the people and the agent, the described action is taken, there will be water; otherwise, not. What, in the last analysis, is claimed here is not a miracle in the sense of a unique contravention of the causal law, but a causal connection of a special kind, which does not fall within the range of physics but that certainly does fall within the range of a science that comprehends all observable phenomena. This conclusion could be avoided only by claiming that the particular complex of premises (including the moral elements) is altogether nonrepeatable, or that if it were repeated exactly, the effect would still be missing. In both cases the story would be of no interest.

Miracle stories, and in particular those appearing in the context of religious systems, have, indeed, the purpose of establishing examples of behavior worthy of imitation or, in an even more general manner, of influencing the future behavior of men. Hence the actual claim cannot be that of *absolute* uniqueness of the phenomenon. Rather, a familiar causal relation is waived for the sake of a relatively unusual one, whose premises occur much more rarely and which is therefore hardly verifiable. In the last analysis all these miracle claims amount to implicitly formulating causal statements that do not apply to customary conditions of everyday life and are not recognized propositions in the present scientific doctrines. Most of these statements construct a relation between physical events in the narrower sense and rarely realized conditions of moral behavior. The same is true in a similar manner for all the various "meta"-sciences which we have mentioned above.

*In discussing "miracles" and "meta"-sciences, it is not the question of the credibility of the stories in which we are primarily interested, but rather the logical status of the miracle concept. We find that, in general, one is not confronted here with the claim of a unique execption to causal connections, but with the vague formulation of a relatively unusual and unexplored causal relation between physical and psychological (moral) elements.*

2. *Astrology*. Casting a short glance at astrology, the oldest and best known of the "sciences," which has no status today but still survives, it is comparably easy to describe its claims. Astrology teaches that there is a connection between a person's fate and his moral character, on the one hand, and the configuration of the stars at his birth, on the other. Astrologers divide the ecliptic, the path of the earth around the sun, into twelve parts, the so-called signs of the zodiac, whose names are those of the star constellations that were visible behind them 2000 years ago. The positions of the major planets relative to these signs of the zodiac at the moment of birth, combined with other elements not important for us here, yield the so-called *nativity* of a man, from which his life can allegedly be predicted in its main features. Thus in the horoscope which Kepler gave to young Wallenstein, one of the great figures of the Thirty Years' War, it is predicted from the "great conjunction of Saturn and Jupiter, in combination with the great wrong that the moon is thrown into the twelfth sign of the Zodiac," that he

has an alert, aroused, eager, impatient mind . . . is not pleased by ordinary human actions and strivings, but strives for new and untried or otherwise peculiar means . . .

In a later horoscope Kepler prophesied a great general misfortune for the year 1634, and in that year Wallenstein was murdered.

In spite of these and many other historically recorded successes of astrology, we today no longer believe in predictions arrived at by these means. Granted all the vagueness of expressions such as "character" and "fate," and all the reservations that must reasonably be made with respect to later influences upon the development of a growing man, there should be, if the premises of astrology were correct, an observable equality or similarity in the lives of all people born at the same moment. Since such a similarity among all born under the same "nativity," has so far not been observed, we have to regard the astrological theory as a doctrine not confirmed by experience and hence not justified. The presence of *some* sort of cosmic influence upon human lives is not sufficient for the justification of the theory. On the other hand, experiences of a more general kind, such as the small biological importance of the exact hour of birth itself, can be used when we appraise the theory. Also the more recent attempts to give the statements of astrology validity in a probability sense by statistical considerations have not led to the desired success. Whether or not at some time in the future sharper and deeper observations will yield a different result, we do not know.

But contemporary discussions of astrology, in so far as they do not fall in the realm of most naïve superstition, usually move along quite different lines from those which could lead to a decision about the actual validity of the theory. Starting from a vague concept of "humanistic science" (Geisteswissenschaft) and trying more or less consciously to challenge the position of the natural sciences, it is said that astrology could still have a different kind of validity from the one the positive sciences claim for themselves. It could represent a kind of "higher" truth which reveals itself only to a different type of man, to the "humanistically" minded. Now, it is certainly a part of the whole of science, as we conceive of it, to study the history, and particularly the psychology, of an intellectual movement that has lasted for centuries and has occupied some of the best minds of that period. But these investigations, whose object is the behavior of certain people—astrologers and believers in astrology—do not lie outside of the framework of empirical science and are not subject to controls other than those of being tested by observation, etc. To this domain, of course, also belong questions like those of the reactions of recipients to prophecies (it is possible to "live up" to a prophecy), questions about the typical forms of subjective delusions in any testing, etc. None of these examinations lead behind the world of phenomena or to a "higher plane" than that of the natural sciences and they are not capable of turning assertions which are scientifically "false," i.e., in contradiction to careful observations, into "right" ones. One may also find artistic value in old astrological writings and a satisfaction of aesthetic feeling in the bold play of imagination of many astrologers; that does not alter the fact that one who depends upon a theory whose claims have no foundation in experience is only misled.

*Astrology is a specific theory about the connection between certain cosmic events and human life. None of its general claims has so far been confirmed by observation. This fact cannot be altered by the interesting study of the historical and psychological background of the theory or the possible aesthetic pleasure which astrological statements sometimes offer.*

3. *"Ausdruckskunde."* Related to astrology in their final aims (but only in those) is a class of studies for which the term "Ausdruckskunde" (science of expression) has been proposed as a common name and which in a wider sense fall under the concept of anthropology. To this field belongs as its oldest part physiognomy and its corollary, *Mimik* (the study of emotional reactions as revealed in men's expression), and as its most modern representative, which at present has gained a certain practical importance, graphology. Our treatment of this subject within a chapter in

most of which rather questionable aspects of human curiosity are discussed is not intended to be depreciatory. It may be justified by the fact that the majority of scholars and educated people still reject any kind of *Ausdruckskunde* as not being a serious science and that indeed some graphologists and physiognomists seem to be in a race with the astrologers as far as fantastic speculations are concerned. On the other hand, the existence of a wide and concrete basis in experience in this field is indubitable.

Nobody will deny that there are observable connections between the bodily characteristics of a man, particularly the features of his face, on the one hand, and his disposition and moral character on the other. But it is very difficult to state anything precise about this correspondence that goes beyond the most general and vague assertions. It may be possible to describe the bodily features by a suitable system of measurements, but the words "moral character" and "disposition" stand as abbreviations for something like the totality of actions to be expected in the future from the individual and can hardly be reduced to distinct concrete observations. One may ask here whether the relations in question are of deterministic or of statistical nature, i.e., whether there are certain bodily marks that are *invariably* correlated with a specific character feature, or if such correspondence exists only on the average. But since in every case of a test the precondition of "otherwise equal circumstances," which is indispensable both in the causal concept and in probability relations, is exceedingly difficult to meet, the question must still remain undecided for the present. At any rate, what one means by "character" is to a certain degree a statistical concept, referring to the *average* behavior of a man.

It seems that lately decisive progress has been achieved by securing a series of practicable general results in physiognomy; we refer here mainly to the studies of E. Kretschmer on *Body Build and Character*. In contrast to the older tendency—Aristotle left us a completely developed system of physiognomy—which went into the most minute details of both body build and character, Kretschmer fixes his attention upon broad and comprehensive types: schizothyme and cyclothyme temperaments( these categories being derived from the analogous ones in psychiatry) correspond to the asthenic-athletic and to the pycnic builds, respectively. Whether this starting point will be capable of leading any further remains to be seen. At any rate, we regard physiognomy as a genuine branch of natural science which proceeds from single observations to theories and predictions, a branch still in its infancy and hence far from mathematization and axiomatization. There is no reason to scoff at it as humbug or, on the other hand, to assign to it the supposedly higher rank of a *Geisteswissenschaft*.

The situation is somewhat similar in the case of modern graphology, except that here one part of the observations, namely, the description of the properties of handwriting, can be rationalized much more easily. To this the comparatively greater practical success of the graphologists is due. Certainly in graphology also much nonsense is brought forward, either by exaggerating details and minute particulars, or by a transgression of the boundaries into the area of prophecies of fate like those of astrology. But there remains a reliable core of possible statements which rest upon the fact that the habitual, mostly unconscious innervations that determine the handwriting and those that determine man's behavior in other recurring situations in life are not independent of each other. Perhaps the connection in graphology is a more direct one than in physiognomy, since in the latter only the permanent bodily features which have impressed themselves firmly during a lifetime, and not those which vary with the momentary situation, are taken into account. In so-called *Mimik,* the two ways meet, but in that area, even at the present, exact statements are much too difficult. Many questions of a general biological interest, such as the limitations of heredity and the interdependence of physical and psychological features, have to be considered here. It is not impossible that a comprehensive future biology (which will also include everything called "psychology" today) will be able to draw important conclusions from the observation of the modes of human expression. This, however, presupposes that the now fashionable fantastic tendencies which seek to interpret the assertions of Ausdruckskunde "symbolically" and to put them in opposition to all positive science will by then have been overcome.

*Physiognomy, graphology, and other branches of Ausdruckskunde form a branch of biology (or anthropology) which is still in its infancy. It is as unjustified to reject all its claims in principle as it is to assign to its assertions, compared to those of the positive sciences, the status of a "higher" truth.*

4. *The Supernatural.* It is a widely held but historically unfounded opinion that the empiricist conception of science rejects connections between so-called psychological or intellectual processes and physical effects on the human body, or at least does not like to admit them. Each of us is familiar with such phenomena as blushing during a conversation, or shortness of breath at imminent danger, watering of the mouth at the sight of certain foods, and many other influences upon bodily organs by way of the intellect. Certainly there are also phenomena in this field which are rarer, less well observed, and of a more unusual kind. There is no reason to declare from the outset, without closer examination, that claims about the intentional formation of swellings by hysterics, or the creation of a facial rash through an imagined contact, etc., are unworthy of belief, or even to think that such occurrences are impossible. Perhaps the exaggerated "materialism" which was in fashion at the end of the last century and which has very little in common with our conception of science, has

led to the opinion that in the positive sciences there is no room for such phenomena. At the present this notion is readily advanced with the intent of making the men of science appear as reactionaries and of giving comfort to those who wish to believe in something "supernatural."

What is it, we should like to know, that can justifiably be called "supernatural"? Perhaps one will be inclined to reply, something that is unique; something that cannot be repeated. But every natural phenomenon, if it is observed with sufficient precision and completeness, is unique; only abstraction, the disregarding of details, the leaving aside of some aspects, creates repeatability. If we describe a phenomenon with the words and idioms of the existing language, for this purpose alone, if for no other, we have to reduce it to repeatable elements. Now, any relation between otherwise known phenomena is once observed for the first time; if one formulates this experience in words, describes it in a report, it will (Chapter 16, 1) hardly be done under the supposition that the experience will never be repeated again. For then the report would have no interest at all. Any record of a "supernatural" occurrence is made with the idea that under rare, unusual, and so far not disclosed circumstances, the situation will recur. It is only ignorance of the circumstances determining the "ceteris paribus" that leads us to the assumption of a special status of certain phenomena, which are then called "supernatural." Accordingly, there exists something supernatural only *relative* to a certain state of scientific knowledge. He who wants to cling to the idea of an absolute supernatural must believe in the dogma that certain occurrences might be observed again and again, but can never be explained, i.e., can never be brought into an orderly relation to the rest of our experience.

Neither the various phenomena which are ascribed, following Charles Richet, to a "sixth sense," nor the often-reported healing by means of psychic and intellectual influence upon the patient, nor even the apparently absurd stories about materializations and similar occurrences lie, in our opinion, outside the range of natural science. Only continued systematic observation can show how far these phenomena agree with presently accepted scientific ideas and how far they require a modification of these ideas. It is a justifiable behavior, and in accord with the economic nature of science, when scientists hesitate to give up well-founded basic concepts of a theory and agree to do so only under the highest pressure of facts. Moreover, of course, it is a matter of individual taste whether one prefers to deal with problems of television, the theory of atomic nuclei, or radio-active radiation, or to study the question of how the materialization of bodily organs of dead people in spiritualistic séances comes about. In any case, no reasonable scientist believes that men will never come to know phenomena that are in disagreement with some theories generally accepted today. All factual questions are in a way always open. Only the question whether an observed phenomenon is natural or supernatural is meaningless for us; it is in its wording connectible with no system of linguistic rules. If somebody claims he saw something, we may believe him, in so far as the *subjective* validity of the statement is concerned; but if he claims *objective* truth for his assertion, then this can mean only that the occurrence is repeatable under certain, perhaps still unknown, circumstances. For a report to be objectively true and at the same time to be in contradiction to all *thinkable* theories of natural phenomena is a statement that cannot be "constituted" in any intelligible manner.

*The empirical conception of science does not exclude, as is often believed, the possibility of interaction between physical and psychic (intellectual) phenomena. It regards in each case continual systematic observation as the only way to arrive at a decision about such claims. A distinction between natural and supernatural events must be rejected as not connectible with any acceptable linguistic usage.*

5. *Occult Sciences.* One may object to the interpretation outlined in the preceding section on the grounds that it is too complacent in the face of actual gross offenses against reason and of indubitable superstition and, further, that it does not sufficiently take into account the justified prestige of scientific doctrines that are today considered unshakable. One will often find the opinion that certain extreme assertions which contradict the fundamentals of our conception of nature can be rejected on quite general grounds without any closer examination. There is often talk about the tremendous distance in intellectual level and dignity that separates most of the "occult" experiences from the objects of science. For us there is only one question of interest: Is there anything except observation and experiment to which one can take recourse if one wants to declare a reported fact "impossible"? This question is of decisive importance, for it touches on the relation between theory and experience and the possibility of inductive generalization, hence on the crucial problem of epistemology.

Two examples may serve to indicate the difficulties of the situation. For a long time certain natural springs have been known that were assigned a special healing effect by the public, although in the chemical composition of the water nothing remarkable could be found. It was consistent with the physico-chemical (and also the philosophical) point of view at the end of the nineteenth century to reject the assumption of a special influence of this water upon the human body as pure superstition. Meanwhile it turned out in some of these cases that considerable radioactivity was present in the water. Hence an "objective" reason was found which until a few decades ago was not as yet conceived of by science. The second example concerns the general principle of energy and our standard attitude toward the inventors of a *perpetuum mobile*. Incidentally, even the phenomenon of radioactive radiation seemed at one time to contradict the energy principle; but a way of avoiding the contradiction was soon found. On the other hand, it cannot be denied that the principle of conservation of energy in its classical form, namely, referring to ordinary space and time coordinates of Euclidean space, is not fulfilled in processes that follow the theory of relativity; and this objection was, indeed, raised against Einstein in the beginning. Numerically, the results derived from the present relativistic formulation of the law of conservation of energy are different from those derived from the classical formula, though the differences are in most cases practically not important. It can easily be seen that the tautological energy principle, abstracted from experience, has been retained only in its general form, but altered, according to the new experience, in its actual content. In view of this it seems best for us to describe the situation in the following way: If today we reject without hesitation a quite naïve attempt at a *perpetuum mobile* mechanism, we rely primarily upon an extensive experience with similar mechanisms, and not upon an absolutely valid principle of greatest generality derived from these observations. In the case of more subtle suggestions, a closer examination, despite the existence of an accepted principle, can by no means be avoided.

In the realm of physiological problems, the situation is naturally much less settled than in physics. In an attempt to interpret certain phenomena of clairvoyance or so-called extrasensory perception, Richet rightly pointed to the possibility of an analogy with the sense of smell, which in the course of the evolution of man has most likely experienced a considerable weakening. It can be imagined that a million years from today this weakening will have progressed even much further, so that the vast majority of men will not perceive any smell at all (and would hence not have a word for it either), but that in a few individuals some faint traces of the sense of smell will be left. What will then be said of a man who claims that with closed eyes and bound hands he can tell whether a bottle had contained carbolic acid a long time ago?

Surely no serious observations can today be quoted in favor of *chiromancy* (palmistry), the art of divination by inspecting the hand. But there is hardly any reason for regarding as absolutely absurd the idea that the life expectancy of a man can be recognized or guessed at from the present state of his organs, even an inconspicuous part of them. The assumption that in the last analysis everything that happens is somehow connected with everything else that happens may not be useful in most situations of practical life and scientific research; but one does well to remember it now and then in order not to condemn new conjectures too hastily and thus eventually to impede scientific progress. Many phenomena that in later developments led to the most successful applications, such as the effects of steam power or electricity, were first observed in the form of playthings. A judicious attitude that remains always amenable to new ideas and does not stick to dogmatic principles but relies only on the result of an unprejudiced examination would above all contribute to remove sensationalism which prepares the ground for all sorts of irresponsible and fake undertakings in the field of the allegedly occult.

*It is not the general principles of science, however certain they may seem, but only the observed facts themselves, on which the principles rest, that must form the basis for appraising newly observed phenomena. A clear-cut renunciation of any kind of dogmatic attitude would soon put an end to the questionable dealings in the field of the "occult," which feed on the lust for sensation and revolt against science.*

6. *Teleology.* One of the attempts to avoid the causality concept of science or to replace it in certain cases takes the form of the theory of final causes, or *teleology.* This is a method of regarding occurrences that are not unusual or rare at all, as "miracles." The sparrow grows wings, *because* he would starve to death otherwise; there is a feeling of pain, *because* only in this manner are we aware of illness and the necessity of care; a man dies, as soon as he no longer has a purpose in life; specifically, the great poet X only apparently died of pneumonia; he really died because he did not have anything more to say to the world. These motivations are often accompanied by the addition that, as compared to the natural sciences, they express a "higher truth." In the last analysis they represent the assertion of a preëstablished harmony: Tout est pour le mieux dans le meilleur des mondes possibles (Voltaire).

Now, from a logical point of view there is certainly nothing to be said against the assumption that the world was established by a higher intelligence according to a predesigned plan. It is not even necessary to explain in detail how much such an idea suggests itself as an attempt at a first orientation in our environment. It can then be retained as a tautological statement and the properties of the plan and of its author can be gradually modified according to continued observation. Thus one will find that sparrows are in fact equipped with the means for finding food, but that other creatures have ample means to destroy the sparrows; that many of the most serious human ailments, such as cancer, become noticeable only after it is too late to cure them; that perhaps Mozart, had he lived under different social conditions, could have lived longer and created many more works. None of these facts is incompatible with the idea of a wise and well-conceived world plan, but they suggest the question whether this idea furthers the insight into experienceable situations. It is certain that a large part of human activity is directed toward changing some of the consequences of the natural world order; but since, after all, man himself is only a part of the world, this activity could have been preconsidered in the plan. As a purely theoretical theorem the assertion of the existence of a preconceived world plan is not refutable; it is superfluous only if the interdependence of all occurrences, including those which are influenced by men, can be subordinated to the "natural laws" abstracted from experience.

Rather recently the philosopher Hans Driesch gave the teleological idea a special and precise formulation. He thinks that in the area of so-called inorganic nature all events are related to one another by the rule of cause and effect, but that the organic processes are determined by purposeful aims. The basic observation he starts with is the following. The egg of a sea urchin, originally intended to evolve into a single larva, will, if suitably divided into two pieces, develop two complete larvae of the same shape but a little smaller size. From this it follows, according to Driesch, that the result of the development does not depend only upon the initial state, as does a physical event, but must be explained by a purposefulness, namely, by the desire of each part of the egg substance to evolve into a complete living organism. On the other hand, if we want to quote an example given by Philipp Frank, we may notice that an iron particle that emits under a spectroscope a specific spectrum, if cut into two parts, shows the same complicated spectrum twice, only with a little smaller intensity. One could then also say in this case that the iron particle has the natural desire to emit a complete spectrum, consisting of innumerably many lines, and it reaches this aim completely, despite the forcible partition. In neither of these cases, however, could one say that the customary schema of natural explanations, which from the antecedent (in this case including the partition) infers the succeeding, would break down.

*The teleological view, or the principle of final causes, cannot be regarded by us as a method which would be able to replace the customary causal (or statistical) method of natural description. Even less does it seem justified to claim* necessity *for the teleological point of view in specific fields of natural occurrences.*

7. *Final Consideration.* In connection with the preceding arguments, which dealt with the basic concepts of science, and at the same time as a transition to the following chapters, which more or less transgress the boundary of natural science in the narrower sense, we should like to make a remark of a more general kind about the fundamental point of view of this book. We are constantly introducing, partly aphoristically, partly in a loosely systematic form, new questions into the debate and we pass over them after a few more or less perfunctory remarks. It should not be necessary to point out explicitly—we have done that at the end of the third Part—that these sketches are not supposed to be "final solutions" of problems, each of which would require a much more extensive discussion than

the scope of this book allows. But the actual position in which a general conception that contradicts school philosophy finds itself suggests another specific explanation.

The opponents of the positivistic and any similar point of view not only treat this view in a generally disparaging manner, but complain in particular that it does not even attempt to understand the crucial problems of philosophy, that it ignores them irresponsibly, and that it passes over all difficulties by a cheap pretension of knowing everything. These reproaches are especially pronounced with respect to questions dealing with the belief in miracles, with teleology, and with similar notions that appeal to the heart and soul. Perhaps they were not quite unjustified when about the middle of the last century the leading opponents of philosophical idealism in Germany appeared in the persons of Moleschott, Vogt, and Büchner, who achieved temporarily some influence, not so much by the impact of the scientific materialism they presented, as by the personal attacks they were subjected to. From our point of view, this movement, and also the somewhat later "monism," advanced by Haeckel, and the "evolutionism" of Herbert Spencer have in common with school philosophy that both regard the contemporary stage of scientific knowledge as a forever safe base for the most far-reaching extrapolations. Generally speaking, the difference was only that materialism started from the latest results of science, whose concrete claims it exaggerated excessively, while idealism was founded upon an older stage of science, which it sought to dogmatize. It is quite characteristic that in their controversy each opponent accused the other of being a mystic and metaphysician. Indeed, there does not seem to be too much difference to us, whether one puts the concept of substance at a certain place into the "Table of Categories" as the "catalogue of all the originally pure conceptions of the synthesis which the understanding contains a priori" (Kant), or whether, in the framework of a most primitive atomic theory, one extols the "immortality of matter" as one of the most important basic ideas of our knowledge of nature (Büchner). One can hardly be prevented from feeling that the latter view is somewhat shallow; but one may also remember, on the other hand, Nietzsche's remark about the mystical explanations, which are supposed to be deep, "but are not even superficial."

The opinions presented in this book do not claim to supply a final and definite doctrine and should therefore be protected against the accusation of exhibiting an attitude of omniscience. While almost all previous philosophical schools claimed as their task to find for philosophic questions answers of the same finality and firmness as were attained in the exact sciences, we, on the contrary, stress the provisional character of all factual propositions, even in these positive fields. Assertions such as: a specific interaction *cannot* exist; *all* occurrences are reducible to the motion of matter and the action of forces, or: everything in this world can be explained as transformation of energy, etc., have no place in our conception of reality. We only suggest analyzing in what sense the expressions in these and other statements are used and examining whether they are consistent with each other and compatible with the present state of experience. At the same time, everything, even the standard by which consistency is judged, must remain open to modification by further research. In agreement with Ernst Mach, we regard it as the most appropriate attitude "to *bear* an incomplete philosophy and to prefer it to any apparently complete but insufficient one." We shall return in the following chapters to the historical and psychological circumstances that produce the subjective want for final truths. The results of the last sections we shall summarize here thus:

*We see in the clarification of the causality concept, due mainly to Hume, the essential foundation of our conception of science. On that basis the fundamental problems in all branches of science can be attacked in an attitude open to the growing stock of experience. At the same time an attitude free from prejudice is gained toward those approaches which at present are outside or on the borderline of well-established scientific fields. The totality of the positivism thus defined is characterized by its understanding of earlier stages in the evolution of knowledge, by tolerance toward contemporary trends of research of all kinds, and by humility toward progress to be expected in the future.*

## PART V

# science and the humanities

Vera philosophiae methodus nulla alia nisi scientiae naturalis est.

The right method of philosophy is no other than that of the natural sciences.

*Franz Brentano*

### CHAPTER 17

# the alleged limitation of scientific concepts

1. *Dualism*. The progress of research and the wide spread of interest in natural science, brought about particularly by the great success of technology in the second half of the nineteenth century, had the result that even in Germany certain elements of science penetrated into the consciousness of general education, and began playing a role which they had always played in the Western countries. A characteristic feature of this development can be found in the well-known work by Albert Lange, which has appeared since 1866 in many editions, *The History of Materialism and Critique of its Importance for the Present Time*. Lange, who tried to reconcile school philosophy with materialism by going a long way toward the latter, suggested clearly that psychology, linguistics, and other fields that are counted among the humanities must approach more and more the method of the natural sciences, lest they have to give up the claim of "furthering even by a single step true and lasting knowledge, in whatever field it may be." The theories of physical energetics and of the origin of species, the most fashionable doctrines of that time, seemed to Lange a good point of departure for philosophizing, in sharp contrast to the "poetic metaphysics" of Hegel and Schelling, who had readily disregarded the simplest facts of science, even those which they had been taught in elementary school. In France it was Auguste Comte who in 1830, when Hegel was still alive, made himself known by his *Philosophie positive,* in which, among other things, the unity of all sciences was propounded; and in England John Stuart Mill followed a similar line. Both have had a lasting effect. In Germany, whose scholastic atmosphere was always inimical toward anything that could be called positivism, Lange tried, to a very modest extent, to propagate understanding for Comte and Mill, but the effect was quite unexpected: it caused a reaction which opposed the "undue prevalence of the ideas of natural science" and proclaimed an "autarchy of the humanities (Geisteswissenschaften)."

The historian of philosophy Wilhelm Windelband was perhaps the first in recent times to emphasize the alleged fundamental difference between natural science and general (political) history; the former, he stressed, represents a generalizing, and the latter, an individualizing way of thinking. Wilhelm Dilthey, who devoted a large part of his life's work to this epistemological problem, set in his *Introduction to the Humanities* (1883) a programmatic basis. Finally, Heinrich Rickert, who had started from the *Historik* of Johann Gustav Droysen, tried in a voluminous work, *The Limitations of Scientific Concepts* (1902 and 1913) to solve the logical problem of a clear distinction between the natural and the humanistic sciences. The conclusions which Rickert and Dilthey drew, or which it was thought could be drawn from their works, were on the whole accepted by the school philosophy in Germany and have found a great many followers among the representatives of the social sciences.

In other countries the controversy was less outspoken. France had her traditional dichotomy into *lettres et sciences* which provided less contact between the groups and therefore less discordance. The English-speaking world acquiesced in the latent antagonism between the domains of arts and sciences. Up to the present time the over-all picture is that of an almost generally recognized opposition between the theoretical tasks of, say, a physicist or botanist on the one hand and a philologist or historian on the other.

For the problems of our book, a discussion of the controversial questions, which are but little cleared up as yet, is of great importance.

*In the following sections we shall attempt to explicate, from our position, some of the main points of the dualistic conception of science, which states an unbridgeable contrast between the natural sciences and the humanities.*

2. *The Characteristics of Natural Science.* In order to understand what is regarded by the followers of the dualistic theory as the basic difference between the humanities and the natural sciences, we must first of all look at the picture they have formed for themselves of the methods and aims of natural science. On this point Rickert and Dilthey do not quite agree, although both of them are more or less influenced by the "mechanistic" theory which about the middle of the nineteenth century was the most popular way of explaining nature. In addition to this it is important that both of them stood on the grounds of school philosophy and opposed Kant only in so far as he seemed to them somehow biased in favor of natural science.

The characteristic feature of the notions of natural science is, according to Rickert, that they strive toward a *simplification* of the picture of our environment. He thinks, however, that a great difference exists between the exact sciences, such as physics and chemistry, on the one hand, and the purely descriptive fields of natural history, zoölogy, botany, etc., on the other. In the first case, the concepts are defined with regard to the natural laws in which they figure and they possess general and absolute validity; they serve like the laws of nature themselves for the exposition of objective facts which exist independently of the creation of concepts and the finding of laws. On the other hand, the conceptual constructions in the descriptive fields are not quite independent of subjective judgments, and their validity is thus somewhat limited in range; but the role of simplifying generalization remains the same. It would be the ideal of all science, so Rickert says, to subordinate everything concerning the physical world to one single comprehensive concept, such as perhaps that of the "atomistic mechanism."

The nature, however, that is the subject of the natural sciences is according to Rickert by no means identical with the world of physics; it also comprises the psychic phenomena of human life, and in this area too a subsumption of all phenomena under a "uniform psychic entity which everywhere obeys the same laws" is possible and desirable. Rickert explicitly recognizes the possibility, and even necessity, of scientific psychology; and here he is partly in disagreement with Dilthey. He even touches upon the idea of a more general natural science which would contain both the physical and the psychic and reduce *everything* to uniform and general laws. In any case, the boundary between natural science and the humanities is not drawn where the physical departs from the psychic.

Dilthey is more strongly under the influence of the physiologist Emil Du Bois-Reymond's notion of the "Limitations of Natural Science" which was expressed in his famous slogan *"ignorabimus"* (1872). What he meant by this can best be shown by his own definition:

Knowledge of nature—more precisely, the scientific explanation of the physical world by means of and in the sense of theoretical science—means reducing all changes in the physical world to the motions of atoms effected by time-independent central forces, or analyzing all natural occurrences into a mechanics of atoms.

The fact that such a reduction to mechanisms of a special kind seems impossible when, for example, one attempts an explanation of the origins of sensations, signifies to Du Bois-Reymond that the scientific method breaks down at that point and is therefore usable only within the world of physics. This conception yields a simpler and clearer delineation of the boundaries between natural science and the humanities than does Rickert's; we shall have to discuss both of them.

*The logical characteristic of natural science, as viewed by Rickert, is the fact that it creates more or less general concepts of absolute validity*

*which have the purpose of simplifying the picture of reality. Its final aim
—in the extreme conception of Du Bois-Reymond and Dilthey—is to reduce all phenomena uniformly to the motion of atoms under the influence
of central forces.*

3. . . . *and of Humanistic Science.* As a counterpart of the notion
that the goals of natural science are generalization, simplification, and absolute validity, Rickert declares that the characteristic task of the other sciences is to comprehend their subject in an individualizing and immediately
realistic manner. In view of his inclusion of psychology among the natural
sciences, he prefers the name "historical" or "cultural science" for the humanities. It is not the subject matter, but the method, the *kind* of treatment
of essentially the same objects which according to him distinguishes the
two groups of sciences. The natural sciences are in his opinion rightly called
"sciences of laws" and as such they are "in sharp contrast to the historical
sciences, which seek to describe what really happened" (G. Simmel).

But Rickert encounters the gravest difficulties when he has to explain
what the conceptual structure of the historical sciences actually consists in.
He cannot deny that the historian, as he pursues his task of describing individual traits of reality, also uses simplifications compared with the totality
of the available information. The writer of history, according to Rickert,
presents ideas which have the purpose of simplifying the exposition of what
he has to say but do not have the character of generality,

and since these ideas can never be quite congruent with the immensely manifold real occurrences, they are also, although they do not have a *general*
content, "concepts" in the sense that in them the aspects essential for history
are emphasized and summarized, in the same way as natural science creates
concepts by emphasizing and summarizing the aspects of reality that are
important for it.

What it is, concretely speaking, of which these concepts consist, "in
which the historical essence of reality is apprehended individually," is
never explained; it can only be inferred from the context that the main
point is to differentiate on the basis of suitable criteria between the "important" and the "unimportant."

Dilthey is less ambiguous in his *Introduction to the Humanities, An
Attempt at a Foundation of the Study of Society and History* about the impossibility of reducing mental phenomena to facts of a mechanistic nature.
The independence of history as a science rests, according to Dilthey, upon
the fact that it is not possible, e.g.,

to derive the full measure of passion, poetic creation, and inventive thought,
which we call Goethe's life, from the build of his brain and the properties of
his body.

According to Dilthey, the realm of the humanities is determined by their subject matter, that is, as far as his expressions can be translated, society and its development. It comprises, besides history in the widest sense, economics, the science of government, jurisprudence, and theology. There are three kinds of statements occurring in these sciences: those which assert real facts as given by apprehension; those which develop the uniformity of certain aspects of facts and form the theoretical structure of the field in question; and finally those which offer valuations and prescriptions for practical action.

The central problem seems for Dilthey to be the question: What are the *common* insights or ways of thinking that underlie the judgments of historians, the inferences of economists, and the concepts of jurists; how are all these related to each other and what determines their certainty? The answers of Comte and J. S. Mill are rejected because supposedly they cripple reality in order to adapt it to the methods of the natural sciences. It does not seem, however, to be the writer's intention to give any explicit answers himself; he presents to the reader an abundance of historical material, critical comments about other people's opinions, and witty implications, but he avoids carefully any clear conclusions. This kind of exposition was surely not chosen without purpose; it represents the type of procedure often preferred in the humanities, which readily takes advantage of the vagueness of linguistic expressions.

*The characteristic feature of the humanities is according to Rickert their individualizing method; according to Dilthey, their subject matter— the totality of those phenomena of human life which are not derivable from the physical qualities of men.*

4. *The Unity of Method.* Before we start making our own position clear with respect to the above-described dualistic notion of science we had better exclude two possible misunderstandings. In the first place, there could not be any point in trying to camouflage differences which undoubtedly exist and to assert that physics and history are "the same." Between chemistry, botany, and meteorology there are also distinctions in subject matter, method, and aim, and the personal outlook of the scientists in these three cases may vary greatly. The question is only whether the contrasts between two fields that do not belong to the same one of the two groups as defined by the dualists are so much stronger and more fundamental than the differences between fields within either group. On the other hand, it must be explicitly emphasized that the question of logical classification has nothing to do with a valuation of the field in question and even less with a valuation of the individual scientists. When Schopenhauer declared that history should not be counted among the sciences he may have given expression to a certain contempt that justifiably irritated some people. The

French usage which distinguishes quietly between *sciences* and *lettres* shows that the differentiation is by no means necessarily connected with a value judgment.

Let us then consider first the validity of the criterion by which the natural sciences and the humanities are distinguished according to whether they generalize or individualize. We may suppose that there is general agreement that the course of history as a whole is given as a *unique* phenomenon. The formation of the earth, and the evolution of the animal and plant species we also know only as an individual event that runs down in time and has not ended yet. Investigations in this field should consequently be counted as "history," and that is indeed done by many of the consistent followers of dualism. Then one may seek to study meteorologic conditions at a certain spot on the earth; e.g., if we examine temperature measurements that were taken over a course of years we will easily find that in this respect no month is exactly equal to a previous one. The weather is thus a unique individual occurrence too, and if we state the general law that it is hot in the summer and cold in the winter, or that a certain combination of air pressure and temperature is usually followed by a thunderstorm, this conclusion is based upon the fact that we single out some aspects of the total phenomenon, aspects that are approximately repeated, and emphasize them. It is quite right to say that the natural sciences arrive at formulations of general laws only by dissecting the immediately given; that they arbitrarily simplify by neglecting the individual distinctions of the separate cases, thus doing an injustice to reality in this sense. Do, however, the humanities really operate otherwise?

The development of the Romance languages from Latin happened only once and it forms in its entirety a unique, closed historical occurrence. Nevertheless, the linguist formulates for it the laws of the shift of consonants—exactly as the natural scientist does—by examining separate detailed events which approximately repeat themselves. Here too, one arrives at rules of a certain general validity by simplification of the immediately observed through the elimination of unimportant elements. No doubt the economist proceeds in the same way when, for instance, he states the law of diminishing return or makes an assertion about the economic consequences of too rapid an increase in population. He necessarily begins with the observation of special, individually distinct cases (which emerge from a more involved complex of phenomena by dissection) and, by disregarding the individual differences, he arrives at general statements. Whether these are then called "laws," "rules," or "hypotheses," or by any other name, is quite immaterial for our present considerations. The point is that if the existence of general theorems which pass over individual variations is supposed to be the mark of the natural sciences, linguistics as well as economics have to be accepted as natural sciences; and on the other hand, paleontology and the theory of descent, rather among the humanities. But this cannot be what the classification is meant for.

Most fields which we have not considered as yet present a more or less similar situation. They represent intermediate cases, showing characteristics of both the humanities and the natural sciences. It will scarcely be possible to apply the criterion of individualization or generalization in practice, unless one thinks only of the extreme opposites, such as theoretical physics in its present form and history as a pure chronicle.

*The idea of a basic logical division of the sciences, into those in which general laws are stated and those which follow a purely individualizing method, breaks down in the face of most disciplines; it seems to fit at most the two extreme cases, theoretical physics and pure history.*

5. *History and Physics.* A criterion of classification may also be valuable if it is only suited to point out sharply the extremes and makes the other possibilities appear as transitional cases. But then it is necessary that the two opposite types be clearly and consistently defined and that to each of them corresponds, at least approximately, some realization. We do not think that this can be said for the division into sciences of the generalizing and of the individualizing types.

Let us admit that there are sentences whose subject is a single individual and whose predicate is a unique action, and other sentences that state something repeatable about a group of people. In calling sentences of the second kind "general" one usually thinks of the content of the statement as being independent of time and location, a quality which is customarily ascribed to physical theorems. But the assertion that all bodies fall equally fast is meant only for bodies near the earth; a theory of trade winds (which exist only once) is also a part of physics; and the assumption that our astronomical calculations will be valid for millions of years can only be called a very daring extrapolation. In fact, there remains merely the truth that physical research tends to statements as general as possible, which comprise as many special cases as possible. But any special conclusion, for however few cases it may hold, even if it describes only a single case, is also a physical statement—even though the textbooks of physics usually are not filled with such propositions. Finally, there exist at any period new phenomena which are not yet subsumed in the theory and can be registered only individually.

On the other hand, there is no doubt that every work of historical study contains a great number of individualized sentences. But these sentences, considered in isolation and individually, form by no means the *total* content of historical writing. At times one finds in the historical text ex-

plicit generalizations, such as: "No people in this situation would . . . ,"
or (in Mommsen, in the middle of the most factual description of the end
of Vercingetorix),

> As after a bleak and cloudy day the sun may yet break through before
> setting, thus fate gives to peoples doomed to perish, still a last magnificent man.

But the main point is not that such assertions are explicitly stated. Nobody
will believe that the twenty or thirty lines in which Mommsen describes the
fate of the Celts after the death of Vercingetorix exhaust what really happened in that epic event or that, conversely, his sentences are uniquely determined by what happened and is known to us. Rather the choice of what
is said—and in this choice above all lies the scientific accomplishment of
the historian—is guided by specific general conceptions of the author and
serves at the same time to transmit implicitly to the reader these conceptions, and hence certain general propositions. Everyone who has watched
his own behavior critically knows that any verbal reproduction of the most
trivial event, whether of one's own experience or not, depends upon the
opinion one has formed of the matter and wants to transmit to the listener;
there is no report without conscious or unconscious prejudice. What an
abundance of general assertions is contained, for instance, in the "individualized statement" that the recession of world culture from the eastern basin
of the Mediterranean in the fifteenth century was compensated by the
spreading out of the Western European peoples over the Atlantic (Jacob
Burckhardt).

Some historians maintain the view that anything contained in a work
of history except individual factual description is but a trimming, not quite
avoidable, but at any rate superfluous and harmful to the aims of science.
What is meant here are insertions with propagandistic effects due to possible intentions of the author to motivate the reader, in an implicit fashion,
toward certain actions or a certain behavior. But if we claim that the sentences describing an individual event are by no means determined by this
event alone, we refer to a fundamental property of language and its relation to reality. The historian using for the description of happenings those
expressions which everyday language offers him (and only occasionally
supplementing or altering them by his own formulations), reduces the
"unique" to a combination of repeatable elements and thus proceeds analogously to the physicist who picks out from the stream of natural phenomena the recurrent features. The scientific work of the historian consists essentially in this reduction and in the conception of general judgments on
which the reduction rests. It might be said that the historian's work is
closer to reality than the physicist's in the sense that the processes of abstraction and simplification which the former applies do not go so far beyond what is usual in everyday language. The contrast between the two

extreme fields may perhaps be sketched by saying that the physicist makes *primarily* general statements and leaves the inferences upon individual cases to the reader, while the historian uses his general judgments *most of all* for the selection and formulation of the sentences that describe the individual occurrence and only states the latter. We shall return to this point below (Chapter 18).

Many historical works of our time consist exclusively or primarily of general statements about the behavior of large groups of people, and many authors regard those theories, and the predictions for the future made possible by them, as the highest aim of historical research. Thus Jacob Burckhardt, one of the greatest historians of all time, puts at the beginning of his *Weltgeschichtliche Betrachtungen* the program:

We pay attention to the repeatable, the constant, the typical as that which appeals to us and can be understood.

Considering that the amount of historical facts that forms our stock of experience grows every day, one should really expect a development of historical writing in the direction toward a generalizing way of treatment. It is immaterial if a special name is chosen for this type of research, such as "philosophy of history," etc. (for further comments on this point, see Chapter 18).

*It does not seem to us to be a useful characterization to assert that physics—in the ideal case—consists only of sentences which are as general as possible, and that history consists only of purely individualized statements. We find in all fields a progression from single observations to comprehensive generalization which corresponds to the essence of scientific work, even though the extent of the generalization that under present conditions can be aimed at and attained is very different for the various disciplines.*

6. *The Alleged Incomparability.* Since from the methodologic point of view we are unable to reach a satisfactory demarcation between the natural sciences and the humanities, there still remains the idea—which, as a matter of fact, suggests itself much more readily—of a distinction according to the subject matter. The natural sciences on the one hand, and history or the humanities on the other, form the two hemispheres of the "globus intellectualis" which we distinguish easily as long as we rely on naïve intuition. Much more difficult is it to draw some kind of exact boundary lines, and on closer inspection the contrast seems to vanish altogether.

One could arrive at an ostensibly clear demarcation if one accepted the above-quoted definition of natural science by Du Bois-Reymond—a definition which even at the time when it was pronounced was much too narrow, and today can only be considered obsolete. Perhaps there are still physicists who see a solvable problem in the reduction of all physical phenomena to a specific system of basic elements (in which, however, atoms in the old sense would not appear). But from our point of view the question whether the *occurrence of sense impressions* can be reduced to physical processes, i.e., can be described in terms of physics, has to be dismissed most emphatically. For in our view all concepts of natural science are only a means for orientation in the world that is given to us through sense impressions. Whether this idea, advanced particularly by Ernst Mach, should be called "naturism" is immaterial and is not decided by a generally accepted linguistic convention.

The basis for a sharp distinction between the two hemispheres being lost, there certainly remain areas closer to the poles which are clearly distinguishable. There is no doubt that the examination of spectral lines is a field of physics, and that a study of the evolution of jurisprudence in the Middle Ages belongs to the area of the humanities. The linguistic terms "natural science" and "humanities" are defined as precisely as are most expressions of ordinary language (Chapter 3, 2) and the practical value of the distinction in many situations of everyday life remains uncontested. The thesis that is under discussion here is that of the entire *"incomparability* of the experience of a mental world with all sensory experiences of nature" (Dilthey). Since the experience of the mental world is given to us through the senses too, by reading and hearing what other men say and write, or by taking notice of their actions and thoughts and feelings, this thesis can only be understood as asserting that man and his behavior do not belong to nature, but to some other category. That may perhaps be acceptable, but the idea that there is an unbridgeable gap, an incomparability between men as spiritual beings and all other occurrences in nature, including men as physical organisms, cannot be upheld at the present stage of psychological and psychophysical knowledge. There is no question here of deriving in a naïve way human passions from the paths of moving brain atoms, but rather of subtle experiences about the interconnection between intellectual phenomena and organic processes. It seems to us that the primary thesis of dualism does not represent an existant theoretical situation but rather tries to give an ideological foundation to the actually existing differences in the practical workings of the different fields of science.

We readily accept the definition that the archeologist August Böckh gave for philology: it is "the knowledge of the already known." That which other people have learned comes to us only through observations of a certain kind and we assimilate it (partly perhaps unconsciously) in the same manner as we do everything else that we learn, by adapting it to what we have known before. We certainly do not see here an insurmountable barrier against the scientific knowledge of nature.

*Granted the great variety of subject matter and the necessarily different forms of observation and elaboration in those fields which according to conventional language are counted among either the natural sciences or the humanities, the demarcation of an area of "mental experiences" which are supposed to be incomparable with any "sensual experience of nature" is completely untenable. It would, among other things, require that between the intellectual behavior of a man and his physical organism no direct connection exists.*

7. *The "System" of Sciences.* There remains, as a last refuge for the dualistic conception of science, the frequently stated assertion that there are two distinctly different kinds of *understanding,* one in the natural sciences, and another in the humanities. This claim concerns a psychological fact which is difficult to define, but which probably was never seriously maintained by psychologists. Its primary source is the self-observation of scholars who classify their own way of understanding as belonging to the humanistic way and hence as "higher." Since it is difficult to believe that the same scholars have also a sufficient knowledge and practice in the natural-scientific kind of understanding, the whole theory must be considered as rather weakly founded. We shall return to the psychological side of the question in Chapter 18, 6.

It may be useful to state once more in what sense our rejection of the dualistic notion of science is meant. We do not want to replace dualism by a naïve monism like Haeckel's which finds pleasure in claiming that it is able to solve all so-called world enigmas with one scientific idea, the theory of descent. We are far from trying to obscure distinctions that indubitably exist. The physician who examines a human individual, whether as psychiatrist or as neurologist, has to fulfill a quite different task from, say, the biographer who critically analyzes the life accomplishments of the same person. One may classify the one problem as proper to the natural sciences and the other to the humanities, and it may be expedient at times to emphasize the difference between the two problems. But in the last analysis it is again a scientific problem to study the relations between the two ways of looking at things and to search for connections among their results. The claim of incomparability, if it has any meaning at all, could only mean that one wants to deny a priori the possibility of research in a certain area, on the borderline or in the no man's land between two sciences.

The ever-recurring attempts, reaching back to ancient times, to find for the totality of sciences a definitive logical classification, a family tree, or a hierarchy, are innumerable. The discrimination between natural sciences and humanities is only the top disjunction which as a rule (but not always) is taken as starting point. We know of the systems proposed by Plato and Aristotle, Bacon and Mill, D'Alembert and Comte, Wundt and Ostwald, to mention only a few names. A mistake made over and over again in these attempts is that they start from a specific contemporary stage of knowledge and try to anticipate its further development, at least in broad outline, for all future time. It can easily be seen how hopeless this is by examining any classification that was designed a century ago. At that time neither biology nor psychology was known as a special science, but customary fields were mineralogy, cosmology, etc. which we should hardly consider relevant today. Other pedantic "systems of science" contrasted such fields as kinematics and physics, grammar and theology, etc. It would seem quite natural to many people for a book with the aim of this one to propose above all a complete "classification" of the sciences. Comte's *Cours de philosophie positive* contained a rank order of the sciences from mathematics to sociology (see Chapter 20, 1) which has become famous. Some of these systems may be useful, but it seems better to us to leave aside any attempts at systematization.

It is of no avail to try to find out exactly what "really" belongs to the field of each separate science. Schopenhauer's attempt at systematization on the basis of the different kinds of application of the Law of Sufficient Reason led to such absurdities as the coördination in one group of astronomy, mineralogy, geology, technology, and pharmacy. In fact, the usual linguistic denotations of the sciences and the demarcations corresponding to them (which vary in time) are intended primarily for practical purposes of organization, teaching, and research and the desire for encyclopedic exposition. Another decisive role is played by the amount that a normally talented man who dedicates his life to scientific work can master; which again depends upon the momentary intensity of development in each field. This also explains the frequent splitting off of new "sciences."

If we look less at the names and the sociologically influenced demarcation than at the subject matter of research, a trend opposed to that of the continual splitting up is clearly perceptible: there is a mutual approximation and gradual fusion of previously separated branches of study. We see at the present time that the fields of zoölogy and botany, which until a few decades ago were still sharply distinct, are unified into a common science of biology, which in many of its parts treats the two subdivisions as a single unit. In physics, electricity and magnetism were once two quite independent fields of phenomena. Soon after their fusion, it turned out that they could not be kept separate from optics. The "optics of all wavelengths" grew into quantum theory and absorbed the theory of the structure of matter, and today we are at a point where the age-old distinction between chemistry and physics is disappearing more and more. Of even greater importance from the epistemological point of view is the fact that biologically oriented psychology, including psychoanalysis, gradually penetrates into the realm of questions that lie at the boundary of the humanities. Thus this historically and conventionally established separation also approaches annihilation. The theory of the "limitations of the concepts of natural science" is old-fashioned today and will probably be more and more refuted by further development. We summarize our results:

*A basic contrast between natural sciences and the humanities, with respect to either method or subject matter, cannot be constructed. Any classification and subclassification of the sciences can serve only a practical and temporary purpose; it is neither logically binding nor final, but depends upon the external circumstances under which scientific work is done and upon the momentary stage of development of the various disciplines. Decisive progress is very often achieved by the clarification of questions that lie on the boundary of previously separated fields.*

### CHAPTER 18

# history and psychology

1. *The Subject Matter of History.* The word "history," apart from all other shortcomings of language, is used in two clearly distinct senses. In the first place it denotes the *object* of historical writing, e.g., the real events and experiences in the past of a people. In the second place, one calls history—and it is this usage that we shall adopt for the time being—the writings of a historian and their contents; e.g., there is a "Roman history by Mommsen." The two concepts are often confused, as, for example, in the well-known phrase from J. G. Droysen's *Grundriss der Historik:* "It is not the past that is history, but the knowledge of the human mind about it." One often does not quite know which of the two meanings is referred to, particularly in the case of the frequently quoted judgments on the value or nonvalue of history. The incidental phrase of Goethe's, "History is really only a complexus of nonsense for the higher thinker," points, we may suppose, to the real events and the senselessness of their succession. On the other hand, Schopenhauer's contempt for history (because it gives less insight into human life than poetry) is directed at the *writing* of history. At any rate, here and in the following sections, we shall always mean by history the *reproduction* of events, mostly that undertaken with scientific intentions.

Even though we refuse in principle to draw sharp lines between the separate sciences and always admit all kinds of transitions, it nevertheless seems useful to attempt a characterization of what history treats. We mean by this a distinction from the field of biology as well as that of physics, chemistry, etc. In both these cases the criterion most immediately at hand (Chapter 17, 4) if one wants to distinguish between a natural science and history, namely, the "uniqueness" of historical events, breaks down. On the one hand we see in the biological evolution of man, in the general theory of descent, in cosmogony, and in paleontology, disciplines which count among the natural sciences and deal with occurrences that are "unique" in the same sense as those of history. On the other hand we have previously remarked (Chapter 17, 4) and shall discuss in more detail in what follows, that scientific history, in principle just as physics does, singles out from the unique course of events partial phenomena that repeat themselves. Only that range of experience whose elements, in the last analysis, consist of repeatable, recurring parts can be described and reproduced in words and expressions of our language. Therefore, the criterion that divides history from the other fields of science must be determined in a different way.

We find, following a suggestion of E. Zilsel, an expedient criterion in the *order of magnitude of the time intervals* in question in the various fields. The whole of human history runs approximately 6000 years, and hence covers about 200 human generations. Cosmogony and the biological theory of descent consider a time interval of about 1500 million years—this is the age of the rigid earth surface as it is estimated today. Thus, the cosmic period of time is to the historical in the same proportion as the latter is to the duration of a few days. It can be said that physics and chemistry deal with occurrences whose "history" is exhausted at most in days or hours; of course, this is also true of scientific observations on the human object, of either a physiological or psychological kind. The occurrences within this narrowest interval of time are comprehended by the human *memory;* the 200 generations of history are covered by what is called *tradition;* and the millions of years of the history of the earth are effective by *heredity.* Investigations within the different stages are conducted independently of one another. The psychologist takes man for granted in a certain historical situation, and the historian accepts man as he finds him at the end of the evolution of the species. Historical events have no significance in the evolutionary history of the world, and physical or psychological processes do not play a "historical role." Without trying to give a pedantic definition and without any claim to have exhausted the question, we state:

*History treats events that happened within the last five to six thousand years and that are connected with each other by tradition; one step above are phylogenic occurrences which influence one another by heredity; one step below, physical, physiological, and psychological processes, whose durations have the same order of magnitude as the length of individual human reactions.*

2. *Historical Truth.* The decisive epistemological problem in the science of history is that of "historical truth." We do not think here of the "higher" truth which is implied when one says that a report may be correct in all its details, and still as a whole be false. What we have in mind is this: for any single concrete assertion, such as "Caesar went across the Rubicon and said . . .," the question of a truth criterion arises. The so-called Aristotelian truth concept, according to which a sentence *"A is B"* is true if *A* is really *B,* does not suffice here; for it is exactly the expression that

something "is really," particularly since we are concerned with the past, that is in need of explanation. Of course, we take it for granted that the sentence in question is "connectible" (Chapter 6) with the appropriate rules of language, that, e.g., "Caesar" is the name of a person and not of a river, "Rubicon," that of a river and not of an abstract property, etc. But what is the criterion for the correctness of a statement that asserts something about the past? We have previously agreed to make every statement verifiable by reduction to element sentences (Chapter 8, 4), but the verification in this sense of something that has passed is obviously not possible.

Our answer to this is that about the past something can be said only in so far as it has left consequences (traces) that can still be examined today. We count among the consequences also all written records of the occurrence (including all facts about the agents and the circumstances of the recording) and possibly personal reminiscences, traditions, etc.; in short, everything that is customarily called "source material." No serious historian, asked for a proof of his assertions, will do anything but cite the sources, some of which are possibly called "indirect." These are conclusions drawn from the experience of regular interconnections between "small-scale" facts and, further, experiences about the possibilities of errors and falsification. But even in order to regard something as the "effect" of a situation one has to apply a large complex of observations which alone allows one to establish a causal relation (Chapter 13, 1). All of this material, taken in the widest sense, constitutes the very complicated range of experience coördinated to a single historical statement. The agreement of an assertion with this entire stock of experience which can again and again be tested by observation is the *only* criterion of the "truth" of any historical assertion.

It is in our view simply meaningless to say that an event may have happened, although "everything we know" speaks against it. If, e.g., *all witnesses* of an occurrence report unanimously that they saw the statue of the governor shake its head, we do not believe it; but that judgment rests upon general experiences of such situations (the nature of statues and the occurrence of delusions), and hence we know more about the subject than the witnesses' reports after all.

It may also be said, according to a remark by Hans Hahn, that a historical assertion contains a *prediction for the future* of a similar nature to that found in physics. The implicit claim is that any future examination of the sources—in the above-discussed sense of the widest possible correlated range of experience—will verify the stated result. This prophecy may be correct or incorrect; it is in any case hypothetical, as any scientific proposition is.

Historians themselves, in general, do not consider this logical question as the main difficulty of the concept of historical truth. They are interested rather, as we indicated before, in the tension between the correctly described, well-established single facts and the "real" or "essential" "meaning" of a historical process. Related to this are the notions of objectivity, freedom from prejudice, conscientiousness, etc., in the writing of history. From a practical point of view these are, indeed, the main problems that every historian has to solve in every single case. It is, then, quite justified if a concrete methodology of historical research concerns itself above all with these questions, just as the physicist has to learn how to draw conclusions from specialized experiments upon more or less complicated connections. But from the point of view of the logic of science we do not recognize a characteristic problem here that would distinguish the science of history from all other ones. *Any* reproduction of a complex of experiences by words rests upon an abundance of conventions. They are implied primarily by the general use of customary expressions and by those conceptional constructs which are closer to the field in question and not accepted with such general unanimity. To the latter belong, in the case of political history, terms such as people and race, state and sovereignty, culture and civilization, and many others. As long as there is no complete agreement among writers and among an author and his readers about the exact meaning or even the admissibility of such expressions, no description even of the smallest factual detail can be unambiguous if it uses these words. Every historical record is a *theory* of the event in question, just as the application of the Newtonian equations is a theory of every single phenomenon of motion. The only difference is that in history the fact that arbitrary definitions are implied is much less conspicuous, even at times purposely not stated, with the effect of inducing the impression of a description uniquely determined by the events. Also, the fact that history has to be written anew over and over again, even if new source material in the narrower sense has not been discovered in the meantime, shows that we deal with a *theory* of events that is determined by the total stock of experience available to the author.

The question of objectivity of the description is often related to that of the importance, or as it is sometimes called, the "historical" relevance of certain events. The fact that Friedrich Wilhelm IV rejected the German imperial crown is regarded by everyone as a "historical event"; what uniform he wore at that moment seems quite unimportant for political history, but could, as Eduard Meyer notices, be rather essential for the history of costume or of uniforms. The selection of what is reported depends entirely upon the aim of the account. It would hardly be necessary to emphasize all this, were it not for the tendency of a methodology of history, influenced by school philosophy, to stress the "objective validity," the absoluteness of certain basic concepts such as that of an event's being "historical," at the same time emphasizing the contrast between history and all theoretical sciences, and even to assign to history a "superempirical" significance (Rudolph Eucken).

*The criterion of truth of an historical assertion lies in the testability of the still observable aftereffects of the alleged fact and of its indirect consequences (sources) including the application of inferences derived from general experience. The text of an historical exposition as a whole, as well as in details, is never uniquely determined by the facts, but always originates in a theory of the occurrence. The theory is implied by generally accepted linguistic conventions, by implicitly admitted stipulations, by hypothetical assumptions about causal relations, and finally by manifestly established purposes or tacit tendencies.*

3. *Explicit Theories of History.* From the foregoing it should be clear that we do not regard as the theoretical component of a historical thesis only what is explicitly pronounced to be a universal principle or presented in the form of generalizing statements. This, so to speak, manifest part of historical theory is frequently called the philosophy of history and —naturally—there are not a few historians who dislike it, just as some experimental physicists like to take a position of animosity toward theoretical physics. But he who defends such a point of view, thinking that he distinguishes thereby between two opposites, theory and reality, draws in fact only an arbitrary boundary line, determined by his own taste, *right through the middle of the theory.*

The contemporary conception of the political and cultural history of mankind ("history" here is meant in the sense of historical past) exhibits hardly a single principal idea which would be accepted by all or even a majority of scholars. The older religious notion, according to which everything that happens is the result of a predetermined outside plan, has lost its attractiveness. Perhaps the decisive weakness of this idea was its placing of all essential historical deeds back into the past and thus giving little room for further development. In contrast to this, newer theories tend to reserve important parts of progress for the future. Leibnitz regarded history as a continual advancement from darkness to an ever-growing clarity. Herder, in his classical *Ideas on the Philosophy of the History of Mankind,* thought that one could observe a continuous ascension of mankind toward higher levels of humanity. All of these idealistic views were far surpassed by Hegel in his bold system, according to which the history of the world is the result of the evolution of a superindividual "world mind," in which only the "absolutely rational" and that which is "intended by the eternal wisdom" happens in logical sequence, accompanied by an unambiguous evolutionary trend from the *freedom of the one* (in the ancient Orient), through the *freedom of the few* (among the classical peoples) to the *freedom of all* (in modern times). Hegel's system seems to be the only attempt yet made to construct a kind of tautological theory of history. The attempt was doomed to failure, because it started with the *end,* with the most general ideas, before even in a single area, however small, a sufficient store of experience had led to a verifiable regularity of this kind. One is reminded of Hegel's grandiose schema in our day by Oswald Spengler's conception, which, though much more moderate, attempts to systematize the origin, rise, and decline of single, separated historical civilizations—this also being a theory with strongly tautological elements.

The starkest contrast to the Hegelian school is Auguste Comte's positivism. Methodologically, he rejects all audacious flights of imagination and recommends the path of sober observation as it is followed in the natural sciences. Comte's leading idea is that the oldest epoch in the history of mankind or of a single people is characterized by the prevalence of theological ideas, that then there follows as a transitional stage the predominance of metaphysics, and that this is finally superseded by the positive reign of reason. This one main movement comprehends, according to Comte, all varieties of the diversified strains of history. Under Comte's influence famous works of history were conceived, such as H. T. Buckle's *History of Civilization in England,* which is a model of positivistic writing of history.

The second half of the nineteenth century brought two new forms of historical theory which are methodologically oriented toward positivism but undoubtedly include also elements of the absolutistic ideology of Hegel. The so-called materialistic conception of history conceived by Karl Marx and Friedrich Engels regards as the cause of all historical events the defects of the social conditions in which men live and which they strive to improve. In contrast to this, a more naturalistic movement, which is based upon Darwin and founded upon the modern theory of heredity, asserts that all history consists of the struggle and interplay of the different, essentially unchanging human races. A favorite antithesis in connection with these ideas is whether single "great men" or national groups "make" history, i.e., are the actual bearers of the historical development. In the same way one could ask in physics whether physical phenomena depend more upon electric or upon magnetic forces, or one could build up a theory according to which, e.g., the causes of all events are mechanical (as the philosopher Wilhelm Wundt did in 1866).

*The explicit theories of history so far proposed consist of weakly founded, very general principles which claim exclusiveness. To make these ideas precise, to adapt them to one another, to determine their empirical foundations, and to delineate their limits of validity, seem to be problems whose solution still lies in the far future.*

4. *Historicism.* Speaking of history (in the sense of the writing of history or the science of history), people think primarily of political and

then of cultural history. To the latter one may assign the history of a language and of languages, of art and of the arts, the history of each single science, of an idea, of a trade, and of any human institution. On the other hand, any kind of philology, archaeology, numismatics, etc., are usually called historical sciences. Thus there must be the greatest vagueness in expressions such as "a historical event," "historical greatness," "an unhistorical man," etc. (We neglect the older, now gradually disappearing designation of zoölogy, botany, and mineralogy as natural "history.") In addition, linguistic usage (as stated above) often unconsciously adopts the same word for the event itself whose description is in question. It becomes understandable in this way that one may write volumes about the "essence of history" and similar ambiguities by just stretching the use of every word only a little bit beyond the area in which a reasonably unambiguous linguistic convention exists.

A favorite, much-discussed, and rather recent catchword is "historicism," which means approximately the view that regards every present institution (or the totality of the present) as the final product of a historical evolution. The word itself, and hence the assembling of certain vague phenomena around the word, date back a few decades only and have not developed independently of the biological concept of evolution. (Littré, 1878, does not yet know the expression "historisme" and Lalande's *Vocabulaire de philosophie,* 1926, calls it "terme équivòque . . . à éviter comme la plupart des terms de ce genre, qui engendrent facilement des discussions verbales"; Runes' dictionary, 1942, treats it as a well-established term.) Often one means by historicism only an exaggeration or overestimation of the historical point of view and regards perhaps the last hundred years as the period in which such a hypertrophy developed. Some opposition to historicism is based on the contention that the study of the evolution of an existing institution, such as the presently accepted system of moral norms, shakes faith in the absoluteness and necessity of that institution in its present form. In this way historicism is actually considered as close to relativistic positivism—which, on the other hand, is often reproached for thinking entirely "unhistorically."

In our opinion *every* science consists of deriving statements about the future from experiences in the past. Kepler studied the "history" of the motion of the planets and from this grew Newton's celestial mechanics. After we have observed long enough the motion of the winds and the clouds, and the shifting of air pressure, we shall perhaps be in a position to say a little more about tomorrow's weather (by means of theories derived from the observations). Human beings and their actions and psychological experiences do not stand outside of nature, and by studying this, though much more complicated, "history" we reach, in slow and small steps, a gradual understanding of the course of events which still continues. Certainly, as we have mentioned previously, in this field the formal derivation of regularities is still in its beginnings and will presumably never reach the stage it has in physics. But historical investigations in the ordinary sense of the term, i.e., those which deal with human actions of the more or less remote past, are not different, in principle, from the observations that form the basis of theories in natural science. If one speaks of the harm done by historicism or of the "damage done by history to the life of peoples," one only hits a shortcoming common to all kinds of scientific activity, which has its roots in the limitations of human capacities: individuals—and analogously certain groups, professions, etc.—that specialize in a specific field of research thereby become less fit for other, wider tasks of life. An excellent physicist is often not capable of serving as an engineer, a perfect engineer is seldom fit to be an executive of a great enterprise, a historian, as a rule, does not make a practical statesman, and a people that too strongly clings to historical reminiscences of its past may miss opportunities that would offer themselves to it otherwise.

*The extraordinary ambiguity of all expressions in connection with the word "history" makes it impossible to follow many of the general discussions, in particular those which deal with the "value and nonvalue" of history. The modern catchword "historicism" indicates a situation that hardly is peculiar to the historical sciences.*

5. *Psychology of Life.* Everybody who seeks to delineate the subject matter or the method of the science of history comes to talk about its relation to psychology; as a matter of fact, most theoreticians and practitioners of the writing of history declare that psychology is the essential basis of history, e.g., Lamprecht, Wilhelm Wundt, Sigwart, and above all Taine, for whom history is "psychologie appliquée." The way in which this is meant can only be understood once it is at least approximately clear what is meant here by "psychology." We should not, of course, be expected to propose for such an indeterminate concept an exact definition. But perhaps there is agreement at least in so far as psychology deals with observations on human beings, concerning such phenomena as do not find an immediate explanation in the realm of the physical. Subclassifications of psychology according to various criteria have often been proposed; we shall here follow a suggestion of Spranger (in a perfunctory and rough fashion) and distinguish between an "elementary" and a "structural" or "life" psychology. The former studies single, isolated, and recurring features, while the latter attempts a global insight into the unanalyzed complexes that constitute the life of an individual or a whole group of individuals. After what we have said above it will appear only natural that we do not consider it correct to classify one of these two areas as a natural science and the other as one of the humanities. The two parts obviously cannot be separated

sharply, have fundamentally the same aim and the same method, and represent only different stages of development. For the application of psychology in the science of history, one is certainly more interested in that part which concerns itself with the more comprehensive complexes.

In order to give an example of what Spranger calls "psychology of life" or "humanistic (geisteswissenschaftliche) psychology," we may look at his theory of the "patterns of life." By this he means the search for and description of certain types of man, for instance, the theoretical man, the economical, the aesthetic, the social, etc. Strangely enough, Spranger starts out with the warning that the "followers of pure empiricism" must reject his point of view since for them there is no "stable or legitimately developing carrier" of experiences. If this is supposed to be an allusion to Mach's conception of the "ego" as an auxiliary concept (Chapter 7) created for the purpose of orientation in our environment, it represents a quite characteristic misunderstanding. For Mach did not deny the scientific usefulness of such auxiliary concepts; and all the simple types treated by Spranger are also only *auxiliary concepts,* formed by abstraction, by an intentional neglect of details, of differences and gradations, and determined merely by the aim of artificially bringing order out of the chaos of phenomena. Thus Spranger finds himself forced again and again to defend his procedure of isolation and idealization against the objection that he makes artificial, forcible cuts through nature, which are "foreign to life," do not correspond to reality, and from which one cannot construct a "history" of mankind. Actually, he proceeds exactly after the model of *all* theories of natural science in their first stages. His character types may be compared to the rock types of primitive geology (petrography), such as granite, gneiss, etc. The difference is that geology does not stop there but goes on working along various lines, trying to develop specific concepts, to establish interrelations, and so on. For the typification of characters, however, or of the patterns of human life, there holds exactly what Mach said about all theories of natural science:

> Nature exists only once. It is only our schematizing reproduction that creates equal cases. It is only in those that there exists mutual dependence of certain qualities.

It is a peculiarity of research in the so-called humanistic sciences, especially in psychology, that its representatives often regard the method which in a certain field is momentarily expedient (and at the moment perhaps even the only one possible) as final and therefore as one to be defended against any intrusion of principles from neighboring fields. One psychologist may think that the abstraction of schematized character forms is the only correct structural psychology, another studies the psychology of life histories by examining a series of individual biographies with regard to common uniform features (C. Bühler); both of them despise the man who deals with a special, simplified phenomenon of volition, and all are afraid of losing the ground under their feet if they are told that even the ego, the individual, is not an "actual, really existing substance," but a theoretical *auxiliary concept* of the same kind as that of the "economic man" or the "depressive life."

*So-called humanistic or structural phychology, which is often considered the basis of the science of history, attempts a global treatment of complexes of psychological phenomena, not further analyzed, which are connected with single individuals or groups of individuals. Its methods are in principle the same as those of any natural science in its early stages.*

6. *"Understanding" in History.* The decisive concept in the application of psychology in the science of history is often said to be that of "understanding." It is not enough, one often hears, to describe an event by determining all of its details. The genuine task of the scientist is not fulfilled until he succeeds in "understanding" the situation; all that remains for him to do then is to give an exposition which makes the reader take part in the "understanding." In the face of this claim we can only try to find out what can be intended by its formulation, i.e., the empirical meaning in the minds of those who make this claim.

It is remarkable that the insistence upon a particular kind of understanding is quite foreign to Kant's philosophy. Schopenhauer treats at length the concept of evidence, but he seeks, in a purely dogmatic manner, to reduce it to the various classes of the "law of sufficient reason." The psychological problem does not appear until the second half of the nineteenth century, and it is clearly influenced by a reaction against the supposedly too strong orientation of Kant's philosophy toward natural science. In fact, in the opinion of almost all those who use the expression with a special emphasis, as was pointed out in Chapter 17, 7, "understanding" is a peculiarity of the humanities as contrasted to the natural sciences.

Customary alternative expressions for the concept of "understanding" are: empathy (Einfühlung), comprehension by deep contemplation, acquiring self-evidence, complete assimilation, etc. Perhaps one might think that this refers to an elementary experience, or to a protocol statement "I understand this" (Chapter 8; see also Chapter 11, 2). But that supposition is contradicted by the existence of so many synonyms; for "I hear a sound" and "I am cold" there are not many equivalent expressions available. Also, most authors think that "understanding" is not a simple process at all, but that it is a rather complicated psychological phenomenon which is capable and in need of explanation. If one looks a little closer at the explanations given, one discovers immediately and infallibly the well-known complex of customary causal expressions: the *causes,* the *reasons,* and the *motives* have to be understood; it is not the detail, taken out of its natural context, but the fact, imbedded in the totality of its causes and effects, that is accessible to true understanding. He who, indeed, regards causality as an *a priori* principle, as a category that came to scientific thought from the outside and was impressed upon it as an absolute regulator, may perhaps base a notion of causal understanding upon such a foundation. In our view, according to which the various causal expressions serve only for the description of regularities observed in the course of our experiences, nothing remains of the entire conceptual construction but the previously stressed fact that we have the *habit,* in all observations, of looking for and determining the regularly recurring elements. Understanding, then, is nothing but the subsumption of an event in a primitive "theory" which covers a limited range of experience. As a pointed formulation of an at least very closely related conception, we quote from Nietzsche's *Will to Power:*

> Understanding means naïvely only to be able to express something new in the language of something old and known.

It is in language that the simplest regularly recurring experiences are conserved or "capitalized" in the form of words and idioms.

The concept of "understanding" takes on a particular form which points to a special field of psychology, if it is explained by saying that we really understand an action only when we have reduced it to an *impulse* known to us from our internal experience. This proposition is quite in accordance with the above-indicated view, for our own impulses are surely known to us only through self-observation of recurrent phenomena in our own psychic life. On the other hand, one may perhaps find the assumption too narrow that only situations known to us from our *own* impulses form the capitalized experience upon which we draw in order to assimilate foreign experiences; that, however, is not important here. We need only convince ourselves that the special concept of psychological understanding which is claimed for the humanities vanishes or reduces to a schema valid for *all* intellectual activity, as soon as one tries to analyze it more closely. This seems also to be the opinion of most contemporary psychologists.

*It is not possible to state a special act of "understanding" in the humanities which would consist of anything else but reducing to earlier experiences, and subsumption under the known, habitual, and repeatedly observed. It is only the desire to introduce an irrational element into science that leads to the assumption of such a basic concept.*

7. *Group Psychology.* In whatever way one relates psychological views to historical research, one is soon led to notice, in addition to phenomena of the individual mind, those of groups of individuals. Usually the expression "group psychology" or "social psychology" is used for studies of

this kind and one may mean various things by them. In the first place, no individual is isolated in the world and a large part of all his actions and psychological reactions is determined merely by the interaction with other individuals; to this sphere belongs, e.g., everything connected with language and other means of personal intercourse. In the second place, there are indubitably typical similarities in the psychological reactions among members of a profession, a nation, a cultural community, or a human race; these questions belong to a kind of "differential" psychology. But the most important phenomena are those in which the two areas overlap, namely, concerted actions, as they are only possible within a community, based upon the type of reaction peculiar to the group in question. It seems clear that many occurrences in political and cultural history may be viewed in this light.

It has been debated vigorously whether there is any justification in speaking of a "soul of the nation" or "psyche of the people," or of a "national individuality," etc. "In truth," the opponents say, there are only single souls, and whatever is observed of a people or of groups must be dissolvable into observations or facts concerning separate individuals. Such objections are quite understandable from those who connect with the word "soul" the idea of a substantial being that may even be provided with some sort of bodily properties. Wilhelm Wundt, who is one of the initiators of social psychology, finds in an attempt to defend it the proper words for a rejection of the metaphysical soul concept (which otherwise he is not so ready to decline):

For whatever one may think about the necessity of postulating a transcendental substance as the carrier of what we call the psychic life, it is certain that in experience we never encounter such a thing; and that, where one perhaps thought differently about this, the assumption of a soul substance proved to be an unnecessary metaphysical ornament or led to consequences which are doubtful, if not directly contradictory to experience.

Sharing this point of view, which corresponds exactly to Mach's dissociation of the ego concept, we, indeed, have no reason to reject expressions such as "soul of a nation," which fill a similar need for convenient formulations and show the characteristic type of prescientific or early-scientific conceptual constructs. As far as applicability and usefulness are concerned, the difference between the concepts of the individual soul and of the soul of a people is at most one of degree.

On the other hand, we do not, of course, claim that there are facts of social psychology that would be in contradiction to observations on single individuals or could not be interpreted as phenomena traceable to single individuals. Only incomplete observations which do not take into account the presence or absence of mutual interference could suggest a contradiction. Experiments are more difficult to carry out with masses; here one must rely more upon the observation of phenomena that occur without the researcher's interference. The relation between individual and group psychology is hardly different from that of elementary and structural psychology. It is very narrow-minded to accept only some of these fields as justifiable and to reject the others. One may study trees, leaves of trees, and woods; each of these approaches is meaningful in its place; each supplements the others, and each becomes harmful if used outside of its proper range (see Chapter 22, 5).

*The collective concepts in the field of social psychology, which have come into use more and more in historical studies, are instructive examples of useful, early-scientific constructs. They serve, along with the analogous concepts of individual psychology, for the global description of historical processess; they will gradually be replaced by a more direct description of relations between regularly recurrent phenomena as detailed research progresses within more limited fields.*

### CHAPTER 19

# psychology and biology

1. *Experimental Psychology.* Not even those who count psychology among the humanities, and claim that a special kind of "understanding" is needed for it, will deny that its aim is the search for regularities, i.e., for uniformly recurring parts of phenomena. For this "understanding," as we noticed previously (Chapter 18, 6), can only be in some way a subsumption of the new under the already known, and hence a determination of the elements that repeat themselves. If, therefore, in this context we connect one part of psychology with the historical sciences and another, with biology, we cannot see the difference between the two parts in their method, but must find it in the subject matter. As we mentioned before, one part treats larger, more comprehensive, and less analyzed complexes of phenomena, such as the psychological reaction of a man toward a specific political event. The other section deals, e.g., with the detailed description of a specific sensation of pain, produced by a certain physical process, its localization, and reproductivity, etc. In Chapter 18, 5 it was pointed out that this "elementary" psychology may perhaps represent a more advanced stage in the general evolution of science, without being fundamentally different from "life" psychology. We can find another characteristic feature of the two groups of phenomena, by applying the customary concept of "intelligence." The parts of psychology closer to the historical sciences treat primarily those aspects of human behavior which are related to reasoning power and intelligence. This is, of course, not supposed to mean that there is a sharp dividing line between human thought and all other psychological functions—a notion advanced primarily by those who wish to build a wall between the human and the animal psyches. Phenomena of emotional behavior that lie on the border or even across the border of "intelligent behavior" also interfere very strongly with history. But for a short characterization of the different objectives which are treated in one or the other section of psychology, the catchword "intelligence" may perhaps be expedient.

Certain studies in the extreme wing of "elementary" psychology, often considered as the closest to natural science, became fashionable four or five decades ago and at that time were established as a separate science under the name "experimental psychology." The opposition that these "secessionistic" endeavors soon encountered was not quite unjustified, for they rested in  part upon an atomization of the questions treated and, in part, upon an overvaluation of the very primitive experimental methods used. The purely superficial imitation of the appearance of physical experiments (including a naïve application of more or less primitive statistics) could not lead to any decisive success. The value of any experiment is always determined by the theory guiding it. The development gained a certain practical importance in the direction of industrial psychology. There is no doubt that the fitness of an individual for a job which consists of the continual carrying out of a specifically limited semimechanical work, such as that of a truck driver, can be determined beforehand by properly chosen tests. But the narrow limitations of this method are immediately apparent; the several forms of the "Ausdruckswissenschaft," mentioned in Chapter 16, whose accomplishments represent a much deeper problem of psychology, seem to be of greater promise.

Since we consider psychology in all its parts, like any other science, as resting upon experience and observation, the distinction between an experimental and a theoretical psychology can for us have only organizational but not logical significance. Other classifications and definitions of psychology, which are based either upon a nonempirical point of view (e.g., Kant: The metaphysics of thinking nature is called psychology) or upon the one-sided emphasis on specific doctrines (associational and apperceptual psychology, voluntarism, etc.) may be neglected for the purposes of this book.

*That part of psychology which deals with sharply isolated single phenomena of psychic life can be considered as a branch of biology; it is not fundamentally different from the psychology which is counted among the humanities and whose subject matter comprises the more complex phenomena usually summarized as effects of "intelligence." What in recent decades has been called "experimental psychology" and developed mainly toward industrial applications represents only a comparatively small sector of elementary psychology and, disconnected from theory, can only be of little benefit.*

2. *Psychophysics.* It is not our task to discuss here individual problems of psychology, even though they may be of high general or "philosophic" interest. We are concerned only with the status of psychology and its relation to other sciences, and hence mainly with its boundary areas. Let us then speak first about so-called psychophysics; then we shall discuss the modern "physicalistic" conception of psychology, and finally the still con-

troversial psychoanalysis. Questions in connection with the holistic concept of *Gestalt* psychology will be considered in Chapter 22.

Vague ideas about the application of physical methods of measurement and hence of mathematical notions to the study of psychological phenomena go back rather far in intellectual history. Johann Friedrich Herbart (1822), among others, stressed the possibility and necessity of such an application. But the idea did not become concrete until the psychologist E. H. Weber (1795–1878) formulated a precise question: Within a series of uniform sensations (e.g., gradually increasing sensations of touch), how does the intensity of the sensation depend upon the strength of the external stimulus? The results that Weber found and that later were supplemented by the philosopher Theodor Fechner culminated in the well-known theorem that sensations increase in proportion to the logarithm of the stimulus, or that sensations increase in an arithmetic progression as the stimuli increase in a geometric one. In this or slightly modified form the Weber-Fechner law can be found in almost all textbooks and it is still almost the only concrete result of experimental psychophysics.

But how can sensations be measured at all? Only a very superficial inspection could lead one to believe that the degrees of temperature shown by a thermometer are a measure of heat impressions. On the contrary, they measure, in the sense of the Weber-Fechner law, the strength of the external stimulus. The actual observations follow this scheme: If the present stimulus strength (such as the temperature) amounts to $S$ units, and if it is increased by the slight increment $\Delta S$, the increase is felt only after this increment $\Delta S$ has reached a value proportional to $S$, say $cS$ (where $c$ is a constant factor, characteristic of the area of phenomena in question). Now, in so far as this fact is sufficiently well established, one may take as the measure of sensation intensity the *number of these passages* that were observed from the start. Beginning with the stimulus strength $S = 1$ and calling the corresponding sensation intensity $E = 1$, the first noticeable increase in stimulus is $c \times 1 = c$, and the stimulus strength $(1 + c)$ corresponds therefore to the sensation intensity 2. At this stage, according to the proposed law, an increment of stimulus $c(1 + c)$ is necessary, such that the new stimulus value $S = 1 + c + c(1 + c) = (1 + c)^2$ is required for the new sensation intensity $E = 3$. It continues in this fashion, and to successive stimuli of the magnitudes 1, $(1 + c)$, $(1 + c)^2$, $(1 + c)^3$, . . . there corresponds the sequence of sensation intensities 1,2,3,4, . . . These are the arithmetic and geometric progressions which the Weber-Fechner law mentions. How it is possible to derive from these progressions the existence of a logarithmic relation may remain undiscussed here.

When this argument is applied to the sensation of pressure caused by small weights at some spot on the human body, it seems obvious that the stimulus strength $S$ has to be measured by the size of the weights. But what is to be taken for $S$ if one is concerned with temperature sensations? If the law is correct for the centigrade scale, it cannot be true for the Fahrenheit scale at the same time, nor for the absolute temperature scale, and vice versa. The Weber-Fechner law describes nothing definite at all as long as one does not state in what system of physical units the stimulus strength is to be measured. The case of temperature, where various scales are customary, shows clearly what holds in every case. For it is by no means self-evident or logically necessary that the strength of a pressure stimulus should be measured by the number of grams which the pressure-causing body weighs; one could as well choose the square of this number, or its logarithm. With the last choice, the result would be that the stimulus and sensation strengths are proportional to each other—if the Weber-Fechner law is correct for the customary method of measurement. Recently it has been shown by experiments that in *many cases,* for that method of measurement which suggests itself most immediately, the simple proportionality holds, and not the logarithmic law. But since a theory cannot very well be based upon concepts such as "most immediately suggested" or "least arbitrary," it is clear that one is still far away from an acceptable theoretical foundation. So long as one does not explicitly state for every area of sensation what system of units is to be used for measuring the stimuli, the Weber-Fechner law does not provide us with a criterion for the evaluation of sensations. The entire question may be comparatively unimportant for the factual content of psychology, but it shows in a particularly instructive manner how easy it is to go astray if one uses mathematical concepts without the necessary critique, i.e., without paying any attention to the "connectibility" of the expressions applied.

*The Weber-Fechner theory, which attempts to introduce a measure for sensation intensity and a specific relation between stimulus and sensation strength, is not "connectible" with the basic concepts upon which physical measurements rest. Without specification of what in each individual case has to be chosen as the physical measure of the stimulus strength, the Weber-Fechner law has no content whatsoever.*

3. *Physicalism.* We now turn to a question of more general epistemological import in asking what distinguishes the subject matter of psychology from other observable phenomena, especially physical ones. We do not intend, however, to go over the entire multitude of previous theses about the relation between the physical and the psychic, or, as one says, between body and soul. In Chapter 7 the conception of body and soul as substances has been discussed in connection with Mach's doctrine of elements. Claims of the complete "incomparability" or "incommensurability" of body and soul, or of the transcendental nature of the soul and

earthly nature of the body, etc., are, in our opinion, just as empty as the contrary propositions of the complete identity of both kinds of phenomena, etc. In our view, meaningful, i.e., connectible, statements here are only those which either serve for the description of observable matters of fact and hence can be counted among the propositions of the respective positive sciences, psychology, physiology, physics, etc.; or they are statements about science itself, which are called epistemological and belong to the logic of science or of knowledge. For the moment we are concerned only with propositions of the second type.

A decisive thesis of this kind is the basic assumption of logical behaviorism, which we state here in Carnap's formulation as follows: Every situation in psychology can be expressed in the language of physics. This means that even those phenomena which in ordinary language are called psychological can be described by means of a system of linguistic rules which is based upon the simplest protocol sentences (Chapter 8) and usually serves for the exposition of "bodily" physics. One may, for instance, treat the observation of an affect in another person (not that of the observer). Is, then, we ask, the proposition "A is angry" dissolvable into a sequence of sentences which describe the visible and audible behavior of A as well as the momentary state of his organs, his heart condition, events in his brain, occurrences in his central nervous system, etc.? According to Carnap this is indeed the case. We know that in the sentence "This beam possesses great strength" the word "strength" (and the entire expression) represents only a short substitution for the description of a more or less exactly determined behavior, a decription which, if carried out, would contain only assertions about sensually observable events. So, according to the above thesis, the expression "angry" plays only the role of such an expedient and practically indispensable substitution for a description of the same kind whose details are not at hand. Common sense would have it differently, and holds that in addition to everything sensually observable about the person A there is still something specific, so to speak a *qualitas occulta,* which is called the affection of anger.

Carnap discussed four typical objections to the thesis of physicalism. The first one points out that we admittedly do not as yet have the requisite physiological knowledge to indicate exactly the physical correlates to the state of affection called "anger." But it is not different when we speak of the strength of a beam without knowing all the structural properties of matter which determine strength. However, we do not doubt that "there exist" such properties, and above all, our assertion indicates only a matter of fact which can be described without this detailed knowledge. Two further objections, which are easily deflated, consist in the assertion that we can acquire knowledge of the emotional status of a foreign person A by other means than direct observation, e.g., by oral affirmation from A or else by a kind of telepathic transmission; but in both cases the evaluation of the proposition "*A* is angry" remains independent of the way in which the knowledge was gained.

The only objection that seems to be more difficult to refute is that the analogy between the physical and the foreign-psychological situation breaks down in so far as the latter can be related to an occurrence in one's own ego. The statement "I am angry" or "I feel anger," whose possibility is obviously one of the foundations on which the analogous judgment about the person *A* rests, has the character of an elementary or protocol sentence and there is nothing analogous to it in the proposition about the beam. Among the "control sentences" constituting the statement "*A* is angry" one has to list this one: "*A* behaves audibly and visibly as I do when I feel 'anger.' " It seems indeed to be a decisive point that there exists a specific extensive group of element sentences—originating in self-observation (introspection, Chapter 7, 6)—which are incorporated into the system of psychological language (or psychological theories), but are missing in the language of physics. If some of the American behaviorists go so far as to deny the scientific value of any introspection (Watson), we cannot agree with them in principle. We think that the subject matter of psychology, entirely within the framework of the empirical conception of science, can be characterized by the fact that in its structure enter element statements of a specific kind which play no role in physics, and which may be summarized in the expression "self-observation" or "introspection."

*The thesis of logical behaviorism according to which every psychological statement (just like a physical one) can be dissolved or translated into assertions about observable facts can be accepted with the reservation that in psychology the stock of basic elements (element statements) has to be supplemented by the results of self-observation.*

4. *Psychoanalysis.* On the border line between psychology and psychopathology stands psychoanalysis, a creation of Sigmund Freud (1856–1939). It comprises a scientific theory of a specific area of psychological phenomena and a technique, derived from the theory, for the treatment of certain illnesses. We are here interested only in the theory, and particularly in its logical aspect. It states essentially that a complete description of the present psychological situation and the ensuing psychological (and physical) occurrences in an individual requires taking into consideration the totality of his previous experiences, which for the greater part have receded into the unconscious. The effective content of the unconscious is primarily formed by "repressions" which originate in most cases in the conflict between sexual drives and external circumstances. By making the repressed experiences conscious again, they may be deprived in part of their harmful influence.

Nobody will deny that every experience leaves in the experiencing subject, in Bleuler's language, an "engram," which may remain latent for a long time and become effective again later on. That does not constitute a contrast between living and dead matter, to which modern physics also assigns a kind of a memory. The older assumption of occurrences without any aftereffects in the area of physics has always been an artificially simplifying abstraction. In the field of mechanics of solids, for instance, we find the phenomenon of "forgetting and remembering": there are deformation processes which under certain circumstances occur independently of past strains and under other circumstances are influenced by them quite decisively (so-called strain hardening). There is also no reason not to admit that the psychic engram implies a continuous process which remains unnoticed. The assumption of such internal processes, which, although "existing," are inaccessible to normal introspection, does not present a logical difficulty; the situation here is no different from that of the "existence" of objects that we do not see because we have our back turned toward them. Finally, it must not be assumed that a sharp boundary exists between the conscious and the unconscious. Even the most sincere person will often not be able to tell whether a motive that determined his action was conscious to him or not.

The schema of a psychoanalytic explanation may be illustrated by the following little example of a so-called Freudian slip. A lady, speaking of kitchen utensils, by a slip of the tongue, instead of "pans" says "pants." The context shows that in an earlier phase of the conversation she had repressed the word "pants" in an enumeration of pieces of clothing, out of bashfulness. This repression, whose connection with sexual feelings is obvious, caused the slip of the tongue. The place of such an incidental slip can in other cases be taken by a continual, serious neurotic symptom, whose "cause" is recognized to be a repressed childhood experience of a sexual nature; by making conscious the engrams which are fixed in the unconscious, psychoanalysts can often make the symptoms disappear. Another example is that of the psychoanalytic dream interpretation: freed from the inhibitions of the waking state, repressed remainders of experiences often assert themselves during sleep in the form of dream images, such that a psychiatrist may draw conclusions from the dream content upon existing engrams and can take this as a starting point for making the underlying experience conscious again and thus bring about a curing of the pathological symptoms.

The extremely vigorous objections raised in many circles to the acceptance of the psychoanalytic theory are in large part of a nonlogical nature and are based upon the intense wish to retain older, more habitual and more favored, "idealistic" notions about psychological processes. There can be no doubt, however, about factual agreement with many observations, and hence about a certain practical usefulness of the theory. But the Freudian doctrine shares with any new theory that by its subject matter is apt to penetrate into nonscientific circles the tendency to spread far beyond the boundaries of the field in which it is applicable. The vagueness of its propositions and the dubiousness of its concepts are here no greater than those in other branches of science in an analogous state of development.

Possibly, from a logical point of view, the objection could be raised that, instead of the concept of strict causality, a statistical relation should be applied to the interdependencies indicated by psychoanalysis—perhaps in the sense that persons under the influence of certain engrams are *more inclined* toward certain Freudian slips, nervous symptoms, and dream pictures than others who are free of them, just as a die that has been tampered with shows more sixes on the average than an unbiased one. The entire field of phenomena like dream images, slips, etc., seems much more similar to the type of recurrent events (Chapter 14, 1) with which the calculus of probability is concerned, than to that type of physical events which led to the concept of causality (Chapter 13). It is a reasonable conjecture that psychoanalytic theory would have received a more correct form, modified in this sense, if at the time of its creation the deterministic conception of all natural occurrences had not been so absolutely predominant in science and if, instead, the concept of the collective as discussed in Chapter 14, 3 had been generally better known.

*Psychoanalysis comprises the scientific theory of a specific area of psychological occurrences: on the grounds of uncontestable observations it constructs a causal connection between certain symptoms and the latent remainders of earlier experiences. Almost all objections raised against it so far are of an extralogical nature. But it seems justified to point out that the totality of the observations in this field seems to correspond more to the assumption of a statistical than of a strictly causal correlation.*

5. *Vitalism.* Every attempt to find the right place of biology within the natural sciences usually starts with the question whether or not biological phenomena can be explained entirely as "physicochemical processes." Generally an answer to this question in the positive is regarded as an indication of a materialistic or positivistic (antimetaphysical) conception of science, while the position of the opposing side, which speaks of specific "vital forces," of the autonomy of the phenomena of life, of vitalism, etc., is considered as metaphysical, or at least as antiempiricist. A closer inspection will show that here words and expressions are used which cannot be assigned a clear meaning.

What can be meant by the assertion that a phenomenon is explained by physicochemical theories? Physics, including chemistry, consists of a system of propositions that serve in a specific manner for the description of certain classes of observable phenomena. The inductive method, discussed in detail in the third Part of this book, allows us to establish tautological statements (axioms), from which conclusions are drawn by deduction. In the face of a new complex of facts we can ask whether the sentences needed for the description of newly observed phenomena are also deducible from the *previous stock of axioms* established for the various partial fields of physics. One will, of course, only require that the *general* axioms (axioms in the narrower sense) be taken from the previous set, and will not deny the free choice of the always necessary additional axioms (Chapter 12, 2) within the range that is left open by the general theory. That is to say, in a more concrete but a little too narrow form: One may ask whether the description of new phenomena follows from the old system of differential equations if suitable assumptions are made about the still-undetermined functions occurring in the equations and about the boundary conditions. If this question is asked regarding any biological process, it must at present undoubtedly be answered in the negative. Contemporary physics consists essentially of what can be found in present-day textbooks of physics. If a physicist or chemist claims that, within the framework of contemporary theories and without the introduction of decisive new assumptions, the origin of life can be described in the same manner as, for example, the working of television, this is an unproved and unfounded assertion. In any case, the empirical conception of science that we represent is by no means based upon such a thesis.

Until a few decades ago, the question was asked time and again whether electric and magnetic phenomena could be "explained mechanically." Several attempts were made to formulate asumptions in agreement with the general axioms of mechanics in such a way that from the system thus supplemented the desired conclusions could be drawn. In the meantime, the new area of experience was expanded more and more, independently of any hypothsis of this kind. Today we know that electricity and magnetism are a more comprehensive field than mechanics and one is more inclined to classify the mechanical phenomena as a partial field of a sufficiently general theory of electricity. A quite similar relation may exist between the biological processes and those which today are called physicochemical. The theoretical foundation for a deeper understanding of the phenomena of life is now in its beginning—"theoretical biology," which is at present so successful, is mainly concerned with this—and nobody can venture to predict in what form it will be possible to assimilate and to reconcile physical and biological theories. But on the path one must follow toward that goal there is no point where one would have to leave the area of empirical science and enter a field of metaphysics or transempirical speculation. Even if eventually it should prove useful to introduce a theoretical auxiliary concept for which the word "vital force" may be suitable, those who think that biology will then be definitely taken out of the range of positive science are still wrong. The electron, although it is not derived from the principles of Newtonian mechanics, is nothing metaphysical.

A similar view toward the question of the relation between physics and biology is presented by Philipp Frank in his book on causality. Some new notions, primarily those of the physicist Pascual Jordan, which relate the explanation of life phenomena to the ideas of quantum mechanics, seem still much too vague to be subject to a critical examination. The stock of experience, too, is still very small; we neither know very much about what to think of the so-called biological catalysts (enzymes, hormones, vitamins, etc.), nor whether we have to regard, for instance, virus particles as the smallest living beings. At this stage of experience one had better forget about establishing general theories.

We need not discuss here incidental attempts to *prove* that the phenomena of life *cannot* be explained by physics or chemistry; it is impossible to state anything about the totality of all possible future theories. (We mentioned certain misconceptions of Driesch in Chapter 16, 6.)

*The relation between biological processes and those which are covered by the contemporary physical and chemical theories corresponds somewhat to the one that existed in the last century between electrical phenomena and classical mechanics. Nobody can predict in what form the two fields of research, which are clearly distinct today, will some day be reconciled with one another. In no case is it a thesis of the empirical conception of science to anticipate one or another form of solution.*

6. *The Evolution of Biology.* The history of biology contains many points of interest in the logic of science. The beginnings of biological research lie in part in the choice of words of everyday language for the denotation of various kinds of animals and plants. The nomenclature, connected with a certain assumption of power and rule, presupposed an immense range of accumulated experiences, a kind of unconscious formation of theories whose importance must not be underestimated. This was the starting point for the attempts at systematization and classification which until the nineteenth century formed the almost exclusive subject matter of so-called natural history, so that the latter could still be called by W. Whewell, in his *History of the Inductive Sciences,* the "classifying science." The transition to the use of a specific scientific language (terminology), of which we spoke in the first Part (Chapter 4, 4), was performed by the great reformer Linnaeus. It was not long after him that, with Lamarck, Cuvier, Geoffroy Saint-Hilaire, and others, natural history reached the stage of conscious formation of theories.

Another starting point in the evolution of biological knowledge was provided by the need for the conservation and care of the human individual, the rearing of the rising generation, and the cure of the sick. The arts of magicians and sorcerers represent one of the oldest forms of positive science. The compulsion to reach immediately practical, useful results as fast as possible forced people to skip many of the troublesome intermediate steps—which, to this day, have not been completely gone through. Out of this situation, after the oldest period of magic, grew the religious systems that anticipated complete solutions of many biological problems, particularly those which resulted from community life, and claimed for them the prerogative of definiteness (Chapter 27, 5). These solutions remained predominant in this field longer than in astronomy, physics, etc. It is sufficiently well known to what extent theological views retarded the progress of the biological sciences, to mention only one instance, by prohibiting experimental research on corpses. On the other hand, there was the indubitable advantage of a uniform convention, accepted by a large group of men, which at least for some time eliminated from discussion certain questions too difficult to be attacked in a rational way.

We know of no absolute criterion which would allow us to say that physics is "more advanced" in *a practical sense* today than any part of biology. But a great many people may agree today that it would be "more important" to solve a certain biological problem, e.g., to find an effective weapon in the fight against cancer, than to achieve new progress, for instance, in the technique of color television. The interdependence of the various branches of scientific work is difficult to discern, but it is clear that in the first place those phenomena were treated which could be more easily isolated from others and from the observing individual (compare the early development of astronomy). Moreover, nobody knows what progress in chemistry, for example, is still necessary in order to make the next decisive step in biology possible. The relative development of the several disciplines is certainly not in all points determined by the logic of science and, in the long run, may also be influenced by planning and organization. But if one goes as far as the biologist A. Carrel did in his widely read book *Man, the Unknown,* and demands a forcible reorganization of the entire work of scientific research for the sake of certain biological problems, this means disregarding crucial epistemological facts. In the demand to forsake "counting, measuring, and weighing" for a comprehensive theory of life, somehow the fashionable tendencies of negativism (Chapter 5) and "holistic philosophy" (Chapter 22) reveal themselves.

The observation that wide ranges of phenomena can rarely be explained by simple statements, consisting of a few generally understandable words, has been found true to a large extent particularly in biology. The popular slogans in the field of the theory of descent, of race theory, of heredity, etc., which are used by everybody, present only a distorted picture of the known facts. An immense amount of diligent detail work, based for the most part upon physicochemical studies, is required in order to clear up the factual situation, and the results can almost never be formulated in the primitive way required for popular consumption.

*The slower development of theoretical biology as compared with physics and chemistry can be explained by the specific nature of the subject matter—its closer relation to human life, the urge for immediate practical results, retardations due to organized prejudices. The mutual relation of progress in the various positive sciences is in large measure determined factually by the logic of science and can be influenced by planning and organization to a limited extent only.*

7. *Genetics.* The part of theoretical biology that has found the widest interest and which, on the other hand, is still subject to continual debate on factual and epistemological grounds is the theory of descent. It rests upon a combination and assimilation of two originally incoherent chains of observations: on the one hand, the gradual variation in the appearance and ways of life of different kinds of plants and animals was recognized; on the other hand, the strong similarity and apparent constancy within lines of the same kind perpetuated by natural reproduction were observed. It is easily understandable that the second of these observations was the older one, which more readily suggested itself and was in the beginning the only one striking the eye. Accordingly the *stability of the species* was dogmatized in the oldest and primitive biological theories which found expression in most systems of religion. Linnaeus still accepted this point of view without any reservations. So much greater was the intellectual courage shown by Darwin when in 1859 he advanced in all clearness the conjecture that the presently existing animal species have evolved in the course of extremely long periods of time by natural reproduction from a few, more uniform types. This proposition became a challenge to empirical research in the field of biology, which has been occupied with it until the present day.

Darwin's doctrine contained, in addition, a second proposition which really accounted for his great popularity, apparently because it was completely anthropomorphic and touched upon the actual interests of society. Darwin thought that the variations brought about by natural reproduction occur at first completely at random, but in the long run only those forms can survive that have proved their worth in life, i.e., in the so-called *struggle for existence.* This principle of selection forms the Darwinian theory in the narrower sense. Other evolutionary doctrines emphasize more the progressive adaptation of the living beings to environmental conditions (Lamarckism) or the analogy between the evolution of the species and the evolution of the individual from the embryo to his full bodily development (the basic biogenetic law of Haeckel). All of these special claims, in so far as they are clearly formulated at all, go far beyond what at the present time is covered by observations; the only thing one can state as a certain result of all previous studies is that the factual situation cannot be comprehended in such a simple formula. What one has to think of philosophical systems that are founded upon such formulas is obvious.

The real research in this field, which today is called "genetics," poses for itself the task of studying the phenomena of heredity, at first within one species. Its foundation is provided by Mendel's law, which was derived from observations and has been tested successfully in innumerable experiments of various kinds. This law consists of a *statistical* proposition about the heredity of certain marks. According to Mendel, there corresponds to every hereditary property a unit, which today is called a "gene." In the simplest case, the genes are present in two different forms, which may be denoted by $A$ and $a,$ and every individual possesses some combination of the two forms, either $A$ and $A,$ or $A$ and $a,$ or, finally, $a$ and $a.$ In reproduction, the individual transmits *one* of the two forms it contains to its offspring in such a way that the probability of transmission is the same for either type, namely, one half. From this it follows, for example, that from the coupling of the type $AA$ with the type $Aa,$ in the long run about one half of the descendants will belong to the type $AA$ and the other half to $Aa,$ while from the coupling of $AA$ with $aa,$ only $Aa$'s can result, and so on. This simple rule, which, as we mentioned, expresses not a causal relation in the older sense, but rather a statistical one, plays in genetics a role comparable to that of Newton's laws in mechanics. But it is a long way from Mendelism to an explanation of the origin of species.

This way is likely to pass through a closer study of *mutations,* a phenomenon discovered by H. de Vries, consisting of discontinuous changes in heredity that occur under special circumstances. It was not until recent times that it was possible to discern a connection between Mendel's theory and the facts of mutation. But it can be said that further progress requires, in addition to the continuation and deepening of experimental investigations, the construction of a system of exact concepts which would make it possible to develop a deductive theory paralleling the observations. The unreasonably heated discussion between so-called Lysenkoists (named after a Russian geneticist, Lysenko) and the classical school of thought is indicative of the early stage of theoretical development. Fundamentals of a logical approach are in the process of creation and well-known scientists are studying questions such as those of an exact definition of species, of acquired properties, etc. It seems that genetics is at present in a stage in which at least some parts are being transformed into tautological (axiomatic) systems and thus attain a certain structural similarity to the exact parts of natural science. This has as little to do with so-called physicalism or a "mechanistic" conception of the phenomena of life as with an abandonment of rational explanations within the framework of empirical natural science.

*The theory of descent presents biological science with a task that it attempts to fulfill by diligent and complicated experimental investigations. Mendel's law, verified by all observations, offers a basic statistical proposition about the facts of heredity. Further progress will most likely be connected with a precise delineation of the concepts involved and with the construction of axiomatic systems in the sense of the exact natural sciences. The short popular formulas and slogans and the philosophical and political generalizations based upon them are of no significance in this structure.*

CHAPTER *20*

# social sciences

1. *Characteristics.* In the "system of the sciences," whose construction was a favorite topic with epistemologists of the past (Chapter 17, 7), the social sciences are usually assigned an extreme place. In a scheme that is more or less governed by positivistic ideas, they take the highest rank among the sciences. This is true particularly in the system of Comte, who regarded sociology as the acme of all scientific endeavors of man. Opposed to this view is the idealistic notion of science as it is still represented at many a German university, where even now the "intrusion" of the positive sciences upon the terrain of the university is regretted; they mean by this the social sciences imported from England and France, which, owing to the lack of the dignity of age and a fully developed method, really should not be called "science" at all.

As far as we relativists are concerned, there is no such "above" and "below," and neither is there a bestowal or a withholding of the title "science." We are not looking for a rigorous definition of what "really" or "justifiably" may be called social *science.* Its subject matter—corresponding to the core of meaning of the customary linguistic usage (Chapter 3, 2)—consists essentially of the phenomena connected with the community life of people. Whether observations on ant or bee societies are to be included in a textbook on human social relations does not need previous agreements or conventions. The line of demarkation with respect to what are called technical or engineering sciences is uncertain and can be determined only by the special aim of an exposition and other organizational points of view; some of the border-line problems in this area (human engineering, etc.) are today attaining a growing importance. The close relations to the subject matter of the historical sciences, political as well as cultural history, are immediately apparent.

From the point of view of the logic of science we cannot assign the social sciences any other position than that of any other discipline. As in any field, one starts here with observations, enlarges them to general hypotheses, and finally seeks to build a tautological system that operates with exact definitions and logical deductions. In this respect, some branches of the social sciences, for example, economics in the narrower sense, are today perhaps more advanced than biology. This has nothing to do with the question of application of mathematical tools in the deductions, nor has it to do with the fact that in sociology, as a rule, only observations and not experiments are feasible. Astronomy does not experiment either, and in geology one surely does not use more mathematics than in economics. Those who like such expressions, which were once fashionable, may call the social sciences with the same justification the logic, the geometry, or the natural history of social phenomena.

This first orientation in the area of social sciences must not tacitly pass over a fact that is of decisive importance for the present state of our literature, and hence for the state of our knowledge in this field. To a much higher degree than in any other area of facts, almost all propositions here are influenced by subjective views, determined by the wishful thinking and the emotional life of the author. (Examples could easily be given.) In general, it is quite apparent that the idea of inducing or preventing a change in one's own environment by what one says, influences, more or less, almost every scientist; this thought determines at least the form, and often also the content, of his exposition. We shall return in the following sections to these and other considerations which we have only touched upon so far, and wish to summarize for the time being:

*The social sciences treat a special sphere of phenomena of great variety; the path of every science, from single observations, through generalizations and vaguely formulated hypotheses, to tautological (deductive) systems, has to be traversed. Neither the practical impossibility of experiments in the narrower sense nor the comparatively limited application of mathematical methods is a specific feature of this field; but such a distinctive mark is given by the stronger connection of the object of research with the area of personal interest and emotional life of the scientist.*

2. *Natural Science, Normative Science.* It was mentioned in Chapter 17, 2 that the idea of the "autarchy of the humanistic sciences" and of contrasting them with the natural sciences has found many followers among economists. We may mention as an extreme representative of this position Othmar Spann, who describes the attempts at dealing with social problems by the methods of natural science in the following way:

Naturalistic sociology reads the individual letters separately, by themselves, as isolated realities, instead of understanding them as members of their totality, of language, of a song, etc. That is why . . . materialistic sociology has until today remained but a science which collects material and which . . . is blind to everything great and essential.

Werner Sombart, too, who in his book *Die drei Nationalökonomien* distinguishes among an evaluating, an ordering, and an understanding economy, believes that only the third is real science; the second, which apparently corresponds to the empirical conception of science, is rejected as totally unsatisfactory. We have commented previously on this relation between the natural and humanistic sciences touched upon here and on the supposedly peculiar kind of "understanding" in the latter (Chapter 17, 7 and Chapter 18, 6). With Sombart the concept of understanding receives yet a special color by the claim of absoluteness and finality. We shall return in Chapter 22 to the concept of "the whole" which plays such an important role for Spann. We merely add here that the classical economists such as Quesnay, Adam Smith, Ricardo, and others, by no means took the position that their field of research stands in fundamental contrast to the endeavors of the natural sciences. Quesnay started from biology, and Adam Smith is quite strongly oriented toward the scientific ideal of geometry, in which there is no question of a mystical "understanding" but only of a clear, simple conceptual structure, useful for the description of a multitude of observable phenomena; his propagator in France, J. B. Say, emphasized particularly the parallelism of Smith's theory to Newtonian physics.

The widest space in all discussions of the method of social sciences is taken by the question whether it is their task to state what *is* or to state what *ought to be;* in other words, whether they are *factual* sciences or *normative* sciences. Often the mere fact that this question can be raised here while it is not asked in any field of the natural sciences gives rise to the claim of a basic contrast between the two. However the physical theorems, e.g., in the theory of strength of materials, lead to prescriptions as to how a bridge *ought* to be built, and the biological theorems in the science of medicine indicate what procedure a sick man *has* to follow if he wants to get well. If somebody sketches the utopian picture of an economic state of the future, he does not act differently from the physicist who calculates the dimensions of a rocket to fly to the moon. The difference is of a practical and not of a logical kind. Unprejudiced considerations lead us to the following view.

One usually regards as the content of a positive science statements that assert something about *relations among phenomena.* Such a statement can be given the form: As soon as there is *A,* there is *B.* This may in suitable cases be replaced by the sentence: If *B* is desired, one has to see to it that *A* occurs. Thus far there is no difficulty. But it happens that in the second formulation the premise "If *B* is desired" is left out, *either* because the author takes it for granted that the reader accepts the aim as a matter of course, *or* because the author derives from his own point of view explicitly or implicitly a specific set of desirable aims. The first is, as a rule, the case in the field of natural science: The beam that is intended for this load *must* have this cross section . . . (*because* it is desired that it should not break), but sometimes also in sociology: Child labor in factories *ought* to be limited . . . (*because* it is desired that children should not be harmed). An example of the second approach is given by an author whose desires include some situation that depends upon the conservation of a free economy, and who asserts: The government *must* under no circumstances support private enterprise by subventions. Misunderstanding necessarily always occurs when between the author and the reader there is no complete agreement on what is assumed as desirable. It is only the unavoidable *incompleteness of the exposition* that creates the difference between a factual and a normative science (for more details, see Chapter 26, 2).

*The classification of sociology as one of the "autarchic" humanities is to be judged by the general criteria earlier specified (Chapter 17, 18); we shall return later (Part VII) to its being placed among the normative sciences, a view which rests upon a specific incompleteness in the exposition of the results.*

3. *Classical Economics.* That part of the social sciences which was the earliest to be subjected to systematic study and first took the form of a scientific doctrine is economics. It is mainly concerned with the organizational institutions which in civilized societies serve for the production and the distribution of goods. Its beginning—disregarding the prescientific period—dates back to the school of the physiocrats about the middle of the eighteenth century. Of course, at first the treatment of scientific questions was not strictly kept apart from the pursuit of practical economic work or the direct influence upon organizational (political) decisions, just as the physician and the biologist were originally one and the same person. The skeptical remark of Cournot, according to which economists did not exert upon the development of economic institutions any more influence than grammarians did upon the development of language, was probably never quite correct. The structural relation between theory and practice may here be similar to that in technology, except that perhaps in economics the gap is wider between the recognition of a connection among certain phenomena and the application of this knowledge to cases occurring in practice.

The physiocrats, of whom we have mentioned Quesnay previously, taught, strongly bound by theological and also naturalistic prejudices, that the produce of the soil *alone* is decisive for the national economy, and they called those working in handicrafts, industry, and trade the "sterile class." Adam Smith, a contemporary and friend of Hume, and recognized as the founder of the science of economics, regarded the *work* done by individuals from the point of view of division of labor as the source of the wealth of nations. He considered all the economic institutions of a well-functioning country (mainly England) as a natural organism which conserves itself by means of its innate regulator; the latter consists of sound egotism under the influence of which every individual acts. The theory of spontaneity of the economy and the doctrine of the necessary and sufficient function of egotism has been maintained in various forms until today. Even more lasting was the thesis that only a free international exchange of goods could develop the natural wealth. Ricardo, who is considered the man who added the finishing touch to the classical school, studied the distribution of wealth and analyzed particularly the foundation of the workless income; in his method he is the most abstract of the classicists. His contemporary Sismondi represents the start of the critical school, which gradually widened the narrow frame of purely economic considerations in the direction of more general sociological questions.

What interests us here is only an examination of the classical economic theories from the point of view of the logic of science. We will not be expected to accept the claim that a proposition such as the "iron law of wages" (stated by the physiocrats and later explicitly emphasized by Malthus and Riccardo) is an "eternal" truth, after not finding any "eternal truths" in Euclidean geometry, or in Newtonian physics, even in its present modified form. But, after all, the old Newtonian mechanics still provides us today with an excellent means for the systematic description of almost all mechanical phenomena, and in the few cases in which deviations were observed they are quantitatively very small. It can scarcely be said that the situation is similar in the case of any statement of theoretical economics. To say the least, the compatibility of many observed phenomena with basic theorems, such as the assertion of complete self-regulation of an economy through personal egotism, is unproved. Moreover, there exist competing theories, above all those of socialism (which, at least in the case of Marx, are presented explicitly as further development of the classical doctrines), e.g., the thesis of the accumulation and final concentration of capital in one hand; and these newer theories also claim for themselves to be practically correct, if not even eternally valid, laws of economics.

The statements of economics, even when they take the form of general theorems, are at best comparable to propositions in natural science of the following types: all bodies heavier than air fall to the ground, unless they are supported; chemical elements cannot be transformed into one another; the average life expectancy of human beings cannot be lengthened beyond 120 years. The first of these three sentences could not be pronounced by anybody in the last forty years without making (openly or tacitly) a reservation with respect to the possibility of aviation; the second was taken until recent times as one of the unshakable foundations of chemistry but is now in the stage of losing its validity; as to the third one, there are hardly any indications at present that it can be refuted. All three of these examples are statements about reality which originated in observation and experience and which are subject to check by future observations. In no area of facts, including economics, can a sentence that is not a tautology mean more. The most vigorous defense of a position, the use of the greatest ingenuity, and the strongest threats of power cannot change this state of affairs.

It is not our task to weigh the claims of the opposing economic theories against each other. Our point is to make clear that here—excepting the above-mentioned interference of extrascientific influences—we do not face a situation different from that prevailing in any other area of facts; mental reconstructions of observed facts must be tested to determine how far their consequences agree with continued observations. The linguistic basis of all existing theories is certainly still so insufficient that a satisfactory examination of their assertions by observation presents the greatest difficulties; but we know that the transition to a more exact scientific language is not independent of the widening of experience and the progress of knowledge. The attempt to anticipate results of factual research by dialectic means, such as, e.g., that of Gottl (*Das Wort in der Nationalökonomie*), cannot lead to any success.

*The very general theorems of classical economics and their elaboration up to the present time are statements about reality which in large part are mutually contradictory. Testing by observation has so far not led to a satisfactory clarification, i.e., to a commonly recognized decision; this state of affairs is reflected in the shortcomings of terminology, etc. In no case can future experiences be anticipated by asserting statements about reality in the form of "eternal laws."*

4. *Marginal Utility and Mathematical Theory.* Disregarding the propositions of most general character, with respect to which an early clarification is hardly to be expected, and directing one's attention to more specific problems which are usually treated in contemporary economics, one will readily find promising beginnings of tautologically constructed theories. The best known among them is the doctrine that has emerged from the investigations of H. H. Gossen (1854), the so-called theory of "marginal utility" or "utilité finale," at present mainly represented by the "Austrian school" and by American economists. Its basic question is this: How does an individual economic subject evaluate a specific kind of goods? According to what criterion does he determine the (subjective) price of the unit of goods in question? The answer is that the *least* utility which the subject under the given circumstances actually draws from the available quantity of those goods determines the price. If, e.g., a farmer has enough

potatoes to satisfy his own demand and that of his family, so that a further amount can only serve for forage, rational management requires that, in buying more potatoes, he pay only the price corresponding to forage. The economic rank of goods is determined by the rank of the *least* valued use that the goods actually find, the so-called *marginal utility*.

Discussions about the "correctness," "admissibility," "significance," logical position, etc., of this thesis and the conclusions drawn from it take considerable space in the theoretical literature of economics. On the whole we agree with the careful analysis that Felix Kaufmann gave in his *Methodenlehre der Socialwissenschaft,* which in many respects stands on the grounds of the empiricist conception of science. Kaufmann points out the tautological elements contained in the statement (which among other things *defines* the concept of rational management), but he does not misjudge the role which the proposition plays as a vague statement about reality. It is of primary importance to realize that such a theory can at most describe one side of a most diversified reality and that exaggerated claims that it contains the true "solution of *the* economic problem" must lead to disappointment.

Connected to a certain extent with the ideas of the theory of marginal utility is the question of application of mathematical methods in economics. It is not worth while to examine the arguments of those who claim that such an application is contrary to the "essence" of economics and to the "non-measurability" of its objectives, etc. One might reply that then any use of multiplication and any addition and substraction of prices would also be inadmissible. In fact, the mathematical methods, whether on the highest or the lowest level, play only the role of unassailable logical conclusions from premises that originally (before translation into the tautological language) do not belong to mathematics, but rather to the particular factual area. The importance and the dependability of the results of the mathematical considerations are determined solely by the adequacy of the basic (factual) assumptions. Accordingly, the "belief in the logical miracle of creating knowledge from nothing" (expression of F. Kaufmann), shared by some advocates of mathematical economics, has no point.

In various groups of problems in economics, mathematical means have been tried out. They were perhaps most successful in the study of such relations as those among amount of production, satisfaction of demand, price policy, and wages. The system of linear equations which express these relations is based upon greatly simplified assumptions, but it does not seem that they therefore lose all practical value. So-called "mathematical economics" or "econometrics," which was founded by A. A. Cournot and developed further by Jevons, Leon Walras, Marshall, Pareto, and others, puts its aims much higher. It introduces, for instance, concepts such as specific costs of production, specific utility, etc. as differential quotients; then the purpose of economic activity may be formulated as a problem of the calculus of variation whose technical treatment supplies a system of equations that superficially resembles the starting point of a field of classical physics. It cannot be said that this procedure, which is governed by the desire to imitate the *forms* of mathematical physics, has had great success so far.

An entirely new idea was recently introduced by John von Neumann and O. Morgenstern. They define an "element" of economic behavior in the form of a game between two persons which depends partly on chance and partly on anticipation of what the other party will do. It seems that this starting point is superior to the older conception, which sees economic action as entirely governed by some extremum principle. It remains to be seen whether it will be possible to build up from such "elements" a theory of complicated economic processes, as, say, the theory of mechanical phenomena was developed on the basis of Newton's laws of particle mechanics.

*By postponing questions of a too general and vague kind, promising starting points for a rational treatment of economic problems were found rather early in the theory of marginal value and related mathematical investigations, and more recently in von Neumann's theory of certain types of "economic games."*

5. *Sociology.* The possibility of reaching more precise results by a more limited formulation of questions should never lead us to ignore the wider area of problems. Auguste Comte may well be considered the creator of a general concept of social science that has not only the economic activities of human societies as its subject. Sociology in this sense (whose first beginnings can be traced back to classical antiquity), however, is so wide in range and so undetermined in its aims that one can scarcely speak of a real construction of theories in this field. This is also true of the successful French school of thought which, in continuation of Comte's principles, was founded by Emile Durkheim at the end of the nineteenth century. We may make a few remarks as to general methodology.

Sociology has one root in the search for regularly recurring patterns in the development of human society, and another root in the observation of the functioning of present-day social institutions. A strict distinction from history would be possible only if the latter were limited to the role of purely chronologic recording, a concept that has its own logical difficulties, as was shown in Chapter 8. A thesis, for example, that has to be considered as sociological is that of the materialistic conception of history: the actions of men and the ideas upon which they are based are, at any time within a society, essentially determined by the actually prevalent and the preceding economic and social conditions. Despite all the vagueness of the expressions occurring in it, this sentence is connectible with the linguistic rules of ordinary language and can be taken as a statement about reality; in other words, whether the assertion is "true," i.e., whether it adequately accounts for the observable facts, depends only to a minor extent upon the still free interpretation of the expressions contained in it. At any rate, neither the acceptance nor the rejection of this thesis (or of any other factual sociological proposition) is anticipated by the empiristic conception of science.

Such an explicit reservation does not seem to be quite superfluous, even in view of the exposition of *Empirical Sociology* by Otto Neurath, who represents the same epistemologic point of view as our book. Neurath emphasizes particularly that sociologic propositions have meaning only in so far as they can be verified in the observable behavior of concrete groups of people. The doctrine of scientific sociology comprises sentences that describe the relations among various elements of human behavior and their relations to other physical elements (material conditions of life, etc.). The recognition of the mutual dependence of such elements forms the basis of social prognoses, or of the supplementation of partially given facts by thought. The extreme physicalistic thesis of Neurath, according to which human modes of behavior, as spaciotemporal occurrences, can always be described by means of a terminology that contains no other expressions than those accepted in physics, can be accepted by us only with the reservation explained in Chapter 18, 4. We believe that there is a class of element sentences, arrived at by introspection, which are expressions of our own drives and which, without belonging to the language stock of physics, form a part of the description of foreign-psychological phenomena.

We also agree with Neurath that sociology cannot be kept apart from history and that the Marx-Engels so-called materialistic conception of history represents a first long-range attempt to establish a relationship at large between the economic conditions of a class of people and other historical phenomena. But Neurath perhaps does not point out clearly enough that propositions which are contrary to Marx's and Engels' are, from the point of view of the logic of science, equally admissible. The statement, for example: "Large masses of people, when presented with certain doctrines in a specific manner often enough, act continually *against* their economic interests" may actually be false, but that can only be determined by experience and not by logical analysis. An examination, from the point of view of logical empiricism, may deny to a sentence the attribute of connectibility, but then the same is true for the opposite statement. If, e.g., it can meaningfully be asserted that the average behavior of people can be prognosticated without paying any special attention to the factor "great man," the opposite proposition can be empirically false, but not meaningless. One can, however, hardly believe that our present historical experience is sufficient to allow a decision on such a factual question.

A modern trend in sociological (and also in psychological) research, particularly striking with American scientists, tries to break up all problems into separate statistical investigations, search for correlations, etc. There is the firm belief that questions like that of the influence of economic conditions upon married life, or of personal social habits upon the occurrence of certain mental diseases, etc., can be completely cleared up by way of questionnaires plus scoring of attributes plus mathematical formulas. Often enough these formulas belong to the deceptive "small-sample theories" which pretend to provide reliable results from any restricted number of observations. But even if the latter is not the case, extremely little can be achieved by such mechanized means. Any real progress in sociology, as in all branches of science, depends on a creative theoretical idea, or, in other terms, on a step toward the foundation of a tautological system. While checking of a theory by observations is a legitimate part of scientific research, experiments without an underlying theory, or at least an idea anticipating a theory, are almost worthless. The much-spoken-of Kinsey report would be an insignificant accumulation of figures if these could not be interpreted in the light of psychoanalytic (or other psychological) theories.

*The recurring patterns in the behavior of groups of people, beyond the area of the purely economic, form the subject matter of general sociology. Since its range of experience consists in part of occurrences of the past, sociology cannot be separated from history. Considering the primitive stage of this still young science it often proves difficult to distinguish between a critique of its factual assertions and a logical analysis of its basic concepts. In no case can substantial results be achieved by a mechanized statistical inquiry that is not guided by a theoretical idea.*

6. *Demography.* A group of problems which today may be considered as a part of sociology but whose treatment goes back much farther in history, forms the subject of so-called *demography,* sometimes also known as "social physics" or often simply as statistics. It started in England in the seventeenth century, the first mortality table having been published by the astronomer Halley in 1693. In 1741 there appeared a German book by J. Peter Süssmilch, *The Divine Order in the Changes of Human Generations, Proved from their Birth, Death, and Reproduction,* a work whose title alone shows how much it stands at the *beginning* of a scientific development. For a long time, the relative stability of certain statistical numbers, such as the annual death rate within a specific age group, was, indeed, regarded as a very remarkable or even "miraculous" fact. All possible attempts were made to reconcile the near constancy of the yearly number, say of suicides, with the traditional doctrines of free will, of divine institutions, or of predestination. It was not until the *Physique Sociale* by A. Quetelet (1835) that the "homme moyen" became a quite rational conception.

Meanwhile, the greatest interest was focused upon the questions of population increase after T. R. Malthus related it to problems of economics. In his *Essay on the Principle of Population* (1798) he made two quantitative assertions, the first of which is trivial: at a constant rate of growth, the population increases in a geometric progression. The second has a very weak foundation in experience: the amount of means of subsistence increases in an arithmetic progression. But it is not the quantitative in Malthus's doctrine that became important; rather it is the fact that here, for the first time, the task of controlling the increase of population was recognized as a vital problem that had to be solved by men. The extensive arguments about the Malthus theory, which were strongly interlaced by nonobjective and nonfactual considerations, quieted down only after it had turned out that the development in the civilized countries led to quite different situations from those predicted by Malthus. Both the birth rate and the death rate have for decades in all civilized countries been continually on the decline, and at least for the latter one may hardly expect a considerable increase again.

To operate, in fact, with constant growth rates, constant death rates, etc., is a highly primitive procedure, a first approach based on superficial experience and hardly reconcilable with a scientific conception of the problem. All we can conclude from the observations is that the ratios (e.g., the number of yearly deaths divided by the number of the total population) *change more slowly* than the absolute numbers (of the deaths themselves). But nowhere in the history of civilized nations do we know of a period of several decades or even centuries in which every one of these ratios did not undergo considerable change in one direction or the other. It is only the study of these changes, their interconnections, and their dependence upon other observable phenomena that can be the real task of demography. Particularly, it is to be expected that the rate of growth of the earth's population will in the long run converge toward zero; for otherwise the population would grow to infinity. It will also hardly be considered desirable that the state of zero increase should be bound up with possibly *high* death and birth rates. However, in what way and to what extent men will some day know how to control their life spans cannot be predicted at the present. On the other hand, almost all exact demographic studies up to now have been limited to a small section of the inhabited earth and are based upon the assumption that certain cultural and political contrasts and interactions between so-called civilized and uncivilized peoples will always remain the same. But it can hardly be doubted that within a space of time of the dimensions of historical processes all of these conditions will experience *fundamental changes* and that all predictions on the grounds of statistical observations of the past may become obsolete. Some of the biologically determined data, such as the sex ratio of the newborn or the longer life expectancy of women, may perhaps form an exception. But even here the possibility of changes through artificial influence can by no means be neglected.

The reservations against the applicability of statistics in the long-range view are valid not only for demography or social physics in the narrower sense, but to an even higher degree for all the doctrines of an economic, financial, and political kind that are based upon the apparently exact foundation of social statistics. All such systems often neglect the fact that their subject matter belongs to the time standards of historical and not of biological processes (Chapter 18, 1) and that therefore every one of their claims has to be limited by a strong *clausula rebus sic stantibus*. Predictions about the course of present or future economic processes, however good the underlying statistical material may be (dating back to the time of classical economics or to a later period), have only a very limited range of application.

*The statistical study of population movements and other social phenomena shows the relative stability, or better, the slow changeability of certain ratios and hence allows statistical predictions for the near future. The disregard of these limits, which are particularly narrow in economic questions, and of the possible alteration of all premises leads frequently to erroneous sociological conclusions.*

7. *Incidental Questions.* Since the production of goods belongs to the most important social institutions, the whole of technology could be included in a sufficiently wide framework of the social sciences. But one often hears of a contrast between the technical and the economic points of view and this opposition has led in the past not only to a sort of class rivalry between engineers and economists, but also to the construction of entire philosophical systems such as that of "technocracy." The so-called technocrats try, among other things, to subordinate economic concepts to technical, or rather, physicochemical notions and think in particular that the theory of energetics provides a rational foundation for the settlement of all economic questions. Behind this search for an "objective valuation" of economic goods and other ideas of technocracy and related trends lie certain problems of the logic of science which we wish to touch upon briefly here.

In the first place, it is easy to see that physics cannot provide a yardstick for the measurement of human labor of different kinds on a uniform scale. The work of the miner in the pit, of the workman who assembles a machine, of the engineer at his drawing table, cannot be expressed as a multiple of some physical "unit of labor." Still more problematical is the "measurability of want," i.e., the attempt to reach an objective scale of economic values from the side of the customer. The economist thinks he has an appropriate system of valuation at his disposal which is more or less precisely expressed in the monetary price. He is particularly proud of having in the institution of capital interest a possibility of comparison between present and future goods (Böhm-Bawerk's theory of capital interest). One must not think, however, that in this manner an objective evaluation, independent of accidentally existing circumstances, is made possible in all cases. In order, e.g., to decide whether in a certain case transportation by railroad or by truck is in the customary sense more "economical," one has to decide first what part of the costs of building and upkeep of the roads is to be charged to the truck traffic (which depends upon more or less arbitrary decisions). In general, one would also have to know in advance how long a certain technical innovation will remain in use without being made obsolete by new inventions, and many other nonpredictable things. Any economic evaluation is valid only within a given or assumed state of technical and social institutions. It does not thereby become practically useless, but it must not be, as it often is, used to provide a standard for the evaluation of the very institutions on which it itself rests.

Older economics saw in the increase of "well-being," either of nations or of mankind, a sufficiently unambiguous aim of economic activity. Today we know how ambiguous this expression is and how many opposing conclusions can be drawn from the positing of such an aim, even if one could take for granted a yardstick for all material goods. One might perhaps try to reduce the concept of well-being to elements such as "enjoyment of life," "standard of living," etc. (O. Neurath). But who can judge to what extent, say, the construction of a beautiful city with wonderful public buildings heightens the "joy of life" of the inhabitants and thus becomes an equivalent for other, more material, goods? On the whole, we still lack sufficient experience about the interaction of physiological as well as psychological elements that contribute to "well-being," and therefore scientific statements are impossible. One might say that sociology is in this respect in the same situation as, for example, medicine was at the time when it was first recognized that there are "diseases"; the thousands of years of evolution which medicine has gone through since that stage cannot be anticipated by making assertions which are scientific *in their form*.

But even the sufficiently vague aim of well-being is far from being generally accepted. The following utterance is ascribed to Mohammed: The angel of God does not enter a house in which there is a plow; which is to say: He who takes advantage of all available material means for his life's work will not obtain true happiness. There are still today many representatives of this "social romanticism," the counterpart of technocracy, except that for them the plow, and farming as a whole, belong to the old and hence hallowed customs and it is only industry, factories, and modern means of transportation that are the works of the devil. To most people, that measure of technical conveniences seems just "right" and conducive to life which they came to know in their youth; everything that was added later they regard as harmful for the spiritual development of the individual. This way of feeling is surely biologically founded, but it does not suffice for a foundation of sociological theories. Incidentally, we may, perhaps, again point to the example of medical science; the reason for its progress is to be found to a large extent in the fact that people have gradually stopped asking questions about what health and disease "really are" and have turned to the systematic investigation of facts within narrower complexes of phenomena.

The opposition between technicians and economists stands in a certain relation to the presently most vigorous controversial economic-political question, i.e., the fight between the followers of *collectivistic* (socialistic) and *individualistic* (liberal) economics. The facts that in the provision of water individual wells were replaced by municipal water supply, and in the transmission of messages the individual courier, by a government mail service, are today regretted only by the most extreme representatives of individualism. But an analogous organizational concentration of trade or other economic institutions is opposed by appeal to the classical concept of "self-regulation by sound egotism" (Chapter 20, 3) and to the incomparable advantages of "competition." On the other hand, the idea that by the mere enunciation of collectivist principles and the start of a primitive apparatus that contradicts previous economic experiences all economic problems can be solved is extremely naïve. It may be predicted that in a later stage of development the entire controversy will be regarded as is, e.g., today the question whether all ailments are to be cured by cold or by hot water. This is by no means intended to depreciate the seriousness and the difficulty of the presently existing problems.

*Many problems of economics cannot be separated from the general problem sphere of the social sciences. In the latter the present situation is marked by the fact that the previous accumulation of experience is altogether insufficient to provide a basis for valid scientific theories. Almost all previous claims in the framework of general sociology go far beyond what is covered by observation and even stand in contradiction to it. One may agree with Auguste Comte when he said that in no area of science is as much to be expected from the future as in sociology.*

## PART VI

# metaphysics and art

Was der Philosoph für einen möglichen Anfang hält, winkt dem Natur-
forscher erst als das ferne Ende seiner Arbeit.

What the philosopher tries to begin with, appears to the scientist as the
distant goal of his work.

*Ernst Mach*

# we shall not cease to ask questions

1. *Three Differences.* Much of what is said in this book will rightly be regarded as in contrast and opposition to what it usually called metaphysics. Now, we do not share at all the opinion of dialectics, that opposites are identical, or, as Hegel expressed it, that being and nonbeing are really the same; the "unity in difference" is for us, to speak with O. F. Gruppe, "a synonym of abacadabra," but we believe that it furthers the clarification of a position if one pays explicit attention to its opponents. Moreover, metaphysical needs, the wish of men to see their lives ruled by nonrational lines of thought, plays an undeniable role in Western civilization. For this reason, if for no other, we have now to attempt to make our relation to metaphysics more precise than before. Many of the views from which the positivistic conception that we represent has developed are characterized as actually antimetaphysical; compared to this, our point of view may perhaps be regarded as rather compromising.

It is, of course, extraordinarily difficult to say anything precise about a phenomenon whose definition is subject to such far-reaching differences of opinion. It may well be claimed that every author who writes on metaphysics more or less changes its boundaries. We shall therefore begin by listing a few points in which our conceptions deviate in an indubitable manner from those of metaphysics, independently of how one prefers to define that concept in detail.

In the first place, we lay greatest stress upon *clarity* of expression, and we feel that this clarity is to a certain extent possible to attain. It was explained in Chapter 2 what we understand by clarity: we seek to use the words and phrases of everyday language, unless otherwise stated, only within their *core of meaning,* i.e., within the area in which there exists a somewhat unambiguous linguistic convention, and not in the zone of vagueness on the boundary of their meaning. To repeat the previously given simple example: we strive to call only *that* object "table" which the linguistic community, on the whole, calls by that name; in all boundary cases, we rather use paraphrases or state explicitly the deviation from the general linguistic usage. On the other hand, it seems to be characteristic of metaphysical writings (which in this point agree with poetry) that they tend to use linguistic expressions in a way that does not correspond to their usual meaning as essentially secured by previous linguistic usage. Such a way of speaking is sometimes called "symbolic" (Chapter 23, 3).

The second contrast we find is connected with the fundamental difference that obtains between us and the school philosophy in the conception of language. If the sign *"A"* stands for any word or expression, *we* mean that any statement that is to interpret *A* can be only one of two things: either it belongs to an explanation of linguistic usage, i.e., to a description (by means of other words) of the complex of experiences for whose designation *"A"* has been actually used within the linguistic community, or it forms a part of a system of definitions by which a new linguistic usage is proposed. The majority of explanations in metaphysics, however, take an intermediate position without attempting to separate these two elements or even recognizing the necessity for such a distinction (Chapter 2, 3). The belief that words such as "nature," "god," "force," or "causality" correspond to certain entities which are to be "discovered" rather than derived from the linguistic usage or arbitrarily (expediently) defined is metaphysical. On the other hand, the metaphysician makes a statement about, say, "nature" as though everybody were supposed to know beforehand exactly what he is referring to. An arbitrarily selected sentence from a principal metaphysical work (Schopenhauer) may serve as a short illustration (also for the previous point):

Nature does not err. Her pace is sure and she does not conceal it. Everything is entirely in her, and she is entirely in everything.

As a third characteristic that separates us from the metaphysicians we point to their *dualistic* conception of the world, which is expressed in their contrasting physics and metaphysics. We believe that about *everything* accessible to experience one can speak in basically the same manner, with the intention of clarity in the above-indicated sense. It is contrary to our point of view, which we shall elaborate in more detail, that there should be one part of the world which can be treated by the positive sciences, and another which, inaccesible to them, must forever be reserved for a different method of approach.

*In three respects our position seems, in any case, to be in opposition to metaphysics: in our demand for clear (and not symbolic) presentation; in our conception of language, which declines to overrate the significance of linguistic expressions; in our rejection of a "bifurcation" of the world, in which one part is reserved for the positive sciences, and the other for a purely speculative study.*

2. *The Common Aim.* To the third of the above-indicated points it could be objected that metaphysics does not deal with the "experienceable" at all, and hence does not separate a part of the world from the rest, but rather has quite different, so to speak, transmundane objectives. That, however, would be but a superficial misunderstanding. All metaphysicians make statements that in some way or other concern reality, the world of experience, and that often enough are intended even to produce changes in the world (via human actions).

It was Kant who undertook the most careful and most conscientious attempt at a definition of metaphysics. According to him only the *sources* of metaphysics lie beyond all experience:

. . . neither external experience, which is the source of physics, nor internal, which provides the basis of empirical psychology, will be her foundation. She is hence knowledge *a priori,* or from pure reason or pure understanding.

But Kant also leaves no doubt about *this:* "Real metaphysical statements are altogether synthetic." As we know, a proposition is called "synthetic" if it actually increases our knowledge, i.e., if it has not the character of a definition. Kant's typical example of a synthetic judgment is the sentence, "Some bodies are heavy"; and this statement is called synthetic because the property of being heavy does not belong to the concept of a body. Kant, at any rate, would not have agreed if any applicability of metaphysical propositions to the world of experience were denied.

One should, however, add that, precisely speaking, metaphysical statements that would satisfy Kant's rigorous requirements are not known. All Kant claims to have proved is the *possibility* of metaphysics, and this proof seems to him indispensible, precisely because the existence of metaphysics cannot be demonstrated directly:

One cannot produce a single book, in the way one would, for example, point to a Euclid, and say: that is metaphysics.

He challenges his contemporaries even "to show a single synthetic statement belonging to metaphysics" and he closes his *Prolegomena* with a "supplement concerning what can be done in order to make metaphysics possible as a science."

Whether Kant would have recognized any later metaphysical writing as genuine and adequate metaphysics that has "advanced metaphysics by one step" may remain in doubt; but it is certain that all metaphysicians claim to increase our knowledge by the content of their metaphysical writings. If, in order to inform ourselves about present metaphysics, we consult an average textbook of philosophy, we find that metaphysics is usually identified with "real" philosophy; logic, epistemology, and perhaps psychology, are only its border areas. Metaphysics is often subdivided into metaphysics of the absolute, whose objective it is to explore the world-reason or the absolute being, God, and a philosophy of the world, which comprises the philosophy of nature and of mind. The second part is to be understood as a general foundation of natural science on the one hand, of the humanities on the other, and a search for their immutable theorems and methods, which are prior to all experience, or as the recognition of the eternally valid elements common to all parts of knowledge. The process that should lead to these results is supposed to be either the dialectic method or the method of induction. The latter means that the transition from observations to general hypotheses and to tautological systems, as is usual in the positive sciences, is considered a metaphysical process, and it is claimed that in metaphysics, at least for the most part, the same thing is done. By the dialectic method one means essentially a discussion of the pros and cons of metaphysical theories, and, to say the best of it, an attempt to test the consistency of the tautological system of metaphysical statements. It is not important for us here to examine how far the actual writings of metaphysicians satisfy the earlier described logical and inductive methods (Parts III and IV); we are now interested only in the *aims* and the *problems* that metaphysics poses for itself, and we come to the conclusion:

*The aim that in the last analysis lies at the basis of metaphysics is fundamentally not different from what the sciences strive for: to create a mental reproduction of the world, to describe reality, and to reveal interconnections that are suitable for guiding human actions.*

3. *Lack of Connectibility*. To recognize a certain similarity of aims shared by metaphysics and the positive sciences is important to us for two reasons. It creates a platform for a clear and fruitful delineation between the two quite different points of view and at the same time it explains the historical fact of their continual close connection in the past. Remarks such as that metaphysics has nothing whatever to do with science, that it is the opposite, the negation, the denial of all science, do not conform to the actual situation, even though they may, in extreme cases of degenerated metaphysical formulations, be justifiable.

So-called "logical empiricism," to which, as we have pointed out repeatedly, the conceptions of this book are closely related, has found a simple and clear formulation for the position of metaphysics. According to this, statements that belong to science are either true or false; sentences of metaphysics, however, are neither true nor false, but "meaningless," i.e., they contradict the rules of logical syntax, are not verifiable, and cannot be constituted from a system of protocol sentences. How we stand toward this formulation is apparent from what was said in Part II, particularly in Chapter 6, and we shall summarize it here briefly.

We do not believe that it is possible to determine *from the start* the totality of logical rules that control the linguistic usage of science. Rather, the language of science develops *together* with its factual content and not independently of it; or even, its development is a part of the evolution of science itself. By an *essentially* new chapter of science, a new linguistic usage is created (not only in the sense of terminology, but also in that of logical grammar). We may refer here to our considerations in Part I of this book and to the statement by Condillac quoted there: "Science is but a well-constructed language." Thus it does not seem possible to us to classify newly introduced propositional systems in an absolute way according to whether or not they satisfy "the" rules of logical syntax, and to declare them accordingly to be meaningful or meaningless.

The essential part of the theses of logical empiricism, however, remains intact in our opinion, if the concept of satisfying the linguistic-logical rules is relativized. For example, we can find that a special chapter of theoretical physics, presented in a specific formulation, fulfills the linguistic rules that were adopted for physics and mathematics and also those rules that govern ordinary language and have not been explicitly or implicitly cancelled. Then we say that this exposition of physics is to the stated extent *connectible*. We recognize in the historical development of all scientific studies a tendency to extend gradually the connectibility (which at present, sometimes even within narrow fields, is still faulty) beyond the boundaries of special areas. In this sense we are in close agreement with the "movement for the unity of science," led by the logical empiricists.

Metaphysical writings are in our opinion characterized by the fact that they satisfy the requirement of connectibility not at all or only to a limited degree, or that they do not even admit the rightfulness of such a demand. This either totally precludes any possibilities of verification in experience or at least cuts down such opportunities considerably and reduces them to a more or less vague form. Most metaphysicians neglect the generally accepted logical rules of everyday language and those of the language of the exact sciences without either indicating or admitting it. Extreme metaphysical groups, such as the mystics of earlier centuries and, in our own time, the "existentialist" group of Heidegger, use a manner of speaking that is hardly connectible even within the narrow framework of their own works or that of their school. One may take as examples those given in Chapter 2, or the following of Heidegger's sentences:

There is nobody who is in the world, and there is nothing but the being-in-the-world, and that is a character—not an action of being.

But there exist at the same time various intermediate stages between the completely "autistic" behavior of these extremists and the behavior of the conscientious scientist who requires of his exposition that it be connectible with the totality of the previous results of research, and that it agree with all previously accepted pertinent linguistic rules.

*Metaphysical sentences are formally characterized by the fact that they are not connectible with an essential part of the rules of ordinary language and of the statements that form the content of science, i.e., they do not satisfy the rules of logical syntax adopted in these areas. In extreme cases there hardly exists connectibility even within an individual metaphysical work or within the school in question. The absence of connectibility results in restricting or sometimes totally precluding the possibility of any verification of the statements by observation.*

4. *Science in the Beginning Stage.* Our remarks, which are to serve as a description of metaphysical studies, admit of a supplementation that goes beyond the question of formal linguistic properties. We have emphasized (Section 2) that the aim of metaphysics is in a certain sense no other than that of science in general, namely, the attempt to describe in a systematically ordered manner the phenomena that comprise our world of experience. But within this framework a more precise determination of the position of metaphysics is possible and necessary.

We have to disregard the extreme cases for this purpose; Hegel's metaphysics admits no bounds at all, either of subject matter, or of method, or even of good taste. In his *Naturphilosophie* (*System der Philosophie,* second part) Hegel treats concrete questions of mechanics and physics, which two centuries before had found a satisfactory solution and one that is in part still valid, as though metaphysics had the last, decisive word to say in every field. As a little sample—with the same effect one could quote almost any other paragraph of the *Naturphilosophie*—the following discussion of Newton's derivation of Kepler's laws of the motion of planets may suffice:

Newton, instead of proving Kepler's laws, rather did the opposite; he wanted a reason for them and was contented with a poor one. The idea of the infinitely small is impressive in this proof, which rests upon the fact that Newton in the infinitely small treats all triangles as equal. But sine and cosine are not equal; if one then says that the two, taken as infinitely small quanta, are equal to one another, one can do anything with such a theorem. At night all cows are black. The quantum should vanish; but if one also disregards everything qualitative in this process, one can prove anything. On such a theorem rests the Newtonian proof; and that is why it is completely wrong.

At a later point the refraction of light at the boundary between air and water is explained by the difference in density of the two media and illustrated by the idea of the "heroic deed of a great man, as conceived by a small soul":

> Just as the viewed hero is effectively existing within me but only in an ideal manner, thus air takes in the optical space of water and dwarfs it into itself.

One may leave such hypertrophies of the metaphysical mind out of the picture, even though it must be noted that so far they have hardly been explicitly rejected by the authoritative representatives of metaphysics.

The majority of the metaphysical writers avoid touching upon questions to which the positive sciences give satisfactory answers accepted by a certain general consensus. The previously mentioned tendency (Chapter 16, 7) not only to take over apparently secure results of science, but even to exaggerate their validity beyond all justification and to claim eternal and dogmatic truth for them is, indeed, very prevalent. Accordingly, one should consider as the genuine domain of metaphysics only those problems which are not treated by science or at least have not yet been treated by it successfully. Such a distinction should find rather wide acceptance even on the part of metaphysicians.

But the difficulty is that there is no "subject of research" which would be independent of the kind of questions that the scientist asks. Living beings are the subject matter of zoölogy, biology, and sociology. Can they in the same sense also be the subject matter of metaphysics? If it were possible to delineate a specific complex of problems, a *direction* of research that is not represented by the existing sciences, this would determine a new positive science. Neither does it lead us any further if we think of the common basis of some or of all special fields; for even the questions pertinent to that are scientific ones and can be formulated in a nonmetaphysical way. The consistent follower of logical empiricism cannot help declaring that metaphysics asks "meaningless" questions about the complex of our experiences and is characterized just by this fact. If we relativize this proposition in the manner introduced by us, we approach the solution a little more closely.

For the demand for connectibility has a slightly different meaning according to whether it is intended for sentences, statements, and results of a theory or for the basic questions from which a new branch of science starts. Before anything in a field is known, the decisive linguistic rules and logical forms which should become valid in the area and which will fuse with the previously accepted formal systems into a wider system are also unknown. It cannot be avoided that new questions which go beyond the previously studied area of knowledge occur at first in a nonconnectible way. It is only after a complex of answers is given that connectibility can be demanded. Therefore, it appears that every science is in the beginning metaphysical, that a new science always *starts as metaphysics* and becomes "connectible" only gradually by assimilation and adaptation to the existing linguistic conventions. In our view, the metaphysical, unconnectible way of research is the prescientific stage, which precedes any disciplined research in the positive fields.

One will not expect that the boundaries of which we speak here are sharp and in every special case uniquely determined. A certain relation of our conception to Comte's theory of the historical development of science is apparent (Chapter 18, 3). At any rate, we are diametrically opposed to the often-encountered opinion that metaphysics is the "queen" of the sciences and that her statements are the "final wisdoms."

*Disregarding certain excesses of "natural philosophy" in the nineteenth century, metaphysics can be characterized as "science in its beginning." By asking questions that are still "unconnectible" one approaches problems whose clarification can be expected only by a further progress of science.*

5. *Antiquity and the Middle Ages.* If we try to demonstrate in the historical development of metaphysics the various aspects indicated above, the task is comparatively easy so far as the older epochs are concerned.

Why, along with Aristotle, do we still regard Thales of Miletus as the "forefather" of philosophy? The answer is, because he *searched* for a *scientific* (even in the modern sense) explanation for the origin of the world and the totality of the phenomena accessible to his observation. Undoubtedly, in the city of Miletus of the sixth century B.C., in which industry and oversea trade flourished, there must have existed a considerable stock of scientific (technical) knowledge that could be described in a way "connectible" with everyday language. The ideas of the natural philosophers, their questions and their answers, disregarded the connectibility. It was certainly not a verifiable statement to say that water or air or any other material is the original "cause" of all things, since it could surely not be formulated in correspondence with the customary linguistic concept of cause and effect that was created for the practical life of that time. But it is evident that in these intellectual endeavors lay the seeds of the later development of natural science.

It seems to be almost a platitude to say that the mystical number theories of the Pythagoreans, in spite of all their obscurity and the insignificance of their results, anticipated by two thousand years questions that only modern mathematics learned how to formulate correctly. A genuine metaphysical controversy was that between the theories of Heraclitus and of the Eleatics, who overstated the ideas usually connected with the word "becoming" in one case and "being" in the other. Here, for the first time, the striving for enlightenment of a group of men who were freed of the immediate wants of life collided with a linguistic structure that was not meant for such purposes and was exceedingly inapplicable to them. Since the later European national languages deviate in their logical grammar only slightly from that of Greek, almost all pseudo questions could be taken over, and until this very day it can be debated in every modern language, e.g., how it is possible to make a "true" statement about an "impossible thing" ("wooden iron does not exist"; the correct form of the statement reads simply: "wooden" and "iron" are the names of two incompatible qualities). At the same time, however, Zeno's paradox of motion (Achilles and the tortoise), originating in the struggle against Heraclitus, points toward a conceptual construct (of the continuum and its problems) that is fundamental for modern mathematics. Of course, we do not want to pass any "judgment" here, but only indicate relations between two different complexes of phenomena—the old metaphysics and modern science.

As a second example we mention the so-called "controversy about universals" which ran through the whole of medieval philosophy. There the question was whether the collectives denoted by general terms such as "man," "plant," etc., "really exist," whether their reality even "precedes" that of individuals, of a single man and a single plant, or whether, on the contrary, these universals are only names, words or abstractions, while actual existence is only a property of the individually determined particular thing. The followers of the first notion called themselves realists and fought on the side of the church against the nominalists, who represented a relatively more enlightened position. In a logically constructed language, such as any formal logistic system (Chapter 10), nothing of this controversy can even be formulated. We do not know (a) concepts and (b) existence of concepts. "Charles" is the name of a particular man, "Frenchman," the denotation of a specific group of men; a long description, which need not be given to those who are familiar with the language and the pertinent experiences, reduces either of these names to directly verifiable characteristics; there is no question of existence or reality, at least in the vague meaning of ordinary language. On the other hand, it must again be stressed that the efforts of the nominalists were the first groping steps in the field of logical syntax, the logic of language, and they raised questions which in our own days have been to a great extent clarified by Russell's theory of types (Chapter 10, 6).

*Two examples—the beginnings of Greek philosophy and the controversy over universals in the Middle Ages—illustrate characteristic aspects of metaphysics: the lack of connectibility in the original questions, and the anticipation of later scientific lines of thought.*

6. *Contemporary Metaphysics.* Present-day metaphysics as it stands its ground in our intellectual life in spite of the extension and deepening of all positive sciences, derives its justification from the allegation that science

as such is not sufficient to answer all questions worthy of interest and must be supported by extrascientific considerations. This point of view is often stated in a vague form, but frequently also with great precision—depending on the extent to which the author in question makes use of the vagueness of expression admitted in metaphysics. We quote a clear and, for our purposes, instructive utterance (1904) of Leonard Nelson, a follower of Kant, about Newton's law of gravitation:

> This law is not a principle, but a theorem; its validity could not be known *a priori;* it had to be verified by induction. For this induction, however, Newton had to *apply* certain general principles of mechanics. For example, he had to borrow from the principles of natural philosophy the assumption that all changes of motion are effects of continuously accelerating forces . . . But it could only be found from the empirically given shape of the orbits of the planets that the acceleration is inversely proportional to the square of the distances of the effective masses.

Here a sharp contrast is constructed between two kinds of physical statements. The law of gravitation belongs to empirical physics; the theorem that the second differential quotient (and not the first or the third) of the displacement vector is determined by the external circumstances of the motion is not supposed to be of empirical origin, but rather to be the result of metaphysical speculations. The complete arbitrariness of this proposition is obvious (see Chapter 12); the development of general epistemologic insight in recent decades probably cut such a view short.

The philosopher Edmund Husserl, who gives his metaphysical standpoint a much less clear foundation, has created with his "phenomenology" the most elaborate speculative system of the present time (see Chapter 2, 6). According to Husserl, the source of all true knowledge is the "pure stream of experience" (Erlebnisstrom), which stands in intimate relation to the experiencing subject and is apprehended by the latter "neutrally" in its "immediate givenness." The things are "open horizons of possibilities," and every psychic act has an "intentional character." The decisive act is that of "Wesensschau," or "insight into the essence" by which the transtemporal, objective essences are intuitively conceived by pure apprehension, so that a complete congruence between the "given and the meant" results. The purely phenomenologic description, with strict avoidance of all deduction, leads to judgments of eidetic generality and necessity and is the *philosophia prima,* which must precede logic and psychology, mathematics and physics, and any positive science at all. We do not believe that the application of this phenomenologic vocabulary can replace any part of the investigations based upon a careful and sober critique of language, as this book recommends them for all areas. If one wants to grasp intuitively or by "Wesensschau" the "essence of the imaginary" and lets the square root of minus one play however small a role in this process, he places himself in the category of one who associates the concept of a dipper with the constellation of the same name; on the other hand, a *"Wesensschau"* without attention to what is customarily meant by "imaginary" is not thinkable.

In his last work Husserl explained in detail what role he claims for phenomenology as compared to the positive sciences. According to him, the latter, and particularly the physical sciences and mathematics, have at present lost the sense they had in their historical beginnings and it is the task of philosophy

to emphasize the original conceptions, i.e., the prescientific and extrascientific universe, which comprehends all of the actual life, including the life of scientific thought, and feeds it as the source of ingenious concepts.

Husserl speaks of the "emptying of all meaning in mathematical natural science through technicalization," of the "world of life as the forgotten sense foundation of science," etc. Naturally, he clings to the *a priori* character and the apodictic validity of "pure" mathematics, rejects a confusion of "real" axioms with definitions, and limits the range of applicability of empirical research to "applied" mathematics, i.e., the mathematical natural sciences. But the essential point is the emphasis upon the necessity of a support of science by metaphysics, the conviction, reportedly also Kant's,

that the objective-scientific method rests upon a never-investigated, deeply hidden, subjective reason, whose philosophical elucidation alone illuminates the true meaning of the accomplishments of positive science and, correlatively, the true meaning of being of the objective world—as a transcendentally subjective one.

*Contemporary metaphysics often claims to provide an indispensable supplement to the present-day stage of the positive sciences. We reply to this that, wherever science shows gaps and a need for further and deeper elucidation, this elucidation cannot be reached in any other way than that of scientific research, and as soon as it is attained, it will form another part of the positive sciences.*

7. *Questions and Answers.* It is an indubitable and often-stressed fact that metaphysics, however frequently it is pronounced dead, at least in the countries of Western civilization, continues to exist in ever-new though little-changed form, and always finds followers. If one examines this fact and tries to find out to what it is due, in the last analysis one encounters the statement which is always given as an answer by metaphysicians when they are attacked, and which was taken as the heading of

this chapter: *Men will never cease to ask questions.* The positivistic conception which this book represents is not taken aback by this, but replies: *We shall never cease to do research* in order to find answers, that is, connectible answers to the questions raised.

Our opposition to metaphysics, indeed, does not consist in our not recognizing problems as such or wanting to prohibit questions—as is often claimed; we emphasize much more strongly than is otherwise done the incompleteness and the fragmentary character of all scientific knowledge and we do not see any end to questions. However, the mere putting of an interrogation before an arbitrary sequence of words and a question mark after it does not make a question; e.g.: "Is there not behind the phenomena that we observe, in addition to the thing in itself, something else, something lighter, more ethereal, a certain something that does not have any properties of a thing in itself?"

It is a well-known statement that a question must be "correctly" posed in order to be answerable. It is often repeated that scientific success is frequently due only to the fact that the scientist formulated a question in the right form. In Wittgenstein's *Tractatus* one finds in the most extreme form:

> If a question can be put at all, then it can also be answered . . . The riddle does not exist.

We have indicated several times our reservations with respect to this absolutism, which is represented by some of the "logical empiricists." In our view it is unavoidable that questions, in whatever field, are posed *at first* naïvely, unconnectibly, and receive only gradually, with the progress of our knowledge, a clarified form. From the child's question, "Who laid the first egg?" develops the problem of the origin of life on earth, about which biologists today have a little more to say than fifty years ago. It is an oft-repeated, but *incorrect,* assertion, which does not agree with our experience, that in such matters we "do not come nearer by a single step, in spite of all science," to answering the original question.

The situation is not very different with respect to the questions that represent genuine metaphysics, such as: Why do we live? Why is there pain? etc. The great metaphysical and, we may add, religious systems start from questions of this kind. From the point of view of the logic of science it must be said that a causal question (Chapter 13) requires that the phenomenon may be considered as an event in a series of repeated cases in which the phenomenon can occur or not occur; beyond that to ask for cause and effect has no meaning. (Why does the wire glow? Because it was heated. That is to say: If under specific constant circumstances the observation is repeated, heating and glowing always occur together. See Chapter 13.) In the question of the reason for our existence there can be no thought of such a series of observations in which the particular consequence does or does not happen; hence the question is unconnectible with the linguistic usage adopted in science and in practical life. The answer, "Because it is God's will" may very well be given formally, but it settles the question only in so far as the rule is added: Why something is God's will *must* not be asked. *It is not positivism that prohibits questions, but rather metaphysics.*

We by no means take the position that everything that is customarily asserted in connection with the so-called reason for existence is to be rejected as nonsensical or meaningless. To posit that problem stems from the same thirst for enlightenment that once led men to ask the (just as unconnectible) question, Why does the night follow the day and the day follow the night? For centuries this problem too had no other solution than the simple answer: Because the gods have made things that way. The question of the reason for the existence of human life, as it is usually understood, is in a certain sense an eminently practical one. For the complex of statements that is given as an answer in the widest sense contains a great many rules of conduct for individuals and whole populations (Chapter 27, 5). We believe that these rules, just like the state of the solar system, can form the subject of a scientific enquiry, and that the continuation of research in this (psychological and sociological) area will eventually disentangle the metaphysical thicket.

There is no field that will *always* remain the special province of metaphysics and into which scientific research can never carry any light; there are no "eternally unexplorable" areas. But neither do we claim that some day metaphysics will disappear altogether; previous development shows no indications to substantiate such a prediction. Men will (perhaps) never cease to cultivate metaphysical, i.e., unconnectible, doctrines, just as they will (perhaps) never cease to write by hand, in spite of the existence of the typewriter and the press. But it is not the understandable survival of the old activities, but the significance, the development, and the range of the new that characterizes progressing time.—Also, there are men on the earth at one and the same time who are thousands of years apart.

*Metaphysical and religious systems, originating in the desire for theoretical enlightenment and for practical rules of action, are primitive, because unconnectible, attempts at the solution of problems that are not yet treated by science. It may well be that such attempts in new or old forms will continue forever; but their range of influence is continually reduced by the progress of science, which extends a system of mutually connectible areas of knowledge over an ever-growing part of the domain of human interest.*

### CHAPTER 22

# a priori and the whole

1. *The Aim of the A Priori.* Two concepts which play an important role in all discussions of metaphysics, one of them rather ancient and the other of recent date, will give occasion here for some further remarks.

"A priori" has meant since Leibnitz knowledge that is independent of experience. But it was not until Kant, particularly through his *Critique of Pure Reason,* that this concept was brought into the center of all speculative philosophy. In the first edition of the *Critique* he says:

> General cognitions which at the same time have the character of inner necessity must be independent of experience and clear and certain by themselves; hence they are called knowledge a priori, while, in contrast, that which is merely borrowed from experience is, as it is expressed, only recognized a posteriori or empirically.

Later Kant commented on this explanation in the following way:

> If we have a proposition which contains the idea of necessity in its very conception, it is a judgment a priori . . . If a judgment carries with it strict and absolute universality, i.e., admits of no possible exception, it is not derived from experience, but is valid absolutely a priori.

As the simplest example of judgments a priori Kant mentions "analytic" judgments (Chapter 2, 2). Since it belongs to the concept of a body to be extended, the sentence, "The body is extended" is analytic, valid independently of all experience, and hence an a priori statement. Another example is the proposition that every change must have a cause; for

> In the latter case, indeed, the conception of a cause so plainly involves the conception of a necessity of connection with an effect, and of strict universality of the law that . . .

The most general case, however, to which Kant and all later authors return time and again, is that of the mathematical statements. The proposition that two times three equals six is true necessarily and generally, an exception is unthinkable, and a test in experience would make no sense;

here in mathematics one has therefore a large, almost inexhaustible class of a priori valid propositions.

Our view toward this notion has been explained in detail in the second and third Parts of this book. There are sentences that are tautological, i.e., that either express immediate linguistic conventions or are transformations of such conventions by means of specific adopted rules. Sentences of the first kind are: "Every primitive sound has a specific pitch," and "A monochrome object is not at the same time blue and red." An example of the second kind is: "In every triangle of Euclidean geometry the sum of the angles is 180 degrees." All of these statements are valid within a fixed linguistic usage, in which, e.g., a primitive sound is defined as one that corresponds to a simple harmonic oscillation, and "Euclidean geometry" stands as an abbreviation for a certain system of axioms. In this frame of reference it may be said, indeed, that the three propositions quoted are "apodictic" and necessarily valid; if it is preferred, they may also be called a priori (instead of tautological). None of these sentences states anything about observable facts. The question, for example, whether to a given material triangle the Euclidean axioms are (more or less approximately) applicable, hence whether the theorem of the sum of the angles holds, cannot be decided save empirically.

Kant's opinion, and that of his followers, is completely different. According to their conception, the axioms and all theorems of Euclidean geometry are apodictically certain statements about reality, and a geometry other than Euclidean seems to them unthinkable (Chapter 9, 5). The attempt to demonstrate that there are synthetic judgments a priori, i.e., apodictically true statements, not derived from experience, about observable facts forms the main content of Kant's epistemology. It may be asked, Why does Kant put so much weight upon this detail? Why does he make it the hinge of the entire theory? The answer to this becomes clear if one considers the purpose that Kant had in mind in the creation of his system. The aim toward which his theory is directed and the problems for whose solution it was built are described by Kant as follows:

And just in this transcendental or supersensible sphere, where experience affords us neither instruction nor guidance, lie the investigations of *Reason*, which on account of their importance we consider far preferable to, and as having a far more elevated aim than, all that the understanding can achieve within the sphere of sensuous phenomena . . . These unavoidable problems of mere pure reason are *God, Freedom* (of will), and *Immortality*. The science which, with all its preliminaries, has for its especial object the solution of these problems, is called metaphysics.

Without any doubt, Kant and most of the representatives of school philosophy use the possibility of synthetic judgments a priori (even if the formulation is a little different later on) to support the construction of allegedly infallible metaphysical theories, which give unconnectible answers to unconnectible questions in such fields of our experience as have not yet been covered by science.

*The concept of the a priori, introduced, as it seems at first sight, for the purely logical purpose of distinction between statements of mathematics and those of natural science, becomes later the support of far-reaching metaphysical theories, which in this fashion are endowed with apodictic validity.*

2. *The Psychologic Basis.* The development of the a priori concept in post-Kantian philosophy does not show a uniform line, but on the whole the tendency to extend its range seems to prevail. Kant had put himself under severe restrictions; all he wanted to admit was that the *forms* in which experiences can be obtained are determinable a priori; among these forms are the pure conception of space and time, as well as the categories of pure reason, quantity, quality, relation, and modality. It is, however, not clear at all how on this basis the validity of a metaphysical statement such as "The world must have a first beginning" can be justified as a synthetic judgment a priori. But in Kant, compared to his successors, the great appreciation of clarity and soberness in thinking and the absence of any inclination toward mysticism have to be noted. Undoubtedly Kant was in his attitude a philosopher of the eighteenth-century Enlightenment; he was called the "Alleszertrümmerer" (the man who wrecks everything), since he attacked explicitly the kind of metaphysics which was borne by an unrestrained imagination. Herbart, who still shared Kant's disinclination toward unbridled speculation, was much more generous in his assumptions of "absolutely valid" prerequisites of experience.

The genuine Kantians moved in various directions. J. F. Fries, who seriously worked on a development and better foundation of Kant's theory in a scientific sense, attempted to justify the a priori by psychologic means, by a kind of analysis of the feeling of evidence—which is closest to our position. The so-called neo-Kantian school, led by H. Cohen, busied itself in outdoing Kant's notions, including the a priorism, by emphasizing the dogmatic side of the system, its architectural structure, its symmetries, and its pretended completeness and perfection. It did not help much that the neo-Kantian P. Natorp tried to reconcile the a priori with non-Euclidean geometry by conceding to the latter a certain "imaginability"; shortly afterward Einstein's theory of relativity made all of these concessions quite inadequate.

Much more pretentious and at the same time much more cautious is modern phenomenology (mentioned in the preceding chapter). Its founder, E. Husserl, finds that Kant "lacked the phenomenologically true concept of the a priori" and that he therefore could not achieve "the only possible aim of a strictly scientific critique of reason, namely, the aim to investigate the pure laws of essence" (Wesensgesetze). It is not clearly stated what the phenomenological a priori consists of, but Husserl explains once that the phenomenologists

recognize with full insight that the general self-evident propositions, as expressed in all axioms ($a + 1 = 1 + a$; or, a judgment cannot be colored) give to situations of eidetic intuition an explicative expression.

Apparently the formulation of tautologies is ascribed to the *"Wesensschau"* in which, according to the opinion (or should one say, terminology?) of the phenomenologists, all knowledge takes its origin. This kind of insight is reached by exclusion or, as they say, by "bracketing" of *all* reality and leads to a comprehension not of the immediately viewed object but of its pure essence and the "essential synthetic truths grounded in it." In spite of the sharp protest of Husserl, we agree with the criticism of Schlick, who cannot recognize in these words and everything that is added to them the description of a real psychological act. In fact, the phenomenologists have not as yet reached concrete conclusions which would show what kind of knowledge results from the *Wesensschau,* apart from tautologies of the above-quoted kind. Husserl has, it can be said, constructed a method of viewing things, but he has not seen anything with it.

Not every metaphysics rests *explicitly* upon a priori foundations. Schopenhauer, for instance, declares in strict contradiction to Kant that metaphysics originates in empirical sources of knowledge and that it therefore lacks the "kind of apodictic certainty which is possible alone through knowledge a priori." Nevertheless, he says, it reaches beyond all experience and supplies the "demonstration of a core of the phenomena distinct from the phenomena themselves." In our opinion, the theorems of natural science are never congruent, especially in their developed (theoretical or axiomaticized) form, with *immediate* results of experience. But we prefer to say that they necessarily remain *behind* experience, that they only reproduce artificially isolated features, and can, by further study, be better adapted to experience. As soon as one speaks of reaching *beyond* experience and of the disclosure of the *true* core, one appeals to the existence of extraempirical sources of knowledge.

In spite of all their many differences, such theories as Husserl's *"Wesensschau"* and Plato's "doctrine of ideas," Spinoza's "knowledge through apprehending insight," Kant's "a priori" and Schopenhauer's transempirical metaphysics, to mention only a few examples, are things of a similar kind: feelings and convictions of subjective evidence try to find an objective expression and thereby hit upon various expedients. No other way than that of psychology, applied to the personalities of the system-building scholars and their followers, can give more insight into the origins and the aims of these constructions. Among the elements that play a decisive role in this psychological act, we may mention briefly the following: (1) the existence of "apodictically valid" (mathematical) propositions which are not recognized as tautological; (2) the existence of well-tested scientific theorems which are practically not doubted; (3) experiences with so-called sense delusions; (4) the general human desire for security and definitiveness; (5) the general tendency of man to overrate ideas of his own creation; (6) the specific tendency to provide certain traditional or otherwise favored assertions with an unshakable foundation.

*Many circumstances concur in making the origin of metaphysical theories, which rest upon the assumption of extraempirical knowledge, psychologically understandable. Kant's a priori is only the most restricted form of such an assumption, and Husserl's phenomenology is, in scientific form, its most recent systematization.*

3. *Description, Not Slogans.* If one asks what we have to offer from the point of view of the empiristic conception of science as a counterpart to the assumption of a material a priori, i.e., of synthetic judgments a priori or similar ideas, our reply is *not* that all knowledge stems from experience. This statement is often regarded as the "dogma" of empiricism.

Giving the words the meaning they have in everyday language, the foregoing proposition would contain in the first place a historical claim about the origin of the present knowledge that men have at their disposal. But such a claim is of no interest here for us. If we should, for example, learn that a certain important theorem was found by its discoverer in his sleep or in a state of trance, it would not change our conception of scientific theories. People living at any time, incidentally, acquire the greater part of their knowledge from books and teachers, and hence by tradition and on faith; only a small part of knowledge is assimilated by an individual from direct experience. But if one considers the learned also as something "experienced," there still remains the question of inherited knowledge. It does not present any difficulties to imagine that certain *engrams,* retained from individual experiences (knowledge consists, after all, only of such residues), are to a certain degree hereditary; at any rate, the present stage of the theory of inheritance of acquired characters leaves such a possibility open, and many observations of the development of nations suggest it. But all this has nothing to do with the problem of the a priori.

We do not defend the above-mentioned dogma—as we do not accept any dogmas at all and rather avoid assertions of such a general and vague character. The thesis, frequently ascribed to positivism, that "the world of the senses is the only reality," must also be rejected as a rather unconnectible sequence of words.

We cannot treat science in any other way than that in which the behaviorist treats all psychologic phenomena: describing their observable manifestations. The present book as a whole attempts such a description and the characteristics of the object in question which are pertinent for us now are primarily those which were developed in Chapters 6 to 9 and later frequently mentioned again. Accordingly, all expressions of knowledge in the widest sense, from the simplest judgments of everyday life to the most complicated propositions of the metaphysicians, can be classified in three groups: (1) statements that are called "tautological," i.e., which are, within a given system, transformable into one another by means of adopted rules of transformation, but which do not by themselves state anything about the world of experience; (2) those sentences which, on the grounds of known correlations between linguistic expressions and experiences, can be verified by observation, so that they classify themselves according to the result of observation as true or false; (3) those propositions which do not belong to a known tautological system and for which the linguistic conventions existing within a community of language are not sufficient to determine the class of experiences that would verify (or contradict) them.

To the third group belong almost all assertions that play a role in metaphysics or that are regarded as a priori, etc. In our terminology, they are "unconnectible" (Chapter 6)—that is, with the linguistic rules satisfied by the sentences under (1) and (2)—but not for that reason "nonsensical." Most of them point in a vague manner to a complex of phenomena that would be accessible to scientific study but has so far not been covered by the sciences (Chapter 21, 4). Even sentences such as the religious saying, "The pure in heart shall know God," or Nietzsche's aphorism, "Wisdom is a woman, she always loves only a warrior," lead, if viewed in their context, to a specific if vaguely determined complex of rules of behavior, which permits a discussion on rational terms (see Chapters 26 and 27). If any statements containing indefinite expressions such as "nature," "God," "freedom," etc., are claimed to be apodictically certain or a priori true, we may not call this claim nonsensical either; but we can only see in it a challenge for a *psychologic* examination as suggested in the foregoing section.

*The positivistic view does not oppose the concept of the a priori and similar ideas by a general proposition of vague content, such as "all knowledge comes from experience"; it rather suggests that all forms in which human knowledge or wisdom manifest themselves be described in an unprejudiced manner. The present book is devoted to the attempt at such a description; this attempt does not lead to a special group of insights which would have to be ascribed to a "transempirical" source.*

4. *Gestalt Psychology*. As all school metaphysics of former and more recent times rests almost always upon the alleged possibility of "a priori knowledge" in one form or another, so the modern popular metaphysical theories revolve continually about the word "whole." *Ganzheitsbetrachtung, holism,* etc., are the slogans by which one tries to rise above the lower sphere of the empirical sciences and hopes to ascend to higher, or at least more important, insights. It seems that the starting point of this terminology was a branch of psychology, which has become fashionable in recent decades, and which is called Gestalt psychology. This theory claims for itself the merit of having superseded an older "purely empirical" conception, a supposedly positivistic doctrine of "objective sense experience," or even a "mechanistic theory of sensations." Let us see what is behind all this.

For a very long time all psychologists and physiologists have related the normal visual sensation that the eye receives of an object to the creation of a small image of the object on the retina of the eye. This conception, and the complex of sentences describing it, is supported by various observations, e.g., the known influence of eyeglasses on vision. In the framework of this theory, according to the elementary laws of geometric optics, each single point of the object is related to a specific image point on the retina. This can be expressed by saying that every point of the object causes a stimulus at a specific point of the retina. Now it is supposed to be "empiricistic" to assert that every single stimulated point of the retina, independently of all others, causes a separate sensation and that the summation of these elementary sensations is done by the sensing subject only because he has acquired practice in this procedure from childhood on. In contrast to this, Gestalt psychology presents the notion that the apparatus of visual sensation and its transmission possesses an "organization" which makes it possible to comprehend immediately the picture of an object as *Gestalt* (shape), or as "a whole."

It may be difficult to describe the difference between the two positions in a clear manner without the use of such words as "summation," "as a whole," etc., which clearly anticipate what is to be explained. But it is certain that there is not the slightest reason for declaring one of these views to be more empirical, physicalistic, or positivistic than the other. If the two conceptions are different at all, one can decide between them only by observation, e.g., by examining the visual sensations in newborn children or the healed blind, etc. Of two theories, both of which can be tested in experience, neither can be more "empirical" than the other.

Let us consider a quite simple case of a purely mechanical phenomenon: a cylindrical piston is to be pressed onto a plastic pad. If the cross-sectional area of the piston is small enough compared to the entire apparatus that it can be regarded as a "point," one will search for a relation between the depth of indentation and the applied pressure, and one may succeed in finding for this an elementary law, i.e., a formula which for a given depth of penetration yields the value of the necessary pressure. But if we take a cylinder of a larger and complicated cross section, the relation between pressure and depth will hardly be calculable, even to a rough approximation, by the above formula; i.e., the necessary pressure will by no means be equal to the sum of the pressures that correspond to the penetration of the single small parts of the cross section. Both direct observation and the mechanical theory show that the force to be applied depends not only upon the depth of indentation, but also upon the *shape,* the *Gestalt,* of the piston (and possibly on other details, such as roughness of the surface, etc.). In this sense, therefore, mechanics would have to be called a "Gestalt theory"! But, to remain closer to the problems of optics: What judicious physicist has ever asserted that the image that a mirror reflects of an object is composed of *mutually independent* reflections of the single points of the object and is not determined by the object as a whole and the totality of its (and the mirror's) optical properties (surface texture, etc.)?

Not even in the most central areas of physical phenomena does the alleged mechanistic or atomistic conception exist or play any role. This is true even to a much higher degree of the classical positivistic theory of sensations. About thirty years before the advent of "Gestalt psychology" Ernst Mach discussed in detail in his *Analysis of Sensations* the physiologic foundations on which the subjective impression of similarity of shapes rests, or how a melody can be recognized as a whole, and many other things pertinent in this respect (see Chapter 5, 4). We may admit that studies of this kind have received particular stimulus (since about 1910) from the work of M. Wertheimer, who is considered one of the originators of Gestalt psychology. But that empiricism or physicalism must therefore be abandoned is a claim taken out of thin air, which can perhaps be explained by negativistic tendencies of the kind discussed in Chapter 5, but not by any epistemologic considerations.

*Gestalt psychology studies specific aspects of phenomena connected with sense impressions. It forms a special chapter, also discussed at length by Ernst Mach, of empirical natural science, of which elementary and structural psychology (Chapter 18, 5), are other chapters. It is completely unjustified to contrast with Gestalt psychology every other psychological approach as "physicalistic" or "empiricist."*

5. *The Whole and the Sum.* The favorite formula by which the followers of the holistic doctrine like to assert their superiority over the lower level of empirical science is this: *The whole is more than the sum of*

*its parts.* This can, indeed, be called the model of a pseudo sentence. This sequence of words would have a meaning only if one could define, for an arbitrary set of objects, in the first place, what their "sum" is, and, in the second, what is meant by their "whole" (and moreover, what is meant by "more"). The concept of a sum is known only for *numbers* and for some kinds of quantities such as forces, velocities, etc. The expression "sum of two triangles" is not defined (the sum of their areas is something else); if it is used, nothing can be meant but the complex, hence the "whole" of the two triangles. In this and most other cases, the "sum" of the things *A,B,C,* . . . is nothing but a scholarly sounding word for the entirety or the "whole" of *A,B,C* . . . and the contrasting of sum and whole is completely meaningless. If the holists wish to express that a complex consisting of *A,B,C,* . . . cannot be completely described by sentences each of which concerns only *A* or *B* or *C* . . . , then they are quite trivial. The distance between two points is not a property of either one of them but a relation proper to their combination, in the same way as the sum or the difference of two numbers expresses a relation between them. Consistently, one would then have to say also that the sum of two numbers is "more" than their sum, i.e., more than the first number by itself and the second number by itself.

Leaving aside the meaningless phrase "more than the sum," it seems at first sight that, at least in biology, the distinction between that which is a whole and that which is only a part can be made in an absolute way. An independent living being, capable of fulfilling its normal functions of life, is on the one hand sufficiently sharply distinct from other individuals and, on the other hand is also clearly differentiated from a single organ, a body part, by its independence. Accordingly, the much talked of holistic biology would have to deal only with the *whole* man, a complete plant, etc., and never with special organs. Everybody who is familiar with the elements of scientific research methods knows that such an exclusiveness does not lead anywhere. But even from a logical point of view, the proposition of an "independent organism" as an absolute whole cannot be maintained. If reproduction is counted among the functions of an independent organism, then for all higher species couples only would have to be considered. Among the lower animals the influence of symbiosis plays an important role, which at present, perhaps, has not been sufficiently recognized; on the other hand, we also know about dissectibility and the continuation of life of the dissected parts. A newer holistic movement does not admit separate human individuals as wholes; only communities in continual connubiality, peoples, races, etc., are proper biological units. In any case, such a demarcation is but a practical assumption, determined by the research aims at hand (or other purposes) and changing with them. The fundamental notion of "holism," however, is that the units or wholes are *objectively* given from the start and that they must determine the direction of research.

We have emphasized previously in the discussion of the contrast between structural and elementary psychology (Chapter 18, 7) how relative all such boundaries are. One may study a single plant as such, or the position of its leaves on the stem, then the cells of the leaves, and finally the chemical compounds of which it consists; or one may examine the dependence of the plant upon its immediate vicinity, its distribution in forests, fields, etc., the total biological composition of the woodland, the flora of the forests, the character of forests in various countries, or the common elements in forests over the entire earth. Each of these viewpoints forms a part of empirical natural science; each change in focus puts new observable phenomena into the spotlight of study. Thus it would also be quite justified to say, "The part is more than a piece of the whole." How far one has to stretch the range of one's view in dealing with a specific problem is a practical question, which cannot be answered in general beforehand. The physician who intends to heal a particular organ of the body has to judge for himself from the situation in each individual case to what extent he has to take into account other organs, the whole body, the personality type, the way of life, the life history of the patient, his ancestral inheritance, his origin, etc.; the slogans of the holists, including the theories about "finality" in biological occurrences (Chapter 16, 6); do not contribute to this decision.

*The customary formulas of the holistic doctrine, such as that of the "whole that is more than the sum," prove to be meaningless or trivial. In biology, too, the scientist can focus his attention only on a specific section of reality and the demand that he consider only "whole's" is of no avail in research. On the other hand, no empiricism denies the possibility of apparently remote interconnections, but the widening of the scope of a problem, in whatever direction, does not lead outside the positive sciences.*

6. *Examples of Wholes.* We had started from the fact (Section 4) that the holistic doctrine was originally oriented along the lines of Gestalt psychology. A melody, it was said, is a "whole," and more than the "sum" of its sounds; the appearance of a man is not determined by the appearance of the parts of his body. But in the same sense a symphony is not the sum of its melodies or themes; the human hand, not the sum of five fingers; and the sound, not the sum of the vibrations. Each of these things can, in our opinion, as an object of observation be a part or a whole. A part can belong to many wholes; a whole can be dissected into parts in various ways. It has been seen previously that the description of a whole never consists exclusively of the sentences that describe the separate parts. But all of this is trivial.

Holistic philosophy, however, which was developed systematically by H. Driesch under the name "Ordnungslehre" (doctrine of order) thinks it can maintain absolute criteria for what a "genuine whole" is. Out of the four "unity concepts"—"river," "mountains," "state," and "lion"— Driesch teaches us that "river" and "mountains" are but "combinations of units, that is, results of accumulation," while "lion" "has, indeed, developed as a living individual out of *Einheitsverknüpfungsgeschehen*" and for "state," "the question whether it is an accumulative whole or a genuine whole is anything but settled." Driesch remarks explicitly that the presence of "Gestalt qualities," according to C. V. Ehrenfels (one of the founders of Gestalt psychology), does not guarantee "genuine unity of a thing." Driesch's doctrine of order, which pours an immense number of new terms upon the reader, is perhaps conceived of as an attempt at a tautological construction for the purpose of describing the most general relations between observable phenomena. (In our opinion this is done by logic; see Chapter 10, 7.) But even if the formal requirements of an axiomatized discipline were to be considered as fulfilled in Driesch's case (which they are by no means), there still remains the complete absence of results that should follow from the retransformation of the tautological sentences into those of ordinary language (Chapter 9, 7). The "doctrine of order" is not supposed to be metaphysics, but its way of using language and its disregard of all experiential basis mark it as an essentially metaphysical system.

We may give an example that shows the role ascribed to the concept of the whole in the social sciences. Othmar Spann, a leading contemporary economist, says in his book *On Living and Dead Science:*

Mind and soul can never be comprehended as something composed of parts or as an accumulation of singles, but being-in-unity, the lightning bolt of the whole, is necessary in order to comprehend the single thing. Everything single must become a member [of a whole] if it be raised from its separateness, its aloneness and nothingness, and transformed into the only genuine existence of the whole. That alone is the fundamental, the original purpose of all social science: to understand what is a whole and what complete contrast there is between that process which tries to construct an (apparent) whole from separate pieces, and that other one which considers the whole as the first, the essential, the underivable (the primary), and all details, as derived, partial pieces . . . The concept of the whole is the true seed of a living science; the concept of separate details, the building stone of dead science, which since the Renaissance and Humanism has become the dragon seed of evil.

Spann answers the question whether the state is a genuine whole, which Driesch left undecided, unambiguously in the affirmative. But such an enthusiastic valuation of the concept of society is not peculiar to the followers of the holistic doctrine. We may again return to the concept of the a priori, discussed at the beginning of this chapter, by quoting the notion of another and differently oriented sociologist, Max Adler, about the essence of society:

> By no means do men learn to understand one another only in society, but on the contrary: all historical society, all forms of social life in economics and politics, are only possible because already *before* any economic historical socialization men are mentally socialized. The concept of socialization, in its empirical conciseness which was not found until the fundamental studies of Marx and Engels, belongs in its epistemological status to the a priori components of our experience pointed out by Kant.

It is apparent that quite the same result, the overrating of the concept of society (with which the scientist is concerned at the moment) is approached in two ways: by declaring the object once as an absolute, genuine whole, and another time, as a priori. It would be an interesting problem of sociology to analyze the specific psychologic motives that lead to the one or the other approach.

*It seems just as impossible to make the concept of the whole the basis of a philosophic structure as to rid it of its relativity and thereby to demonstrate an absolute or genuine whole. Sometimes it is the desire to give to the object of one's own interest more dignity that leads one to declare it a "genuine whole" or an a priori.*

7. *Conclusions.* Above (Chapter 22, 2) we have enumerated a series of points that make the origin of the a priori concept psychologically understandable. If something similar is to be done with the holistic doctrine—disregarding subjective motives such as the last mentioned—the following matter of fact could be pointed out: there are beyond doubt groups of phenomena or of sense impressions that are more strongly connected with one another than with others; it is the primitive drive for as simple a conception of the world as possible that leads to a dogmatization of these conditions and to stating as theoretical and absolute what is only a practical, superficially evident unity.

Returning to the fundamental results of Mach's critique of language and knowledge, we realize that the origin of the customary concept of "body" and "individual" is due to the existence of such *relatively constant* relations (Chapter 7, 5–7). Hence the following question, which we find in a well-known exposition of Gestalt theory, is a particularly characteristic pseudo problem: "How does it come about that the wholes which separate themselves in sensory dynamics correspond so generally to individual things in the practical meaning of the word?" ("sensory dynamics" means here the visual process). This question is of about the same kind as: Why do the rich always have the most money? And the author discusses explicitly those cases in which a group of "things," e.g., stars, is seen as a whole, a constellation, and he does not deny that we sense a painted constellation also as a whole, although it forms with the canvas together only *one* thing.

This, of course, does not mean that we want to reject Gestalt psychology in so far as it presents a freer (to use a fashionable word, more dynamic) conception of the nature of rather complicated visual impressions (Chapter 22, 4).

In biology, the occurrence of practical units is even more apparent. The smallest mosquito, every infusorian, is a complete organism—in a certain sense. But even the smallest particle of iron, if heated, emits a complete spectrum and the most enthusiastic holistic philosophers (see above) declare man himself to be a "derived, partial piece" of a whole, i.e., society. It is not the occasional usefulness, or even the practical indispensability of stating a "whole" for limited scientific purposes, that we deny, but we are of the opinion that this notion is based in part upon an arbitrary, expedient delineation, and in part upon unconscious, long habitual custom, and that there are many instances in which it has to be modified or completely given up. The subjective feeling that something is a "whole"—and this is true analogously for the feeling that an insight is evident a priori—does not disclose an "ultimate truth," but is the result of an uncritical view, whose function is exhausted in yielding a first orientation in a definitely limited area.

If one believed the metaphysicians, all of us positivists are suffering from a kind of blindness of soul, or "blindness toward ideas," which makes us incapable of recognizing true ideas, although even we cannot dispense with them. But we would not think of denying the usefulness and the value of any intellectual means where they are expedient. We have, however, learned from the history of science that no thought, or concept, can elude criticism and lead a life of bliss beyond and above all experience or float in the air as an eternal "idea" far above earth-bound knowledge. We do not believe that the conceptions of this book are ultimate truths either, but merely an attempt at orientation within the acquired stock of knowledge, an attempt that will remain subject to continual modification. If the metaphysician, the phenomenologist, the a-priorist, and the holistic philosopher tell us that their sentences express "situations of eidetic intuition, recognized with full insight," we do not consider it unnecessary to analyze these statements and to examine to what concrete experiences the various expressions in them refer, what amount of linguistic prejudice is contained in them, and what psychologic condition has led to their construction. The more certain, self-assured, and pretentious a conviction appears, the more it is still in the beginnings, in the uncritical stage of knowledge.

*There is no lack of psychologic motives and expedient reasons for the use of the concept of "the whole" in various spheres of knowledge. But we see in it a model example of metaphysical postulates: an auxiliary concept, useful in many places, has been elevated to the rank of an "absolutely valid idea," which then is sold as a source of fundamental knowledge.*

### CHAPTER 23

# poetry

1. *The Origin of Myths.* It has often been stated that the boundary between metaphysics and poetry is a vague one. This assertion rests upon the assumption that to both denotations, metaphysics and poetry, correspond cores of meaning in which the application of the respective expression is unambiguous. In the case of metaphysics, this area is to be sought where the aim of information about the world and the purpose of instruction are clearly emphasized. Poetry has its center in creations that *apparently* do not attempt to transmit knowledge and to formulate assertions, but rather use the means of language unintentionally, as it were, for the description of unique experiences. But as any metaphysician likes to accomplish more than the scientist who formulates judgments, similarly there is no poetic work that does not, at least implicitly, express specific conceptions of some section of reality. Considering that, except during school years, the thoughts of the vast majority of people are hardly ever touched by scientific influences, but very much by works of fiction, it will be realized what high importance the art of poetry has in the formation of the intellectual state of an epoch.

There seems to be agreement that the origin of Greek philosophy, its pre-Socratic period, was in close connection with cosmogonal myths which, it is believed, had replaced the still older myths of the gods. But one can hardly regard these myths as pure poetry in today's sense of the word; rather they must be thought of as the first attempts at systematic explanation of the world, attempts that have been continued until this day in the form of metaphysics. The study of other ancient cultures than the Hellenistic does not offer an essentially different picture. We may reasonably assume that after attainment of a certain degree of material wealth the practical needs of life directed intellectual activity into two different, though originally not clearly distinguished, paths: on the one hand, attempts were made to supplement and to improve the rather primitive technical "theories" that had proved useful in everyday practice; on the other hand, there appeared a desire to interpret in a hardly controllable way the most conspicuous natural phenomena and to influence by such interpretation the social behavior of men. Presumably, the earliest attempts at interpretation of the world, after they had lost their validity as such, later played the role of the oldest recordings that were taken as poetry and myth. It is, at any rate, difficult to imagine that the oldest myths were conceived in the same way in which works of fiction are created today, namely, under the common agreement between author and reader to renounce literal credibility. This renunciation represents a fundamentally changed attitude toward the text and must be regarded as the essential characteristic of what we today call a work of poetry or of fiction. Homer's epics precede that change, which received its decisive break at a much later period, perhaps only with Dante's *Divine Comedy*. We mention here this great poem, which erected a "tremendous world, state, and church structure," because it can claim to be taken as a didactic work, but at the same time uses consciously figurative allegorical elements and poetic forms in the modern sense.

Much, very much, has been written in the last hundred years about the beginnings of poetry and its connection with other cultural phenomena. If one wishes to go back to the very oldest stages of evolution, to prehistoric times, one may study contemporary primitives; by this approach L. Lévy-Bruhl, for example, has discovered many valuable facts. Traditional history of antiquity, influenced by the predominant school philosophy, approaches these questions in a much less open-minded way. An audacious attempt to derive today's scientific way of thinking, and particularly the foundations of mathematical concepts, directly from myths was made by G. F. Lipps; but we recognize in his approach a product of metaphysical thinking, anticipating by far positive research work. We, too, believe that (Chapter 21, 5) many propositions of the Pythagoreans are to be regarded as predecessors of later mathematical problems; but in order to demonstrate concrete connections, a great amount of research, not only in the historical but primarily in the epistemological direction, would be necessary.

*Mythical poetry and metaphysics are in their origins hardly distinguishable. Probably, earlier metaphysical systems, which no longer were accepted as literally true, gradually assumed the role of myths of world origin and the gods. It was not until much later that the art of poetry came into existence with a changed attitude toward subject matter. We shall be able to understand this evolution in its details only when scientific study of the processes of knowledge in their logical and psychological aspects has progressed much further.*

2. *Other Sources of Poetry.* Myths and primitive metaphysical systems are certainly not the only and probably not even the most important

sources from which the later art of poetry has developed in all its varieties. The spoken word that, as a routine, *accompanied* certain types of human actions, such as those of warriors, of certain craftsmen, etc., represented from the earliest times an application of linguistic means for purposes other than purely communicative. One may think of yells of encouragement or of intimidation in a fight, of the connection between word rhythms and certain processes of manual work, or of the sedative effect of suitable verbal sounds: in all these cases we notice an accomplishment of language that lies outside its function considered by us so far—the formulation of statements. But the characteristic peculiar to today's poetry and fiction is that the functions *combine*. Every poem, except in rare extreme cases, contains judgments and implicit propositions and thus becomes subject to logical analysis. Although it is a commonplace that poetry and logic have nothing to do with each other, that they are even opposed to one another, whatever can be said that is factual about the content of a poetic work, and even about the so-called "irrational" element in it (Chapter 24, 7), represents in our view a logical examination. On the other hand, in a work of fiction, such as a novel, where the purpose of communication is manifest, the rhythm and the sound of the language used play a certain role.

It is also a common prejudice that poetry is characterized by its lack of *purpose*. This is surely not true of its beginnings, since, undoubtedly, magic formulas, exorcisms, and prayers belong to the earlier forms of poetry. Even though we today do not believe in magic effects of words (Chapter 1, 4), we know the receptivity of people, individually and in groups, to any kind of poetic performance, songs, theater, storytelling. The fact that the creative artist does not always have in mind the concrete effect upon his listener or reader does not distinguish him from the scientist whose research activity has been subjectively disconnected from the original practical aims of the research.

The contrast between poetry and science is often characterized by saying that the poet intends deception while the scientist aims at investigation of truth. On the other hand, the contention that the works of poets represent truths in a higher sense is one of the strongest foundations of negativism (Chapter 5). Among the areas in which the two attitudes, the scientific and the poetic, approach each other, one ought to mention, in addition to metaphysics and the so-called poetry of ideas (Ideendichtung), primarily *history,* which finds some supplementation in sagas and legends and in the historical poetry of epic or dramatic form (see Chapter 23, 6). Sociologic utopias and the poetically adorned expositions of some chapters of natural science (so-called science fiction) play a lesser role. All of these phenomena may be regarded as hybrid forms without too great importance. Often, however, a study of boundary cases contributes decisively to the clarification of a complex of questions.

The problem that arises in the pursuit of the aims of this book and to which we shall devote a few remarks is to characterize those linguistic creations which are customarily called poetic and nonscientific. We regard this primarily—for the moment excluding musical-esthetic by-effects (see Chapter 24, 7)—as a problem of the logic of language. Such a study may be open to the objections that are often raised to an unfamiliar formulation of questions: it seems useless, since it has no immediate influence upon practical action, and it seems inadequate, because it arbitrarily singles out special features of a more complex reality.

*Starting points of the development of poetry can be found in various situations of practical life. Often one observes transitions between poetic and scientific work. It is a problem of the logic of language to draw a boundary line between these two types of intellectual activity.*

3. *Poetics.* There exists a rather superficial characterization of poetic language whose recognition is almost generally agreed upon. It is customary to say that the poet does not use the words and expressions of ordinary language in their common, "literal" sense, but with a "figurative," symbolic meaning. The older textbooks on poetics adduce entire systems of rules of translation from one language into the other. There we find listed tropes, word figures, and figures of speech. To the tropes belong metaphor, prosopopeia, allegory, metonymy, synecdoche, etc. Word figures are additions, omissions, transpositions of words—all measured by the customary grammar. Figures of speech are alterations of sentences, i.e., modifications of the ordinary (linguistic) syntax. The whole theory refers primarily to the so-called metrical language, but it is clear that prose writing also, although to a lesser degree, is included in it.

Today all these rules are not held in very high regard; they are neither taught nor learned systematically, but that does not necessarily mean that they are no longer applied. Owing to the extended popularization of reading they have gradually become a part of the language stock which the individual assimilates unconsciously in his childhood. Even the little initiated is hardly disconcerted by the words of a poem: "The hours fly, the sun stands at noon, and when it sets . . . my friend must pale." There is no need for him to *translate* the words into ordinary language (which is the purpose of the rules of poetics), but he apprehends the text like someone who has mastered a foreign language sufficiently well to react directly without going the long way of translation.

One of the reasons why so little attention is paid to the classical rules of poetics is that it is believed that an essential part of poetic productivity consists in re-forming the language and therefore in not being limited to the previously customary metaphors. We regard as decadent, even as apoetical, any production, even in prose, in which, in some fashion, a new language does not manifest itself. Here, of course, we are not thinking of so-called neologisms, artificial word creations, etc., but rather of changed forms of expression and exposition. One has to read contemporary criticisms of the classics in order to see how strange and obscure, how contradictory to many rules of language (even those of poetics), every line of a poem by Goethe seemed at the time of its appearance. The extent and the manner of language development through poetry vary greatly from nation to nation. The French are much more conservative than the Germans; they allow only small modifications in the forms of words and verses. The remodeling is directed there toward much more essential aspects of linguistic presentation, of which we shall speak below.

The possibility of such rather radical changes of language leads us back to the starting point of this book, to the questions, raised in the first chapters, concerning the relation between language and knowledge. According to an appropriate expression of F. Gonseth, who, however, had in mind only problems of the logic of science, one is faced here with a "paradox of language,"

that it is possible to give to certain words, and by the use of these same words, a meaning that they have never had before.

The words, idioms, and sentence formations of ordinary language, indeed, receive their meaning only by being applied, and they change with each new application (Chapter 3, 7). Certain applications which are further removed from everyday life and, so to speak, take advantage of the "overtones" of the word meanings, are called (without much justification) *symbolic*. That communication in this fashion is possible at all is due to the same faculty by which children learn their mother tongue. The language of science in its more mature stages develops in a somewhat different way; it strives in principle toward vigorous tautological systems. But faced with the works of poetry we behave as children who, at the same time with the content of the communication, assimilate the new elements of language. We shall see later that there is much more in point than merely small alterations in meaning, euphemistic ambiguities, etc.

*A conspicuous and essential characteristic of poetic works is the fact that in them words, idioms, and sentences of everyday language are used in a changed way. These changes do not occur according to constant rules of translation in the sense of a fixed poetics, but it is rather regarded as an essential task of the poet to expand language continually by new and original forms of expression and exposition.*

4. *Rules of Language.* The forgoing remarks do not refer merely to the so-called "form" of a poem or to the "style" of a work in the sense in which this expression is used in the history of literature. We do not be-

lieve in a fundamental distinction between "form" and "content." In our conception, linguistic rules reach far beyond what is usually called grammar or stylistics. For us, linguistic rules include all conventions, no matter whether they were ever explicitly formulated or not, that determine the relations between the spoken (or written) words and corresponding experiences.

If a novel begins with the words, "A simple young man traveled in midsummer from Hamburg, his home town, to Davos-Platz in the Graubunden area," these words mean something entirely different from what they would mean if they stood in a letter from John Smith to his father. It would require a long explanation and would not be at all easy to demonstrate exactly what is meant by this beginning of the novel, i.e., to translate its first sentence into the factual language of life or science, such as, "Let us suppose that a young man . . ." It is by no means sufficient to say that the reported occurrence is "invented," historically untrue, or pure fiction or "imagination." For obviously the sentence contains many elements that are not fictional, e.g., that Davos really is a town in the canton of Graubunden, and that one can conveniently "travel" from Hamburg to Davos in midsummer, which determines approximately the century in which the novel takes place and the social class to which the hero belongs. To a certain degree the author feels bound to the empirically possible; he maintains throughout the entire novel situations which exist or have existed.

The logical place of narrative poetry is in the vicinity of the *Gedankenexperiment* (hypothetical experiment) of the physicist. We suppose that a young man traveled in this manner, and we further suppose, . . . , and further . . . Then it is claimed, in the first place, that the assumptions do not contradict one another according to our experience and, in the second place, that this or that further chain of events follows according to general experience from the assumptions. Thus, what the writer presents is *experiences* about the interconnections of observable phenomena, and primarily of phenomena that belong to human social life. He uses for this another language and applies other linguistic conventions than those used by the scientist, the historian, the psychologist, or the sociologist.

If we turn from the more customary form of fiction to the so-called historical novel, to the fictionalized biography, to poetic descriptions of historical events, or, on the other hand, to the fairy tale, the legend, the fable, or any of the innumerable intermediate forms of the epic, it becomes apparent that in every case somewhat *different* linguistic conventions apply. If animals are introduced as talking, it is agreed between the author and the reader that it is not *this* observation which is the real subject, but something quite different, e.g., in Reynard the Fox, to show how a sly man can take advantage of the vanity of a fool. Conventions of a different kind again govern the drama; one may think, for instance, of the monologues, or the special methods used for introducing the characters in the first scenes, or the artful language of the dialogue contrasting to real speech. We are so used to the change of linguistic rules in these cáses that we follow most of the transformations almost unconsciously. "Nobody mistakes," says G. Mannoury, "the fiction column of a newspaper for the latest news."

An important feature common to all linguistic conventions in the various branches of poetry and distinguishing them from the language of science is their relation to *connectibility* (Chapter 6). The single poetic work, if it is to be taken seriously at all, remains, of course, consistent with a set of special conventions implicitly assumed at the beginning. But two novels or two dramas are not directly connectible with one another. They follow common general linguistic conventions; otherwise they would not be understandable at all. But these conventions admit of a usage of language in which many different meanings correspond to the same words and expressions and, above all, the same experiences can be expressed (approximately) in many different ways. If we call the single work of art a special theory of a section of reality (see Chapter 24, 2), we must say that each of these separate "theories" is written in a different language, so that they are not connectible, in principle, in the way that scientific theories are; connectibility is not even attempted in them. This does not mean that two poems must necessarily contradict each other (and hence one of them, at least, experience); for the concept of connectibility, as introduced in Chapter 6, refers to linguistic consistency and not to agreement with observation.

It must by no means be assumed that it is the *same* whether a certain experience is described in ordinary language or in any type of poetry. Such a separation of "form and content" in the sense that equality of content is compatible with different forms is a primitive auxiliary concept whose unrestricted application would be in contradiction to our entire conception of the role of language. We have remarked in Chapter 3, 3 that even in the narrow framework of everyday speech two expressions never are exactly equivalent. At most the two cores of meaning may more or less overlap, but in the boundary zones there *must* exist deviations; it is even the aim of poetic metaphors to suggest implicitly meanings that belong to the outer zone. (Only within the framework of a completely axiomatized system can there be complete substitution, Chapter 4, 5.) If one translates from one national language into another, everybody knows how certain changes of meaning are unavoidable. But we have emphasized (Chapter 4, 2) that the logical grammars of most of today's civilized languages have become so similar to one another that there the difficulties are relatively small. The logical syntax of the language of a poetic form deviates to a much larger extent from that of ordinary language; here there can be no question of a translation in the actual sense, but only of a vague correlation with respect to roughly delineated "contents." For this reason, any claim that a work of poetry "signifies" this or that or expresses this or that experience, if formulated without the above reservation, seems entirely inadequate.

*Each type of poetry is based upon certain conventions which we have to count among the linguistic rules. What the poet reports, using these conventions, are experiences about vital interrelations between observable phenomena. The special linguistic rules that hold within one work of poetry are such that connectibility among different works is not granted. An adequate reproduction of the reported or the "content" in the language of every day or in the language of science is not possible, owing to the great differences in the logical grammar.*

5. *Lyric and Experience.* Many might agree with our remark that poetry also expresses only experiences about observable facts, in so far as narrative and perhaps dramatic poetry are concerned; but it seems that for lyric, i.e., "purest" poetry this could not be the case at all. We are shown, however, by the testimony of a poet who cannot be denied competence in this·respect, how mistaken such a reservation would be. Rainer Maria Rilke explains in his autobiographical novel *Malte Laurids Brigge,* that

verses are not, as people imagine, simply feelings (those one has early enough) —they are experiences. For the sake of a single verse one must see many cities, men, and things; one must know the animals; one must feel how the birds fly and know the gesture with which the little flowers open up in the morning. One must be able to think back to roads in unknown regions, to unexpected meetings, and to partings one had long seen coming; to days of childhood that are still unexplained . . .. One must have memories of many nights of love, none of which was like the others . . . And still it is not yet enough to have memories. One must be able to forget them, when they are many, and one must have the great patience to wait until they come again.

Here a poet, to whom we owe more for the creation of new forms of expression than to most contemporaries, emphasizes most explicitly the empirical character of lyric poetry.

But we also find relevant for us in the quoted sentences the indication of "feeling" as an alleged source or subject of poetry. There is no other word that suggests itself as quickly as this one when one speaks of lyric poetry; one even thinks often that one has said enough by explaining that lyric poetry deals with feelings rather than knowledge, etc. That may be true, but only if one realizes at the same time that feelings in a certain way rest upon knowledge, that they originate in experiences and memories which have lost their clear isolation by a kind of assimilation process. Thus Rilke continues:

For it is not yet the memories themselves. Not until they have turned to blood within us, to glance and gesture, nameless and no longer to be distinguished from ourselves—not till then can it happen that in a most rare hour the first word of a verse arises in their midst and goes forth from them.

It may be added that the memories thus assimilated are called feelings in ordinary language and that the cheap lyric verse that Rilke rejects ("feelings one has early enough") is that whose subject is not a self-gained and transformed experience, but rather borrowed and imitated feelings.

Inspiration and feeling, imagination, instinct, vision, and intuition are the elements from which poetry springs—or, more precisely speaking, these are the words with which people try to describe the phenomenon of poetry. We too cannot avoid the words, which, after all, have been created for such purposes, but we believe that one should not stop at the point where one demonstrates with these words the contrast of poetry to any other kind of intellectual accomplishment. To overcome this superficiality was the problem which occupied the positivist Nietzsche (the Nietzsche until about 1882) again and again. In his works of that time, *Human, All Too Human, Aurora,* and *Joyful Wisdom,* one will find many enlightening remarks about the roots of poetry, the origin of feelings, and their relation to reason and science. We may quote as an example the following:

Feelings are nothing ultimate and original; behind the feelings there stand judgments and evaluations, which in the form of feelings (inclinations and disinclinations) are inherited by us. The inspiration that is based upon a feeling is the grandchild of a judgment—and often of a false one!—and in any case not of your own! To trust one's feelings—that means to trust one's grandfather and grandmother and their grandparents more than the gods which are within *us:* our reason and our experience.

Thus Nietzsche dates the origin of feelings even further back, from the individual sphere of experience into that of inheritance. The question (of heredity) raised here is accessible to empirical research. But in whatever way it will be decided, the essential point remains that the "basic forces" of poetry, such as feeling and inspiration, do not represent something to be contrasted to the intellect and cognitive faculty, but rather have their roots in them or are at least of a common origin with them.

*It is true even of lyrical poetry that it expresses experiences. Feeling and inspiration are aftereffects of old experiences that in our memory have lost their individuality.*

· 6. *Poetry and Science.* The older forms of "didactic" poetry, the poetic description, etc., are rightly no longer regarded as works of poetry. They were attempts at combining the linguistic conventions of ordinary language or the language of science with some superficial elements of poetics, such as meter and rhyme. A counterpart to this, at present very popular, is to present history mixed up with fiction, particularly in the form of the biographical novel. Some superficial traits of science are retained, but with respect to the logic of language liberties are taken which customarily are reserved for fiction (e.g., in the presentation of invented or composed conversations); it may be anticipated that this popularity will pass after a certain time. On the other hand, the historical novel, which seeks to be nothing but novel and not history, cannot be sharply distinguished from other kinds of epic poetry. To introduce single persons who have "really" lived, partly ascribing to them arbitrarily changed features, can hardly be completely avoided in any work of fiction.

The strongest ties to reality, i.e., to an experienceable matter of fact, to which poetry is bound lie in the creation of human individuals, of their character and fate. We call the interdependencies that can be observed in the behavior of one and the same person under different circumstances his *character* or—if the passive side of the behavior is more emphasized—his *fate*. It would be a task of psychology to describe such dependencies systematically; but almost all of our knowledge of characters and fates, except that gained by personal experience, we owe to works of poetry. We allow the epic and dramatic poet every freedom of invention with respect to the occurrences he describes; but we demand that he reproduce the correlations which exist *within one individual* correctly, i.e., in agreement with repeatable experiences. And for the poetic creation there exist rules of simplification and typification similar to those of any scientific discipline. Thus Faust, Don Quixote, and Peer Gynt have become for us factual information about German, Spanish, and Norwegian characters, and in the varied world of Balzac's novels we find an instructive concept of the French citizen of his time. Undoubtedly the knowledge of the poet forms one of the most important premises of his accomplishment.

In strong contrast to this there are certain theories, somehow akin to the rejection of the older didactic poetry, which declare a work the more "poetical" the less it has to show in factual content and in information. We may disregard entirely such extreme excesses as so-called Dadaism. But the first steps in this direction are taken by all those who demand of the poet only that he be naïve and free from the burden of all knowledge, who do not tire of contrasting mind and art, reason and feelings, logic and beauty. To be sure, certain features of reality are reproduced in such antithetical pairs and the practical usefulness of such classifications for limited purposes will not be denied. But one must not believe that they represent fundamental insights or absolute truths.

The leaning toward negativism in the form of "rejection of knowledge," not only of the details of scientific research but of all rational information, is particularly pronounced in contemporary literature. In a novel by Thomas Mann the type of a successful poet is described in the following manner:

It seems that a noble and active mind blunts itself against nothing so quickly as the sharp and bitter irritant of knowledge; and it is certain that the youth's constancy of purpose, no matter how painfully conscientious, was shallow beside the mature resolution of the master of his craft, who made a rightabout-face, turned his back on the realm of knowledge and passed it by with averted face, lest it lame his will or power of action, paralyze his feelings or his passions.

But what the poet here rejects arrogantly is not at all knowledge or science as such—without which he would be on the intellectual level of a child or a South Sea native, and could not even write. The rejection is aimed only at the relatively thin slice which goes beyond the knowledge that the "master" assimilated in his childhood and became accustomed to, and that with a little perseverance and proper application could possibly be still absorbed by him. Everyone may draw the line for himself beyond which the acquisition of further knowledge and insight seems disturbing to him, but he must realize that it is an *arbitrary* boundary line, determined by personal inclinations and the limitations of his own capacity, and cutting right through the middle of the store of available knowledge. All demands for naïveté of the artist, etc., have only a relative significance, within one generation, one stage of cultural development, against the background of a clearly defined educational level—within the framework of a personality equipped with specific capabilities.

As an essential characteristic of poetic creation one often finds mentioned the free play of the imagination, which leads to more or less arbitrary inventions in contrast to the "truthful" expositions of science and practical life which are in agreement with reality. The relativity and the narrow limits of this characterization are obvious (Chapter 23, 2). It has often been debated whether the work of Newton or the works of Shakespeare show more original imagination; slight changes in the meaning attributed to the word "imagination" make various assertions possible. The poet, even where he gives free rein to his poetic imagination, reproduces the full and unabridged truth, not the superficially observable truth which is the domain of the active man, and not the piecemeal, one-sided truth of the scientist. According to Bergson, the positive sciences work with symbols, while metaphysics and art conceive of life as a whole and reproduce it free of symbols. It can just as well be said that the poet uses words symbolically, not in their sober sense which everyday life and science give to them. What of the "one-sided truth of science"? The drama, for example, takes *one* feature, one episode out of the life of a man and puts the figure viewed in this light before us as a whole. A work of art in relation to life can be compared to the artificially isolated, pure musical tone in its relation to a noise. The scientific point of view focuses its attention upon a specific, intentionally isolated sequence of phenomena—it is neither more one-sided nor more many-sided, neither more useful nor less applicable, than art, but it works with different kinds of summarization and abbreviation, and it uses a different language. Each of the two types of linguistic conventions grew out of certain needs; each has its proper range of applicability, and neither can, within its own sphere, be replaced by the other.

*Slogans, such as free play of imagination, being unburdened by knowledge, symbolic (or nonsymbolic) manner of expression, etc., do not yield a characterization of poetry as compared to science. The special linguistic conventions that poetry uses are much more subtle, much finer, and subject to continual evolution; they could only be established after careful logical analysis.*

7. *Assessment.* The favorite way to discuss the art of poetry (and other phenomena of this kind) consists in pronouncing so-called *value judgments.* By value judgment is meant a classification in a reference system which is not further specified but must be guessed from the context. It is well known how low Plato, in his *Republic,* valued poets and artists; we find here one of his most unfortunate arguments. According to Plato, there exist three different kinds of "tables." In the first place, there is the true concept of a table, created by God; in the second place, there are real tables, made by craftsmen; and in the third place, there are the imitations of real tables in the paintings of artists. Artists, including poets, are therefore twice as far removed from the truth as craftsmen or the men of practical life. We have discussed the relation of (1) to (2) in Chapter 2, 7; and we shall return to the "imitation" by art in Chapter 24, 2. It does not seem to us to be a very meaningful proposition that imitation as such has a particularly low "value." All the other objections that Plato raises to the poets can be summarized by saying that the poets do not serve the same purposes as statesmen, scholars, and craftsmen.

On the other hand, there are also highly positive valuations of poetry. The poets, it is said, contribute to our knowledge of human life much more than the philosophers, not to mention the scientists. All, or at least the most important, inventions and discoveries were predicted or anticipated by poets, e.g., the theory of descent, by Goethe. Many scholars consider it a particularly effective confirmation of their ideas if they can adduce verses of poets that express something similar. A special form of value judgment is the prophecy that in the end there will only be poets, or—in other cases —that the art of poetry will die out entirely, etc.

If we remain, according to our general method, on the grounds of the description of observable facts, we have to offer the following brief characterization of the work of poets and its relation to science and metaphysics.

Many questions that deeply affect men and seem of vital interest to them (particularly those which originate in the problems of society) have not as yet been treated, or not sufficiently so, by the positive sciences. If these problems are approached by the methods that characterize primitive science, metaphysical attempts at solutions result. Another approach springs from the previously mentioned constitutional property of man, according to which accumulated, unanalyzed residues of general experiences under certain circumstances transform themselves into moods, feelings, and similar dispositions. An especially adapted linguistic method, that of poetry, makes it possible to express such states of consciousness—at times by taking advantage of acoustic by-effects—and to communicate moods and feelings by linguistic means to readers and listeners. Even the most prosaic of the poetic forms, such as the novel or the short story, becomes a work of poetry when it tries to convey a specific mood of life by using suitable linguistic conventions. In lyrics, where musical and esthetic acoustic effects play a more important role, the situation is more easily discernible. Rilke describes the situation in the lyrical language itself.

Sorrow we misunderstand,/love we have still to begin,/death and what's hidden therein/await unveiling./Song alone circles the land,/hallowing and hailing.

The history of world literature confirms our conception by showing how the state of knowledge of any epoch is mirrored in its works of poetry. When in the seventeenth century with Bacon, Galileo, Kepler, and Descartes the inductive sciences took on concrete forms and brought the peculiar term "law of nature" into the foreground, starting in France, language—that is, grammar, style, and poetic forms—began to be normalized. Men felt like "lawmakers" of nature and language; this was the age of "classical" poetry. It was not until the eighteenth century that the so-called Enlightenment took root. Minds found themselves freed of the pressure which religion and superstition had exerted upon thought and upon the scientific world perspective. Didactic poetry flourished anew and found its climax in Voltaire; but the influence of the new philosophy penetrated even into the most remote regions of lyric poetry. Goethe's poetic lifework, which reaches far beyond the horizon of "Enlightenment," stands at the threshold of the nineteenth century, in which biological and, gradually, sociological problems begin to influence poetry. The unity in the development of the different branches of civilization in every epoch has often been stressed. The few examples given here are only intended to indicate that the poetic works of an epoch, too, even though in a linguistic form very different from that of science, express in a specific way the state of experience and knowledge of that age.

*We disregard claims about the value or nonvalue of poetry and merely seek to determine what function it fulfills. In areas of life that are not sufficiently explored by science, poetry expresses, by means of linguistic forms which have been created for that special purpose, experiences that are present in the consciousness of the poet in the form of moods, feelings, or inspirations, with the aim of communicating these states of consciousness to the reader or listener.*

### CHAPTER 24

# art

1. *Beginnings.* It is generally assumed that the fine arts, music and poetry, vocal and dramatic arts, have something in common. One speaks about *art* and *the arts* in general, of artistic accomplishments, etc., without, of course, being able to define exactly what is meant by "art" or "artistic." Far be it from us to select one of the numerous "definitions" that have so far been proposed for the concept of art or to add one more to them. The science of optics does not start with a definition of light or sight either. All we intend to do is to discuss some characteristic features of the complex of phenomena to which the word "art" points and to discuss a few of its relations to previously considered branches of human activity, and particularly to science. Since poetry also belongs to the "arts," some of the following comments will serve at the same time as a supplement to the preceding chapter.

It is usually assumed that a study of this kind has to start with a historical review and must say first something about the *origins* of the pursuit of art. In fact, if it were possible to give some reasonably well founded, sufficient explanation of this point, much would have been gained already. But it happens only too easily that attempts at such a historical theory of art get lost in boundless conjectures. Sociological and psychological investigations of more recent times about the thought of the primitive have given us some information about details, but we are still far from possessing a reliable picture of the early development as a whole. So much seems to be definite—especially according to results of Lévy-Bruhl (Chapter 23, 1)— that the origin of art cannot be separated from the origins of scientific thought at a certain early stage of evolution. The primitive confounds the notion of his own self, his shadow, and an artificially produced picture and forms from them a single idea, similar to that which we call *soul;* in all of his theories about outside occurrences, the identity and mutual interchangeability of person and picture play an essential role. The primitive magic world conception also stands in close correlation to other elements in which we see the beginnings of a later pursuit of art, such as word rhythms, dance, and song. A clear distinction between endeavors directed toward the satisfaction of vital needs, food, and sexual drives on the one hand, and "artistic intentions" on the other, probably was not made until much later. Investigations into the origin of music, which according to Darwin is traceable back to the biogenetic evolution of man (bird songs), point in the same direction.

Today there is no contrast that seems so marked as that between science and art. A few points of contact are perhaps still recognized, e.g., in the sphere of certain forms of poetry (Chapter 23, 1 and 6), but one does not permit, if for no other reason than good taste, any idea of a connection between scholarship and such extreme forms of artistic performance as the dance. The fact that this notion is transitory, that, at any rate, it was not a matter of course for the medieval idea of science, is shown in the grandiose world picture that Dante creates in his *Divine Comedy*. There we see, "as women, not yet relaxed by the dance," the souls of great scholars pausing in the performance of the round dance, among them the philosophers Thomas Aquinas and Albertus Magnus, the jurist Gratianus, and others. Just because this, even as poetic license, seems so farfetched to us, it is perhaps well suited to characterize how much the outlook toward the relation between science and art has changed. There existed, at any rate, once an idea of a mental attitude which comprised the scientific as well as the artistic. As a minor point it could also be mentioned that until about the end of the eighteenth century scientific, even mathematical, publications often were adorned by artistic drawings.

*The opposition between science and art is the result of a process of differentiation which has developed in the course of history. It was not until the nineteenth century that it received its present decided form.*

2. *Not Deception, but Theory.* In order to have a more concrete object in view, let us turn to a special branch of art: painting. It is today almost entirely confined to the creation of pictures intended for framing, free from any relation to the environment and independent of later use. Older forms of the painter's art, such as the direct decoration of buildings and the ornamental art, which was highly developed in the Orient, nowadays play a minor role. The picture or painting, the drawing, and any similar kind of pictorial work, reproduces, except in extreme cases, a definite object, an occurrence, or a situation. The questions arising here and debated by the theories of art at great length lie in this direction: What does such a reproduction "mean"? To what requirements is it subject? Must it be true to nature or merely "artistic," etc.? The layman is reproached by the artists in that he, wrongly, clings to the *object* or the content of the picture; on the

other hand, the public often protests against the work of the artists because their pictures do not *correspond to nature* but distort it arbitrarily, etc.

It would be an impossible assumption that the fine arts have as a goal the complete reproduction of anything "real." Even a life-size plastic reproduction that imitated exactly the color, surface texture, etc., would still appear in many respects different from the object reproduced; but were such a thing undertaken at all, it would not be considered as a work of art in the usual sense of the word. Such technicalities as change of scale, framing, omission of details, and many other simplifications, which are as a rule used in the art of painting, preclude any idea of deception from the start. Everybody who looks at a picture accepts a priori certain conventions, which go far beyond the above-mentioned technical elements and are comparable to the linguistic conventions that determine the various forms of poetry (Chapter 23, 2). If a layman finds that a portrait does not sufficiently resemble the subject or that any picture is not sufficiently "natural," it signifies, in general, that he does not accept the conventions that the artist presupposes. French painting of the nineteenth century created specific new conventions which were in direct contradiction to those of classical art, and it was opposed and in disesteem until the public was prepared to *accept* the new conditions. Such a process is repeated, on large and small scales, time and again, and the study of these developments comprises a large part of the history of art.

There are, however, also art historians who see their task just in describing the previously accepted or even only the older of the previously accepted types of artistic creation; they claim that those are the only possible and admissible forms and demand their continued imitation by present and future artists. In this context, then, ideas such as "absolute beauty," "intrinsic aesthetic values," "the ever-unchanging standard of nature," etc., appear, which we shall discuss later. The analogy with the attitude of the school philosophers in the field of science is obvious; there it is the "absolute and eternal truth" that is sought, and found, as a rule, in the stage of knowledge of the recent past.

From our point of view, the goal that the artist seeks can be characterized in the following manner: he wants to express himself *about* the object which he exhibits, and he uses for this communication certain conventional forms which he, to a certain extent, modifies freely. *This* is what a Descartes looks like, says his portraitist, Franz Hals; these are the eyes of the skeptical thinker, who still keeps many things he knows to himself. This transition from green to brown *is* the river landscape, declares the landscapist Jacob van Ruisdael, and he accomplishes with this something similar to what the physicist does when he says that sounds are air vibrations. Every painting, every artistic creation is a *theory of a specific section of reality.* Instead of words and word images, which are the means of communication for the scholar and the poet, the painter can use more direct elements as "signs." We do not want to contrast the "real" world to a world of "delusion," but—as was said in Chapter 3 with respect to the usage of words—one should say more precisely: between the (entirely real) experience of the picture and other practical experiences, lying outside of art, there exist according to the rules of art, about which we are in reasonable agreement, more or less exactly defined coördinations. It is the wider task of the theory of art to describe these coördinations, or, if one prefers, to explain them.

The concept of a "world of delusion" serves as the basis for a school of thought that regards art primarily as providing *illusion* or intended deception. The artist, accordingly, exhibits a world that is more beautiful and more pleasant than the real world, and the fact that the spectator or listener feels himself transferred into the former raises feelings of pleasure in him. This is undoubtedly true for a wide area of popular art, in our time particularly for the motion-picture drama with its inevitable happy ending. But the word "art" certainly covers also phenomena of a quite different kind, which cannot be explained by a simple desire for illusionary pleasure. Psychoanalysis, which endeavors to describe deeper connections between different phenomena of the unconscious, has introduced the concept of *sublimation of the drives* by the practice and enjoyment of art.

*Imitation or deceptive reproduction of nature cannot be the goal of art. The artist expresses himself about a subject, about an occurrence, and uses in this process certain conventional means; he acts in this respect similarly to the scientist who invents a "theory" for a group of phenomena. Only to a limited extent can the desire for illusion be an explanation of the aims of artistic creation.*


3. *Condensation and Beauty.* Against the comparison of a work of art with a "theory" it will be objected that according to the customary conception a theory is either true or false and hence must be accepted or rejected without further ado, while this does not hold for the work of the artist. But this conception of a theory is not the one we represent. We have, particularly in the third part of this book, pointed out time and again that the acceptance or rejection of a theoretical system is not a matter of logical conclusion, but of *decision.* Today one prefers energetic thermodynamics to the doctrine of caloric because the former describes a larger area of phenomena in a more uniform and consistent way and allows us to classify them satisfactorily within a wider field. The criteria "true" or "false" do not apply here; rather could one speak—if not quite exhaustively—of a matter of taste. At any rate, in contrast to the above-mentioned widely accepted opinion, there is no question here of a logically determined decision.

The decisive points of view in the evaluation of scientific theories were summarized, as we noted in Chapter 12, 3, by Ernst Mach in his notion of the "economy of thought." Even more strongly than in science, our feelings (that is, a certain unanalyzed habit of thought within us) revolt against the application of the word "economy," which is reminiscent of an entirely different area of human life, to a question relating to so-called esthetic sensations. But it nevertheless seems that at least *one* essential feature of what is called artistic value is pointed up by this. We require of an artist that he exhibit an experience in a *generally valid* form such that by the *one* picture, limited as it is in its means of expression, many single experiences, which we have had or still expect to have, are called up in us. The ideas of concentration, condensation, limited means of expression, are inseparable from the concept of art. Theodor Fechner in his *Vorschule der Aesthetik* went so far as to claim that a "principle of economic use of means or of the smallest exertion of force" is fundamental for all artistic practice. A brush stroke, a spot of color, which an artist adds can elucidate a situation, enlighten us about typically recurring interrelations, give us new and decisive insights—and it is in such accomplishments that we see the climax of artistic performance. Even the most abstract work of art, whose creator would most vigorously deny that he wanted to "exhibit something" at all, does not speak to us in any other way than by calling up in us the memory of repeatable experiences through allusions, whose vividness makes the genius of the artist. If in Mozart's "Don Juan" overture we apprehend the sudden advent of fear and its gradual swelling into desperation, this is based upon a remote resonance to acoustic impressions experienced in similar situations. It must also be remembered that absolute identity can never be achieved in two ways, such as through a picture and its description, or through a piece of music and a poem; the two forms of expression can only vaguely point toward approximately the same factual situation (see what we said about poetic works in Chapter 23, 4).

The customary discussions about any subject in connection with art and the practice of art revolve about a word that supposedly encompasses everything in point here: the word "beauty." Art is the realm of beauty as science is the realm of truth; any theory of art rests upon esthetics as the doctrine of the beautiful, etc. Indeed, the expressions and idioms derived from the word "beauty" and its synonyms suggest many of the associations that are related to the idea of works of art. But in what way here the one concept can be explained by the other is not comprehensible. As in the case of all such abstractions, linguistic usage gives the word "beauty" an immensely wide zone of indeterminacy. We may give, only to mention two extreme propositions, first the pedantic definition of Kant,

Beauty is the form of finality in an object, so far as perceived in it apart from the representation of an end,

and on the other hand, the poetically heightened verses of Rilke's *First Dui-
nese Elegy,*

> For Beauty is naught but Terror's beginning which barely we endure, and
> thus admire because it patiently disdains to break us.

Can it be imagined that an expression of such broadness of meaning is
suited to form the basis of a scientific theory? One could, of course, have
in mind—and this may have been Kant's idea and that of other system-
atizers of esthetics—to build a theoretical system in which the word "beautiful" is restricted to a meaning that is limited compared to general linguistic usage and fixed by a definition. Such endeavors could, however, find
their goal only in the construction of a complete tautological system, which
would offer a well-ordered description of certain aspects of a group of phenomena, here of the creation of works of art, in the sense that we discussed
in Part III. What the estheticians drive at as a rule, namely, to be "lawmakers of the arts," would not be accomplished in this manner (or in any
other).

Every one of us is familiar with situations in which he may assert that
something is "beautiful" or "ugly." But we also know that in this judgment
agreement can rarely be reached among all individuals who otherwise
speak the same language; at any rate, it occurs much more rarely than in
the cases of alternatives like right or left, red or green, etc. From this state
of affairs it does not follow that those words ("beautiful" and "ugly") are
inapplicable in practical life; but it does follow that they must not immediately appear in a theory that claims to be scientific, i.e., to be connectible with other parts of science. The so-called search for absolute and
objective beauty is inconsistent with the logic of language.

*The acceptance or rejection of a specific work of art by an individual
or a group rests as little upon logical decisions as the acceptance or rejection of a scientific theory; similar criteria (of economy or concentration)
guide the "value judgment" in both cases. There is no constituted linguistic usage (based upon element sentences) for the word "beautiful," its synonyms and derivatives. The demand for objective, absolute, universally
valid criteria for those experiences which can be called "beautiful" or "ar-
tistically valuable" is logically inconsistent.*

4. *The Doctrine of Proportions.* The desire for orientation and the
habit of seeking relations among all kinds of observations lead quite naturally to the question: With what other *elements* are phenomena connected
to which we, in one manner or another, apply the word "beautiful"? If put
in this way, the question has nothing paradoxical about it; its range, however, is considerably limited as compared with the customary goals of "esthetics" as a part of philosophy. Some of the studies of school esthetics de-

viate from the above formulation in the wording rather than in actual fact; they ask, for example, for the "conditions" of the beautiful or the "causes" of the sensation of beauty.

We may disregard entirely empty paraphrases, such as, the beautiful is that which takes part in eternal beauty (Plato), and pass over general remarks such as that of psychoanalysis, according to which enjoyment of beauty originates in the sexual sphere. The oldest (and most often repeated) theoretical explanations are based upon a group of ideas characterized by the notion of *proportion,* adequate ratios, simplicity, and regular repetition of elements. We may take as a typical example the so-called "rule of the golden section" or the "pure proportion." When the ratio of two dimensions $A$ and $B$, where $A$ is the greater one, repeats itself as the ratio of $A + B$ to $A$, this is supposed to be a sure sign, according to some authors, of the visually beautiful. The endeavors, carried on since Aristotle, to prove that this or a similar geometric relation holds in all objects which are conceived as beautiful, particularly in the parts of the human body, the orders of columns, and other elements of historical architectural styles, are innumerable. Here one can hardly avoid being caught in the most outrageous contradictions. The most "perfect" geometric figures are, according to this school of thought, the circle, the sphere, and sometimes also the straight line, because in them certain distances, or directions, remain constant. But in human figures nobody will find any approximation to the form of a sphere or of a straight line as particularly beautiful, and in columns it is usually not the circular cross section that is valued. If the observations are examined in an unprejudiced way, there may remain something in the general idea that, in those cases where our attention is not absorbed otherwise, the repetition of symmetries, the recurrence of simple ratios, etc., gives the spectator pleasure. This may hold true for purely ornamental decoration, and to a limited extent (on superficial inspection) for some works of architecture and music. The human body, and, on the other hand, anything that is in a serious sense considered a work of art, is confronted by us with an abundance of reminiscences from all spheres of life, such that the impressions which come to the fore in our consciousness are quite different ones. The enjoyment we derive from a Greek tragedy, a sculpture by Michelangelo, or a symphony by Beethoven can only in a very farfetched manner be connected with the formal view point of adequate proportions. The situation is not very different with respect to other so-called "formal laws" of art, such as the "three units" of the drama, etc.

The experience of joy, the occurrence of sensations of pleasure, are usually considered by school philosophy as simple and not further analyzable "determinations of our soul." Although we cannot accept this metaphysical expression, what we mean is not very different when we say that sentences such as "I feel pain" or "I feel pleasure" belong to the element statements (Chapter 8), which can be used for mutual communication without great difficulty. It is not until one asks *why* in a specific case pleasure is felt, or more precisely, with what other observations (or element sentences) the sensation of pleasure proves to be regularly connected, that scientific problems arise. The above-mentioned more or less geometric motivation of the beauty sensation, based on regularity, harmonic ratios, etc., forms only a very humble contribution to the answer. There is no doubt in our minds that the effect of a work of art upon the spectator or listener depends not only greatly upon the most complicated properties of the object itself, but also upon the entire stock of past experience of the one who receives the impression, his upbringing and education, his knowledge, his oldest memories, contained in unconscious engrams, as well as upon all occurrences that are still active in his present state of consciousness.

*The criteria of beauty cannot be exhausted in a larger or smaller set of rules about geometric or arithmetic relations, etc. If there is an element statement of the kind "I feel that this is beautiful," every such sensation is accompanied by an extremely complex aggregate of phenomena; this aggregate is determined not only by the object attended to in the assertion, but to a high degree by qualities of the asserting subject.*

5. *The Range of the Beautiful.* Kant correctly observed that the statement, "This object is beautiful," rests in every case upon various experiences which lie outside the immediate observation of the object. He expressed this in the previously mentioned definition, according to which we call "beautiful" that which seems useful, without being aware of a specific use. Considering all the vagueness of the expressions "use" and "usefulness," the definition states probably merely this: for every object viewed, *general* experiences of which we are reminded in its contemplation determine primarily our judgment about its beauty.

This conception appears more clearly and less pretentiously in the so-called *principle of association,* which was stated by Lotze and later by Fechner: he who finds an orange beautiful not only sees it as a round yellow spot, but he sees

a thing of appealing smell, delicious flavor, grown on a tree, in a beautiful country under a warm sky, with it; he sees, so to speak, all of Italy with it, the country to which a romantic longing has always attracted us.

In other words, in viewing a natural object or a work of art, in listening to a piece of music or a stage play, residues of earlier experiences are awaked in us, without our being clearly aware of them; nevertheless, they form the essential components for the formation of an esthetic judgment.

Another component, highly effective in the apprehension of a work of art, is our *training,* our familiarity with certain elements of technique, with the conditions of creation, the possibilities and limitations of the kind of art in question. Goethe's remark that "only limitation proves the master" is not an incidental one, but hits the core of the concept "art." He who does not know the limitations or has no understanding of them, or does not, in a certain sense, accept them as valid, cannot gain any relation to a work of art. One has to be *trained* for the appreciation of art. The assumption that what "is" beautiful must appear so even to the entirely uneducated and untrained is refuted by unambiguous observations, among others by the differences in taste between peoples of different civilizations. If in some cases it seems that an inborn sense of art appreciation can be demonstrated, this is no disproof. For in the first place we are still far from knowing the relevant laws of heredity, and on the other hand, the really inborn cannot always be clearly distinguished from that which has been acquired through earliest childhood impressions.

Some theories of art avoid the concept of the beautiful and work instead with the concept of "artistic value." It is even thought sometimes that one can construct definitely infallible scales for the evaluation of artistic achievements. As long as it is realized that any valuation means a classification in an arbitrarily created system of values, there is nothing that can be said against that. But pronouncing, without clear indication of the reference system chosen, a judgment about the relative artistic value of Asiatic art as compared with modern Western painting, or something similar, means using a language that is not connectible, not scientific.

A more recent esthetic theory, which was particularly fashionable about the turn of the last century, tends to identify the beautiful with the useful, the expedient, and all that promotes life. The authors of this conception, Ruskin and others, had in mind primarily architecture and the artistic handicrafts, and focused their attention above all upon pragmatic purposes (the discrimination of "trash"), which they actually reached in many cases. In contrast to this, E. v. Hartmann, among others, defends the theory that the esthetic experience is actually defined by the absence of any other effect upon the experiencing subject. An improvement of language, i.e., a clarification of the theoretical situation, can hardly be recognized in either of these lines of thought.

There is an interesting remark by Popper-Lynkeus about esthetic *equivalents*. It is well known that mathematicians and admirers of mathematics often experience an esthetic pleasure in mathematical arguments, which corresponds entirely to the pleasure otherwise observed in, say, listening to a musical work. A similar attitude is occasionally exhibited toward certain instances of scientific or technical progress, discoveries and inventions, which are apprehended by some practically uninterested people with "esthetic" feelings; for this a certain amount of technical understanding is, of course, indispensable. These and similar observations (e.g., with respect to military pomp, pageantry, athletic performances, etc.) show how extraordinarily varying the object of esthetic sensations can be, and how often it can belong to the sphere of the prosaic and, in the ordinary meaning of the word, inartistic. On the other hand, it is known that in a so-called "naïve" attitude any useful, harmful, or neutral *natural* phenomenon (sunrise, lightning) under certain circumstances is apprehended as beautiful, while a "sophisticated" form of esthetic pleasure is often provided by objects which, in the customary way of speaking, are ugly and despicable (Baudelaire, *Les fleurs du mal*). That shows how widely the concept of esthetic equivalents can be stretched.

*The range of objects to which the notion of the beautiful is applicable is very wide, and almost unlimited. The esthetic judgment is determined in any single case by general experiences of the past which have prepared within the judge a certain disposition and may in part be unconscious in him; by special information about the branch of "art" in question; by momentary attitudes that are due to external circumstances; by habits; and perhaps by inherited characteristics. The study of all these influences is the task of the science of art.*

6. *The Science of Art.* If we leave aside the numerous attempts at the creation of a "normative" or "objective" theory of esthetics, there still remains a sufficiently large area of study which may be denoted as *empirical* esthetics or empirical science of art. This field belongs to the "humanities," and we remember what has been said in Part V about the relation between natural and humanistic science. There is no fundamental contrast in subject matter, in method, or even in the kind of understanding that comes to the fore here, but rather a change of emphasis with respect to the various elements that constitute a scientific exposition (Chapter 17, 7). The description of the complex of phenomena to which the word "art" points takes naturally at first the form of a historical, in certain cases a geographic-historical, study. Any historical investigation unavoidably contains, as we know (Chapter 18, 2), certain hypothetical elements, which lie, e.g., in the selection of the details described and in the use of fixed words and phrases, etc. From historical descriptions, especially if one stresses the so-called humanistic point of view, there gradually develops, as one tries to perfect them, rudimentary "theories" in the form of general statements about repeatable individual events. As a very far-removed goal appears a closed deductive (axiomatic, tautological) system, which would display the relevant aspects of one or the other particular field.

There are quite a few attempts at reaching the final goal by circumventing all difficulties in a cheap way by the introduction of hollow phrases which in the opinion of the particular author express something definite. As a typical example we may quote a schema, proposed by a well-known representative of the Comparative Science of Art with the intent of giving the scholar a "sure feeling of the objectivity and completeness of his method." It is this:

| 1. Material and Technique | World | |
|---|---|---|
| Stimulus: Creation<br>Goal: Skill | Significance | Appearance |
| Objective limitation | 2. Subject matter<br>Stimulus: Culture<br>Goal: Interpretation | 3. Form<br>Stimulus: Nature<br>Goal: Exposition |
| Artist | | |
| Subjective freedom | 5. Content<br>Stimulus: Soul<br>Goal: Expression | 4. Shape<br>Stimulus: Meaning<br>Goal: Effect |

The numbers in this scheme do not indicate only an incidental sequence, but they will prove . . . to be ascending from the lowest to the highest values.

Whoever has acquired even the first elements of critical thinking with respect to language will know how to appreciate this schema. The level of a great part of the existing esthetic and art theories is about the same as this; connectibility hardly exists even within the narrow limits of the work of one school of thought.

A special question which for a long time has bothered the art theoreticians is how to define the range of contents that can be suitably expressed by the individual arts. If we keep to the conception that a picture, a poem, a piece of music are expressions of the artist *about* a certain subject, rendering his own experiences and observations, it seems meaningful to ask whether every form of expression is equally well suited for any subject matter. Since, according to what we learn from the existing works of art, this question must apparently be answered in the negative, various problems arise in determining the boundaries between painting and sculpture, between fine arts and poetry, poetry and music, music and architecture, etc. It does not seem as though one could find here more than a series of more or less obvious practical rules of a rather vague kind.

The allegedly close relation between music and mathematics is also only of a superficial kind. It belongs among the above-mentioned ideas of the "theory of proportions" (Chapter 24, 3). Certainly in music the repetition of elements, symmetrical or parallel arrangements, etc., play a more important role than in, say, the art of painting (although here, too, a uniform distribution or balancing of "masses," the repetition of color shades, etc., have some import). But what in a Bach fugue, whose rigorous form

the connoisseur admires, is considered, after all, as the very essential is its
rich emotional content, i.e., the abundance of images and reminiscences
roused in us which stand in some sort of relation to our most intimate
experiences. It appears, incidentally, that Oriental music is much less
"mathematical" than that of the Occident, and sometimes even quite inaccessible to formal (mathematical) analysis. In European poetry rhythm,
construction of verses and stanzas, and particularly rhyme, form the most
conspicuous "geometric" elements; Oriental poetry has instead of, or in
addition to, these the "parallelism" of verses.

A more important side of the empirical description of the phenomenon
of art is based upon the order concept which in the sphere of art is called
*style*. Many details of stylistics may be questionable and its expansion to a
"style philosophy" may not make much sense, but there is, after all, no
other way of describing something than to point out common elements
within groups of phenomena. The saying that one must not "label" artists
and should treat them as individuals only, that one does violence to them
by any classification into groups, and so on, contradicts the essence of
scientific methods. *Any* statement, formulated in an existing language, is,
in a certain sense, a classification, and science in particular cannot do anything but classify by description.

*Rejecting the phantom of a normative theory of absolute esthetic
values, there still remains a sufficiently wide field of research for an
empirical science of art. Based upon geographic-historical points of view,
it will seek to describe and to classify the observable phenomena in the
area of art practice and to comprehend their connections with other facts
of the individual and social life (as a part of psychology and sociology).*

7. *Irrationality.* It is often said that anything in connection with
art and artistry can only "be understood psychologically." But that is not
intended to mean that all considerations about the practice of art are to be
subjected to the methods of *scientific* psychology. It expresses rather a
special form of the negativistic attitude and its proper formulation may
perhaps be approximately this: art is something *irrational* (or at least,
there is a strong irrational element in it); therefore one cannot make
rational statements about it. Roughly the same is expressed by saying that
everything in art belongs to the "sphere of feeling" and cannot be comprehended by reason.

What can be meant by the claim that an occurrence, a phenomenon is
*irrational?* We need not spend much time on philologic word explanations;
for no enlightenment can be expected here from etymology. But it seems to
us to be an error of judgment of the worst kind when we read in the
*Kantstudien* of 1928, in a criticism of a book about *Truth, Value, and
Reality,* the following:

What is it that . . . irrationality really signifies? . . . Why did the author deviate here from his usual habit of considering first the mathematical meaning of irrationality?

We have pointed out in Chapter 4, 6 that the class of numbers, for whose denotation the word "irrational" is customarily used in mathematics, could just as well have been called transcendental, imaginary, hypertrophic, un-calculable, or anything else. In no case can one derive from the obviously arbitrary use that is made of a word for a technical term its meaning in ordinary language.

It seems that people who classify the experiences accessible to them as rational and irrational want to point out the following distinction. In the first class belong all those experiences for which a satisfactory (complete, exhaustive) description in connectible, clear language is possible. Here "clear and connectible"—we repeat what we have discussed before—means a form of language in which the words and idioms are used not "symboli-cally" but according to the core areas of a sufficiently general linguistic convention or in the sense of a (scientifically) constituted linguistic usage. Then all those phenomena that cannot be described in terms that satisfy these requirements of completeness and matter-of-factness are irrational. To the positivists, the empiricists, the pure scientists, the so-called material-ists or followers of the enlightenment has been ascribed the claim that everything in the world can be explained rationally in the above-indicated sense, and it is therefore stated that they deny the existence of any irra-tionality.

This is not the position of this book. If we should be forced to make such a choice, we would rather say that everything experienceable is *irrational:* a description in the words of any form of language, either ordinary language, or the language of a kind of poetry, or the scientifically refined language, cannot take the place of the experience itself or exhaust it, but, in any case, can only speak *of* the matter and exhibit only one or several features of that which is experienced. The various forms of lan-guage, where they are applicable beside one another in competition, only emphasize different characteristics of the same complex, and to classify them according to an absolute schema of values is impossible. The require-ment of a *complete* comprehension of reality by a theory, by a poetic or otherwise artistic exposition, can be *approached* from every side, but reaching it is impossible from any side; the state of such accomplishment cannot even be characterized in a constituted linguistic usage. Therefore it makes no sense to declare for any *special* area of study, e.g., the works of art, that it is just the one that we shall never know thoroughly, never be able to clarify *completely.*

The primitive statement, "I perceive this as beautiful," can be given, according to ordinary linguistic usage, the form, "Now I have the sensation of beauty." But if this elementary occurrence, this *reception* (Chapter 7, 3) is to be described in its connection with other receptions, we deal with a problem in no wise different from that of the description of any, say physical, process. For that we have the various linguistic forms, the scientific, the colloquial, and the poetic language at our disposal, and it was one of our basic contentions that exactly the same thing can never be expressed by different languages. Each description points to a different and singular side of the matter. The poetically inspired description of the "whole" of an occurrence is just as one-sided as the exact reproduction of a neatly isolated single feature of it. The statement that certain matters of fact, e.g., the beauty sensation, can only be "apprehended by feeling" makes no sense to us.

It is sometimes said that language should be made effective primarily through its *sound,* by the choice of words according to acoustic and other esthetic criteria. In this manner, it is supposed, one can speak directly "to the heart," avoiding the intellect, and thus catch spheres of experience that are inaccessible to the prosaic language of everyday life or of science. We do not deny the possibility of such an influence, which is one of the essential components of poetic accomplishment and is somehow related to the function of music. Perhaps it is only in the limiting case of completely axiomatized exposition that any by-effect of this kind is entirely excluded. In any other form of language the "overtones," the borderline meanings of words and the associations suggested by acoustic reminiscences (even in the written language), make their influence felt upon listeners and readers. The higher or lower degree to which these influences are effective characterizes each type of language. The study of such effects can be a subject of psychology. At any rate, in their existence we cannot recognize a contrast to the intellect, an opposition to the mind, or an eternal division of the world into rational and irrational sectors.

*We cannot accept it as connectible information that questions concerning art and beauty are to be settled by the allegation that they are irrational and cannot be formulated and answered in plain words. Anything that is said in any kind of language, that of everyday life, of science, or of poetry, is but an allusion to or a reminiscence of other (nonlinguistic) experiences and can never replace them or exhaust or fully reproduce them. The matters of fact connected with artistic creation and enjoyment of art are not outside a world describable by the same means.*

## PART VII

# human behavior

Les loix de la conscience, que nous disons naistre de nature, naissent de la coustume.

The moral laws which we say to be an outgrowth of nature are in fact an outgrowth of our customs.

*Montaigne*

### CHAPTER 25

# we will, we ought, we may, and we must

1. *Starting Point.* The customary treatment of the chapter of philosophy called "Ethics" is based upon the idea that there is a stock of propositions, or correct statements in this field, which exist independently of anything men do and which we have to discover and then investigate. In the same way, a few centuries ago, European sailors discovered land between the 40th and the 120th degrees of west longitude, which had always existed, although unknown to the Europeans, and which was then more and more explored. America had been discovered by steering from Europe consistently toward the west. Thus, school philosophy thinks, it should be possible by consistent study, by the concentration of our mental forces in a specific direction, to find those (existing, unchangeable) principles which determine the correct ethical conduct of men. There is no doubt in the general opinion of philosophers that such principles *exist.* "Toutes les bonnes maximes," said Pascal, "sont dans le monde, il ne faut que les appliquer."

Against this conception we have to object above all that a problem makes sense only if it is possible to decide somehow, after carrying out certain procedures, whether or not the problem is solved. If a continent in a certain part of the earth is sought, one can at least in the case of a positive result say at a specific moment: it is found. But how would one determine in the search for the correct, true, and eternal ethical principles that one has arrived at the desired result (or at a partial result)? Even if it were possible at some moment to reach a *consensus omnium,* the question would still remain whether the next generation will agree. In point of fact, in spite of centuries of endeavor one has so far not been successful in demonstrating any substantial ethical theorems that would enjoy unanimous recognition; and there is no hope that the goal of a "normative" ethic will be reached in the future.

Some philosophers accommodate themselves to this indubitable difficulty by accepting the original problem in an essentially restricted form. Innumerable predecessors, it is said, have looked for the unknown (and indefinable) land and have found various things. We, too, shall now take part in the expeditions but pay attention primarily to the further exploration of the already discovered, comparing the older findings with the new, seeking relations between them, etc., without attacking the central question: how close are we to the actual goal? This point of view is usually called the *historical* treatment of ethics; the vast majority of the ethical studies of the present are dedicated to it.

If within the framework of this book we direct our attention toward the study of human behavior, we want to pursue neither normative nor historical ethics. The first task we believe to be void of content, undefined and undefinable, and the second, too narrow, since it takes the concept of an independently existing ethics for granted. According to our principles, we talk only about things that are susceptible to observation and continued testing and we can characterize a branch of science only by delineating a specific area of *phenomena* that are in question there. Such a delineation is indicated by the term "human conduct," although still in too vague a form. For in this notion one could include, after all, anything concerning technology, politics, or history, and many other things. But what we have in mind is a much smaller group of phenomena and we think that for its characterization all those words of ordinary language can be used with advantage which are indispensable in all *concrete* discussions of the subject. These are—in the English language—the so-called auxiliary verbs *will, ought, may,* and *must,* and further all the hardly enumerable expressions and idioms which, either derived from them or independently introduced, serve to paraphrase the same situations. That which one ought to do, or must do, is also called "duty"; the concept "freedom" is related to "may"; and from willing one arrives at expressions like "volition," "satisfaction," "dissatisfaction." Rule, commandment, law, liberty and coercion, free will, right, custom, virtue, moral value—all of these are expressions which the original desire of men for practical regulation of community life and for theoretical orientation in this sector of experience has gradually developed. It need not be stressed here explicitly how uncertain and variable according to locality, time, and occasion linguistic usage is; nor that we do not consider it our task to find out what "right," "custom," etc., *truly* denote (Chapter 3, 2). We only want to describe in the following some of the characteristic aspects of this area of phenomena.

*As in the discussion of the causality problem, where (Chapters 13–15) we took the customary causal expressions as our point of departure, we see a fitting approach to the so-called problems of ethics in the question: what is meant by sentences of the form "Man wants and ought to do; he may; he must; he must not . . ."? The description of the complex of phenomena to which these expressions point is for us the task of scientific ethics.*

2. *Will.* Among the four auxiliary verbs chosen as a heading of this chapter, the first one, "we will," takes a certain special place. For it is generally assumed that what someone wills, or does not will, at least in the vast majority of cases, is known to himself and he is aware of it, i.e., he does not have to learn it by communication from others. Although it is a quite common claim of many moralists that an "inner voice" also tells us what we ought to, may, and must do, even the most extreme representatives of these theories admit that about duties and ethical commands, at least in details, one can be *instructed*. But it is taken for granted that it is immediately evident to anybody in what direction his momentary will points, on which side there is immediate satisfaction or dissatisfaction for him. As is well known, it was Schopenhauer who laid particular emphasis upon the independent character of the will, the direct awareness of what is willed, and the identity of well-being and ill-being with obeying and disobeying the will. Almost all philosophers have developed special theories about willing, but no particular conception, even with respect to the basic assumptions, has so far asserted itself against the others. There is not even agreement as to whether the will is a phenomenon reducible to other psychological, intellectual, or emotional elements, or whether it is something original, *sui generis*. Such a situation indicates that one has not even reached a reasonable statement of the problem in this field. We certainly do not consider it our task to seek a definition of what is called "I will"; we know what the situation of linguistic usage in such cases is.

Like all elements of ordinary language, the auxiliary verbs in question are created primarily for the purpose of meeting the needs of everyday life, for communication about routine matters and usual occurrences. It is immediately known what it means if we say, He got up, because he willed it; he remained seated, although he did not want to. But if one tries to analyze the exact and complete meaning of these phrases, one has to go through long explanations and has to adduce remote theories about the conceptions of free will, external and internal compulsion, etc. If, on the other hand, one deviates ever so little from the area of everyday occurrences, the expressions become *indeed* uncertain. There are no longer sufficient linguistic conventions that could decide how far a hypnotically suggested action is to be ascribed to the "will," where the border line between conscious willing and instinctive actions or reflexive movements lies, etc. It would be a problem of physiology to make a comprehensive survey of these phenomena and to create for them a systematic description; in this the original terminology will surely no longer play any essential role.

To go farther into these questions is not our task at this point. We only state that in the area of daily experience—in a certain core of linguistic application—it is known to any individual without the use of further explanation ("velle non discitur") what he does or does not "will" at the moment. We shall leave open the question whether the willed is *completely* identical with that which gives pleasure, whether the will is a predominantly intellectual or an exclusively emotional phenomenon, to what extent the will is connected with movements, actual or imagined (Hobbes, Mach), etc. For a preliminary orientation, the following remark may suffice:

*In most situations of daily life, the individual, without having to be instructed, is immediately aware of what he wills at the moment or does not will, what gives him pleasure or displeasure, to what he feels attracted and by what, repelled. On this matter of fact rests the original use of the word "will" and related linguistic expressions.*

3. *Ought Sentences.* The customary application of the expressions "ought" and "may" is based upon entirely different grounds from those which lead to the concept of will. There are, to be sure, philosophical theories which claim that it is somehow inborn in man to know how he *ought* to act in certain situations. But these theories refute themselves by quoting different—and not always reconcilable—rules of behavior as binding, so that necessarily the individual cannot recognize at least a part of them as valid for himself. We also note an easily discernible external difference: ought sentences are almost always pronounced in the plural form, with a view toward a group, and mostly, without tense; not a specific individual, "you," but "one" ought; the decision of the will, on the other hand, the decision between satisfaction and dissatisfaction, concerns primarily the individual.

If we consider how the meaning of an ought statement may become a part of the language stock of a child or a primitive, we find that in every case it is the *personal imperative* which stands at the beginning of the development. Person *A* gives the command that *B* take a certain action or bring about a certain state of affairs, and *A* has well-recognized powers at his disposal for the enforcement of the execution, to wit, means for the inducement of pleasure or pain sensations. From this point the meaning of the command sentence develops in various directions. In the first place, the immediate threat of force recedes more and more and changes gradually into a potential form of power, i.e., a power whose presence is proved only by past experiences. Then, again, experience, observation, and reflection develop an understanding of the interdependence of various commands and of their connections with circumstances of all kinds. The individual finds himself entangled in a network of demands which either are made of him or he makes of others. Among these demands, certain types distinguish themselves by their general character: they occur repeatedly and in various connections; they appear in the relation between various pairs of individuals or between groups of people. In the course of time, in this class of general command sentences, the person of the commander recedes into the background as the attention is focused on the content of the command. The commander also makes it known that he too is a recipient of commands and only passes them on. Finally the last step is taken: the complete cutting off of the command from the concrete, visible person of the commander. In a more primitive stage, extraempirical persons are interpolated as the bearers of the general commandments and they are endowed with all suitable qualities such as power, permanence, and unlimited insight. Later on, the more personal qualities are disregarded and an entirely abstract justification of the prescriptions is retained; these are then called the *moral law,* or something similar. At this stage there appears the expression "one must" or "one may" as an absolute order, completely separated from the person of a commander, and essentially independent of a person to whom it is addressed. Such moral laws are made known to the individuals of a community by immediate communication, by education, and by other forms of information.

More or less synonymously with the independent, absolute "shalt" and "shalt not," the words "good" and "evil" and other derived expressions are used. That which agrees with the absolute "shalt" is the good, that which contradicts the shalt-rule, evil. We do not overlook here the fact that later linguistic development has brought about some differentiation in the meaning of the two pairs of expressions and that today they are often not used in exactly the same sense. Originally, however, there was only one alternative between the (morally) accepted and rejected.

*From individual imperative sentences, originating with a person and addressed to a person, there gradually evolved a system of impersonal and dogmatic shalt-regulations. These are disseminated by various means of communication among the members of communities.*

4. *Moral Value.* The next step in the evolution of general shalt-sentences is the introduction of the concept of "value" (moral, ethical value). If simply the good and commanded are called valuable, the evil and prohibited, valueless, one has said nothing new. The essential role of the value concept lies in its supplying us with a *rank order* of human conduct: there are highest, most fundamental virtues and less meritorious actions, down to incidental offenses and the worst, most despicable crimes. There can be no doubt that the conditions of community life create a certain practical need for such systematization.

Nevertheless, it is one of the most interesting psychological phenomena that man in the course of the evolution of his mental capacities came to accept the existence of an absolute and objective order of values, an order that is supposed to be entirely independent of his own actions and to remain permanently unchanged. Without a doubt, even in our time, in the sphere of the present life of civilized people, a great many thinkers defend the point of view that in every man there is a certain faculty called "practical reason," enabling him to distinguish unfailingly and objectively what he must do or must not do, what is morally good or evil, praiseworthy or blameworthy, honorable or despicable. One would think that reasonably unprejudiced observation would show very soon how dubious, changeable, and self-contradictory such "instinctive" decisions are in most cases. Whether, for instance, courage or compassion is the higher virtue, whether or not regard for one's own or another person's life takes precedence over the duty to destroy it, derived from some ideology (e.g., the military)— about such questions there is agreement neither in concrete single cases nor in principle, even among the contemporary members of a limited social group. But apparently the desire, nursed from various practical sources, for the establishment of an unassailable scale of values is stronger than the critical capacity that most thinkers possess or assume their readers to possess. A logically more acceptable theory is perhaps the "heteronomous" doctrine of value, which shifts the origin of norms into an extrahuman sphere; according to this conception, there are specific sources, the records of revelation, which, by means of interpretation, let us know what is in agreement with the norm (Chapter 27, 5). This heteronomous theory of ethics is, however, almost unanimously rejected by modern philosophers.

The *autonomous* doctrine of value, or "axiology," as represented by contemporary school philosophy, can perhaps be characterized best as an "intuitionistic" conception. It is claimed that there exists an "original intuition," common to all men, which makes everyone recognize the good, and that the task of ethics is but to interpret this intuitive insight and to draw the explicit detailed conclusions for every single action. The various schools of thought, which sometimes dispute violently with one another, deviate very little among themselves on this basic conception. The rationalists assert that the doctrine of ethics is of logical origin; the "empiricists" appeal to the "experience de nos jugements et de nos sentiments de valeur," without which we would be "blind to value." But even those who do not offer any conjectures about the origin of value but only accept the existence of an objective scale already stand more or less on the premises of intuitionism. We shall return to this point later (Chapter 26, 4).

Remaining on the grounds of what observation in fact shows, this can be said: we see that the individual, under the influence of his origin, environment, training, education, and acquired experiences, arrives at value judgments. The congruence of a part or all of these preconditions within a class of individuals results in a corresponding agreement on valuations. Nowhere can we find a criterion for singling out one among many different, mutually contradictory value scales as "objectively correct."

*The dogmatization of the shalt-sentences, going a step further, leads to the idea of the existence of an objective scale of values of moral actions. This phenomenon can be explained psychologically by the strength of the practical need for uniform and unassailable valuation. An unprejudiced observation does not yield any indication of the existence of a moral intuition, common to all men and independent of their conditions of life and their state of mind at the time of action.*

5. *General Doctrine of Values.* The concept of moral value is frequently considered as a special case of a more general doctrine of value. One means by that primarily the arranging of a group of phenomena (experiences) in an order of succession to which an objective validity is assigned. Closest to moral valuation is the esthetic, of which we spoke in Chapter 24, 5. The scale of the good is then paralleled by a scale of the beautiful, and great emphasis is often placed upon the analogy of the esthetic and moral spheres as is indicated in the classical concept of *kalokagathia.* All inquiries into the general value concept and other theories in which an (objective) evaluation plays a role, are usually assembled in a "philosophy of values," also called "axiology." This is then often regarded as the "real" philosophy, as contrasted to purely epistemological studies.

The actual situation in the philosophy of values may perhaps be illustrated by a programmatic speech which was presented on the occasion of the Descartes Congress in Paris in 1937. According to this, axiology covers to an equal extent three completely coördinated areas: the "raison logique ou théorique," the "raison éthique ou pratique," and the "raison esthétique" (logical, moral, and esthetic judgments). In the first case one deals with the distinction of true and false; in the second, of good and evil; in the third, of beautiful and ugly. In all of these cases, human judgment is autonomous, not subject to any external command, neither divine nor natural, and at the same time is "objective, apodictic, and universal." Of special interest for us here is the reference to logic and mathematics.

That which holds for "theoretical" reason and the mathematical truths derived from it holds equally for "practical" reason and the moral truths derived from it. As it was formulated by our Grotius: In the same way as even God could not accomplish that 2 times 2 be not 4, so He cannot bring about that something that is evil according to sound judgment be not an evil.

According to the conception represented in this book, logical and mathematical theorems are tautologies which do not say anything about reality; they are linguistic conventions and transformations which follow adopted rules. If, for instance, the theorem of the *tertium exclusum* is assumed as valid and from it the conclusion is drawn that in addition to black and nonblack there is nothing else (which is but a convention about the use of the expression "nonblack"), this statement can be applied to the world of experience only in a very incomplete and approximate way. In the first place, one needs an empirical demarcation of the objects to which the distinction black or nonblack applies, that is the range in which the sentential function "$x$ is black" is defined (Chapter 6, 2); then it must be agreed upon when an object is to be called black. The usefulness of logical and mathematical formulas in practical life is undeniable, but in their application they lose their exactness and thus their apodictic character.

Now one could, of course, think of constructing a tautological system of propositions that aims either at esthetic or at ethical phenomena. Such a system could serve for the simplifying *description* of these fields of experience, just as geometry yields an idealized description of spatial phenomena. But it would not be independent of arbitrary assumptions (neither is geometry), nor is it clear how the transition from descriptive statements to shalt-sentences is to be accomplished without further arbitrary assumptions. A line of thought about whose possiblity probably nobody is in doubt, is to establish a logical order of command sentences. In such a system it would be evident what demands are contained in others, or have others as their consequence, or which are in contradiction with one another. In so far as this is regarded as the task of ethics, ethics would indeed become a part of logic; but it would then contain anything but valuations. Questions of this kind were treated in a reasonable manner by Karl Menger in a book with the subtitle *Foundation of the Logic of Morals*. Most of the philosophers of value confuse logical classification of shalt-sentences in the sense mentioned with the concept of valuation.

We have pointed out in Part III that the existence of so-called apodictically valid mathematical theorems (namely, tautologies) suggested to philosophers the idea that in the area of the natural sciences, too, statements of the same exactness and generality could be found. We now see that the influence of mathematics reaches still further: there are even attempts to set up principles of moral behavior with the claim that they have the same certainty as the theorem "2 times 2 equals 4." This shows what epistemological progress has been achieved by the recognition of the tautological character of mathematical and logical formulas.

The following example may illustrate our conception of the value problem. Assume that a person is assigned five qualities: (1) he is tall; (2) he is strong; (3) he is healthy; (4) he is honest; (5) he is handsome. In case (1) we have a fairly well-established procedure of measuring tallness (at least if no greater accuracy than plus or minus ½ inch is required) and a fairly well-defined reference value, the average height of a man. The statement is, for all practical purposes, unambiguous. In case (2), there are various contradictory ways to measure strength, but one may easily come to an agreement about which one should be used, and may also find a definition for the normal strength as the reference level. As to statement (3), the instances that determine the state of health are highly controversial, and it is still more difficult to define something like the man of normal health. Statement (4) refers to the behavior, i.e., to the past actions of a person and those expected from him in the future. Without any additional specification with respect to the class of people and the classes of actions referred to, it is almost impossible to reach an agreement. To rely on some innate or a priori knowledge of what honesty really means leads us nowhere. The same is true, to a still higher degree, in case (5). Except for the most extreme samples, no major group of people will concur in their judgments, and any attempt at establishing objective viewpoints is doomed to failure. The main point is that statements (1) to (5) present a gradually increasing amount of unavoidable uncertainty and ambiguity.

*The conception of a general doctrine of values (axiology), which is to comprise logical, esthetic, and moral valuations, has no foundation whatsoever in experience. It rests, among other things, upon a misunderstanding of the tautological character of logical and mathematical theorems. In no concrete case has the attempt to make plausible the transition from logical propositions to shalt-sentences or valuations yet been successful.*

6. *Must and the Free Will.* Let us return to our starting point, the auxiliary verbs mentioned in the heading of this chapter. We have seen that "we will" (approximately) denotes an original attitude open to the immediate consciousness of the subject in question, and that "must and may" refer to a system of norms, set up by human beings, or accepted by them as valid. There still remains the "must" to be studied which in many respects occupies an intermediate position.

Linguistic usage is divided. On the one hand, by "must" is meant an emphasized "ought." A norm, a regulation which is provided with greater executive powers, appears as a compulsion, as a "must." On the other hand, "must" is also applied in the sense of a biological function and is thus related to the "will." Man must eat, must sleep, must once die: such sentences express descriptions of observed connections which are given the attribute of causal necessity (Chapter 13, 4). In this way, the use of the word "must" has two kinds of roots—one of them in the system of human norms which become known to the individual by communication, education, and training; and the other one in inborn qualities of human nature, which are independent of human actions and observed by experience.

The above-mentioned sentences of the form, "Man must die," can easily be replaced by simpler statements, such as, "Every man dies"; then they are what is called "natural laws." But there still remains a problem of the "must" which is indicated by the German saying, "Kein Mensch muss müssen" (nobody must). That is to say that the actions of groups of people (government) aimed at making an individual respect the generally recognized norms can never have such an impact that a statement of the form of a "natural law" would be possible, such as: Under such and such circumstances this specific behavior of the individual occurs *necessarily*. The philosophical problem that starts here and whose discussion has been going on for centuries is that of the "free will," i.e., the determinacy or indeterminacy of human actions.

General experience teaches that we cannot predict with certainty what *another* human individual will do in the immediate or the more distant future. Human actions do not behave like the movements of the stars, but rather like those of dice thrown on the board. The analogy with the dice game is twofold. We see that the decisive result of the action of somebody else (the result of a "decision of his will') is influenced until the last moment by many very complicated and for us incalculable details which seem unimportant individually; on the other hand, predictions, made collectively for a class of cases from the knowledge of the circumstances determining the class (men under such and such external circumstances act thus and so), hold true with a certain frequency. It may be said that those human actions for which such classes can be established possess the type of a collective (Chapter 14, 5) and hence can be objects of probability statements. In no case, however, can the actions of an individual be assigned the property of determinability. Perhaps the essential motive for the assumption of "free will" is that we foresee *our own actions* of the immediate future (our own volition), *but not those of other people*.

The desire to retain, even in the case of the dice game, the older and more customary method of causal description led to the formulation that the result of a single throw is "objectively determined" and that we merely lack the knowledge of the various causes that determine it. The same point of view is often defended with respect to the actions of the will; one says, they may be absolutely undeterminable, yet they are "objectively determined." In our conception of language this is an empty sequence of words, for it cannot be shown by what kind of observation one could distinguish between indeterminable phenomena which are in fact determined and those which are not.

These remarks show that we agree neither with the determinist nor with the defenders of so-called free will. For the latter believe that, after all, a fundamental difference exists between the behavior of the thrown dice and that of the freely acting man; the action of the man is, they say, not only indeterminable, but also "really" indeterminate. Such a proposition is then further combined with the assumption that there exists, besides the world of humans, another, higher world, filled with more intelligent beings, who behave toward humans as a father to his children, the prophet to his people, etc., and who foresee even the "really indeterminate" (Chapter 27, 5).

*The customary concept of the "must" points on the one hand to norms with increased force of execution, and on the other hand to observed regularities, so-called natural laws. From the conjunction of the two ideas results the problem of free will. We can remark to this, here, only that human actions, or certain classes of them, seem indeterminable to us in the same way as the individual occurrences in a dice game or any other collective.*

7. *Primary and Derived Concepts.* Against our attempt at a characterization of the questions of ethics by the areas of applicability of the four English auxiliary verbs, some may point out that these do not always have an immediate analogy in other languages. There are fairly equivalent verbs in German: *wollen, sollen, dürfen, müssen.* In French one has *vouloir* and *devoir* for "will" and "ought"—the substantive *devoir* is that which one ought to do: the duty—and for "may" and "must" there are several paraphrases possible which are partly due to the peculiarities of the French forms of negation. The two fundamentally different meanings of the English "must" can be well differentiated in French: "l'homme doit mourir," "il est obligé de travailler"; but the linguistic usage does not show any consequence (c'est de son devoir de travailler). It cannot be claimed that French diction expresses a somehow higher stage of epistemological critique.

But these and other philological or historical details are not essential. We only want to make the point that from the life of man in communities many relations have evolved which, variously interlaced and by no means easy to describe, have found their first primitive classification in the abovementioned word forms with all their vagueness and ambiguities. It was not until a later stage of the development that abstractions such as "free will," "duty," "freedom," "obedience," "law," "ethical behavior," etc., came into use. These expressions contain implicitly a specific, almost unconsciously formed theory, comparable to the practical rules of the handicrafts that precede any scientific or technological study. Far be it from us to deprecate the pragmatic usefulness of such rules and of the various slogans in which they find their expression, or to underestimate the intellectual accomplishment of this stage of evolution, or even, which would be particularly wrong, to overemphasize the relative merits of the later critical, scientific treatment. But we cannot recognize as ultimate wisdoms and final conceptual constructs, not to be altered by further research, any of those abstract terms which are the result of *first and primitive* theoretical efforts. It is too early today to predict in what form and in what comprehensive systems the doctrines of human behavior will be organized in the future within the framework of an advanced universal biology and sociology.

According to a remark by Bergson—who bases upon it a considerable part of his theory of ethics—men are "created" for small, closed communities and it is only in the course of the development of civilization that they seek to transgress these boundaries and strive toward the "open" community which finally comprises the whole of mankind. We may disregard here the implication of the act of "creation" and the contrasting of a natural destination and the actual behavior of men. But it seems to be a correct observation that the earliest societies consisted only of narrow groups of family members or companions in arms, with the aim of defending themselves against interference from the outside. At this stage a need for terms such as "ought" and "may," "will" and "must" can easily have arisen; but concepts such as "freedom" and "duty," "right" and "law," or more elaborate distinctions between law and ethics cannot have developed yet. From this we again draw the conclusion that the auxiliary verbs mentioned are the *original* forms of expression for the description of ways of behavior.

*The relations into which human individuals entered by joining in smaller or larger groups led to the use of expressions such as "ought" and "may," "will" and "must." The attempts at a systematic description of such relations, that is, the first primitive theoretical endeavors, have then created the more abstract terms "ethics," "value," "law," "duty," etc., whose application implies a far-reaching extension of the original foundations. It is our task to study the matters of fact to which these linguistic creations correspond.*

### CHAPTER 26

# law and ethics

1. *Positive Law.* By "the law," "statute law," or "positive law" one usually denotes the complex of regulations which, in fixed wording, by the power of the state are forced upon the members of a society as rules of conduct. But there are also many other, in part very different, meanings of the word "law," and from the contradictions and overlappings of linguistic usage ensue innumerable pseudo problems. One speaks of natural, divine, unwritten law, of the law that was "born with us," of immanent and transient law; in every case a small shift in meaning or emphasis in the use of the word is sufficient to create confusion. This is, of course, not to deny the seriousness of such problems as the description of the relationship between, say, the empirical sense of right and wrong on the one hand and the traditionally and formally fixed norms of law on the other, or to underrate the importance of the historical study of its evolution, etc.

If, in the first place, we consider the stock of formally recorded statutes, such as are given, in any civilized country, in the collections of State laws, ordinances, municipal regulations, court decisions, etc., we find characteristic of them the consistent use of a *special,* rather exactly defined *language.* This language is, of course, imbedded in the general language of everyday life of the country and is supplemented by definitions in the usual sense, i.e., reductions of new or unusual expressions to more customary ones. But it is not this reduction that creates a proper, "juridical" language, but rather the fact that words, locutions, and forms of construction of ordinary language are used *without* explicit explanation in a slightly altered, mostly more limited, in many cases antiquated, sense. Thus, e.g., § 862 of the German Civil Law Code states:

> If possession is disturbed by a prohibited form of force, the possessor can demand from the disturber the removal of the nuisance. If further disturbances are anticipated, the possessor can sue for abstention.—The claim is rejected if the possessor possesses unjustly with respect to the disturber and the possession was acquired within the last year previous to the disturbance.

These sentences are preceded by some statements (axioms) which explain the use of the word "possession": possession of an object is acquired by the attainment of the *de facto* power over the object; possession is ended by the possessor's abandonment of the *de facto* power over the object or the loss of it in another manner, etc. But it is not the view of the jurists that this should be a *complete* axiomatic system, i.e., that by the word "possession" in the entire text of the law nothing must be understood but what is contained in the foregoing explanation; rather, a certain familiarity with general linguistic usage is taken for granted. Even more in the case of the other technical terms such as "prohibited form of force," "to disturb in the possession," "to possess unjustly," a knowledge of ordinary language is presupposed. The "prohibited form of force" is explained in § 858 in a way that presupposes familiarity with the expression "disturbance of possession"; the concept of "unjust possession" is reduced to the "prohibited form of force," and finally, the relation "with respect to him" is introduced without any explanation. All of this shows that the language of the jurists must be learned by *habit and usage,* as is ordinary language itself. The area of its connectibility comprises a part of everyday language; the exact boundaries are very difficult to determine. But the greatest emphasis is placed upon the entire corpus of law being a linguistic system connectible within itself.

Popular objections to jurisprudence often take the line that all statutes should better be formulated in the "natural" language, the language of the people. If only the possible omission of foreign words is demanded, this is but a superficial and quite irrelevant request. But a partial abandonment of the connectibility with ordinary language is *unavoidable* in the face of the vagueness and changeability of the latter, if the text of the law is to express in a reasonably clear way precise matters of fact. The essential point for jurisprudence is to use a linguistic form that is sufficiently isolated and shielded against the continual changes in colloquial language. The tasks of interpretation, subsumption, and the whole application of the law are not thereby made more difficult, as is often believed, but on the contrary, they are facilitated, or even made possible only by this kind of isolation.

By no means is the interpretation of laws, which forms the main task of the practical jurist, a purely logical process. He establishes relations between two languages (if the correspondence between ordinary language and experience is taken for granted) and in doing so he has to use one of them, namely, ordinary language. A man who secretly feeds his own lamps from the current of a public electric network is ordinarily called a thief. But can a judge sentence him for theft if the definition of theft in the (German) criminal code begins with the words, "He who . . . takes away another person's movable object. . ."? "Movable object" is not defined in the law, and the customary linguistic usage is, also as far as the term "take away" is concerned, completely undetermined. The judge must, therefore, base his decision upon other norms than those written down, at least as long as special legislation in electrical matters does not provide the necessary supplementation. But there will always remain areas in which it is not a logical conclusion but rather a spontaneous personal decision that determines what is "the law" in a concrete case. It is a purely terminological question whether those incidental "norms," which in the application of the law are customarily adduced along with the explicitly written ones, are to be subsumed in the concept "positive law." The study of these norms, as a counterpart to the explicitly formulated legal texts, is a difficult chapter of the science of jurisprudence. Ihering demonstrated masterfully on a great example in his book *Geist des römischen Rechts* how the relation between written and unwritten law has developed historically.

*The law of a country is primarily recorded in a system of regulations, which possesses a special linguistic form, detached from the general linguistic development. An essential task of jurisprudence can be characterized as the establishing of transitions between the artificial language of the law to the currently used everyday language. In this it has to rest upon further norms which are not explicitly formulated and thus more or less vague.*

2. *Normative Science.* It was inevitable that school philosophy and the jurists following it tried to give the science of law a philosophical superstructure similar to the philosophy of nature of the Hegel-Schelling type. Here one not only searches for the "true essence" of law and seeks the "pure" and "absolute" law, but one also discusses in detail the question of the *existence* of the law, where an interplay between the words "be" and "ought" plays the leading role. The following quotations from a recent work (which otherwise contains many instructive remarks) may illustrate our point:

If the concept of "being" is conceived of not in the narrow sense of *natural being,* the causal determination, but if one means by it in the widest sense the being posited by the mind as such or the object of cognition, then the state and the law as well are, of course, as objects of cognition, also beings. Thus one may speak of a being of the ought, only it is a being of a different kind from that of nature.

And further:

The cause of the ought-like being, of the reality of value, of right and lawful actions, is not the *ought* or the value, morals or the law, the norm in its specific proper sense, but rather the thinking, feeling, willing, the fact of the existence of a psychological experience of the norm. And this fact of existence —as cause, as motive—has the corresponding behavior as an *effect.*

We agree with the *Doctrine of Pure Law* (*Reine Rechtslehre*) of Hans Kelsen in that "be" and "ought" are not the same, that they lie, if one wishes to express it that way, "in different planes," etc. But to pronounce statements about a specific "kind of being of the ought," etc., is not connectible with the rules of ordinary language or any constituted form of language.

According to a customary classification, jurisprudence and ethics belong to the *normative sciences,* whose task it is to set norms, i.e., to *find* ought sentences and to justify them. We have pointed out above (Chapter 20, 2) in the discussion of economics that any science, as soon as it strives toward practical application, arrives at a stage where it establishes rules or commands. The bridge *ought* to have these dimensions (in order to maintain a certain security against breaking); the patient *ought* to submit to this treatment (in order to be cured); the healthy man *ought* to keep to a specific way of life (in order not to get sick). In all these cases, the ought sentences can be transformed into the usual form of conditional statement sentences: if the bridge is built to the stated dimensions, it does not break; otherwise, it does. In contrast it is believed that the sentences occurring in the "normative sciences" are "genuine, absolute" norm sentences, which do not admit of a reduction to conditional statements.

The idea of the existence of *genuine* normative sentences and thus an absolute distinction between the normative and positive sciences is not compatible with a reasonably critical attitude toward language. We have seen in the preceding (Chapter 25, 3) that general ought sentences are derived from personal commands, in which the persons of the commander and of the recipient of the command come to be disregarded and where the reference to the existence (or nonexistence) of an enforcing power is entirely removed into the background. It is only this origin in personal commands that gives meaning to the sentences in which the word "ought" or a synonymous expression occurs, hence to any regulation, commandment, or prohibition. No theories, however much extended, about the essence or the kind of "being" of the "ought," etc., can change this fact.

The outright pronouncement or formulation of commands can in no way be called a science, even if this certainly vague term is given the widest interpretation linguistic usage permits. But if one means the *justification* of commands or norms, one finds oneself again in the sphere of the *usual* forms of science. For a sentence construction of the kind: One ought . . . , because . . . , if it is not completely meaningless, can be immediately transformed into: If . . . , then . . . In other words, a norm together with its justification is nothing but an ordinary statement. To the extent in which the words and locutions then used are based upon a constituted linguistic usage, the statement is connectible and, in general, verifiable.

The idea of a normative science could only originate in the fact that in jurisprudence as well as in ethics customarily the ultimate justification remains in principle *tacit*. The laws, regulations and customs that are valid in a country at any period, including the unwritten norms upon which the application of laws is based, rest in the last analysis upon the tacit assertion that, their fulfillment assumed, community and private life in the state will flourish, and certain aims, about which agreement is taken for granted, will be reached. This assertion, of course, owing to the multitude of conditions and ways of life in question, falls into extraordinarily many detailed statements and systems of statements. Its explanation and justification form —in addition to the internal questions of consistency, dependency, interpretation, subsumption, etc.—the actual subject matter of the science of government and law. This science is thus a part of a general sociology in Comte's sense and fits quite readily into the framework of the natural sciences and humanities about which we have spoken in detail in Part V of this book.

Ethics, or the science of morals, is less distinct from jurisprudence, if this is taken as a part of sociology, than is usually believed. The norms set by ethics may claim a more general validity, beyond the locally and temporally limited institutions of the state. But if the norms are given a justification at all—and it is only in this way, as we have seen, that they can become objects of science—the justification can only be of a sociological kind, i.e., it must deal with the relations among people in an orderly community life. We shall return in the next chapter to the explicitly *extrascientific* forms of ethics.

*To call jurisprudence and ethics normative sciences, in order to give them thereby a special and in a sense preferred and unique position within the framework of the sciences, does not appear to be compatible with our critical attitude toward language. In so far as one is concerned here at all with investigations which in the widest sense of the word can be considered as scientific, they form parts of a general sociology. In this branch of science all propositions have to fulfill the same requirements of verifiability and agreement with experience as in any other part of science.*

3. *Right Originating in Wrong.* The following situation is as a rule regarded as an essential conflict in the field of law and morals. At any time, within a civilized country, there exists a practically unambiguous system of regulations which make up the statute of the country or the positive law. In a similar manner there exists, in somewhat wider spatial boundaries and in much vaguer form, within a group of countries belonging to the same civilization, a certain stock of moral codes and ethical norms which are more or less generally recognized and accepted and as a whole do not conflict seriously with the more essential legal regulations in the separate states. Conduct that is in harmony with these recognized fundamentals of law and

morals is in the general linguistic usage called good, virtuous, commendable.

On the other hand one knows that juridical and moral codes do not have an unrestricted lifetime but in the course of history undergo in part essential changes. We do not think here of those alterations of single precepts for which the possibility and the process of amendment are provided in the existing statutes themselves; regulations modified in this manner derive, in a way, their validity still from the older laws. But there are other, so-called *revolutionary* actions, which have as a result that within a specific group of men, from a certain moment on, new legal codes become valid. As far as the nonlegal, ethical norms are concerned, provision for amendments is not made at all; they rather appear from the start with the claim of eternal, unassailable validity. Nevertheless, it is a fact that in the course of historical development, in addition to gradual transformation of opinions, the most important ethical foundations have been altered in a decisive way by the forcible intervention of single persons or groups; more precisely: basic principles that once stood in strict contradiction to the existing ones have later, owing to certain influences, found general acceptance.

The conflict to which we referred above finds its usual expression in the question: Can actions that are in contradiction to existing legal and moral codes and that aim toward their forcible change be approved of? If this question is answered in the positive, we conflict with the above-indicated and generally accepted definition of commendable conduct, a definition that can hardly be given up. In the case of a negative answer, one pleads against essential progress, at least in the form in which it has taken place repeatedly in the past. And in both cases one loses any assurance of the merits of the present state of affairs, which, after all, was also created and solidified by destructive and forcible means. The conflict can take various and very violent forms. The proclamation of the superman, the idolization of the great "historical personality," who stands above all laws, the contrasting of slave and master morals (with preference for the latter) on the one hand, and the commendation of civil virtues, of (Christian) obedience and of eternal peace on the other hand, are only a few of these forms.

So long as all one is concerned with is to give to a particular action one of the predicates "good" or "bad," one faces only a problem of definition, which can be solved in one way or another; the question then is, in the sense of the expression introduced by us (Chapter 6), a nonconnectible one. As to the practical conduct with respect to revolutionary actions, there can hardly be much doubt. The powers that defend as valid the accepted state of affairs in law and morals cannot at the same time work toward its annihilation, and hence they must oppose any revolutionary tendencies. The theoretical problem of how "wrong becomes right, immorality turns into morality" is subject to a historical, and hence in the widest sense a sociological, study. There remains *one* question that highly interests us and is connectible but, with the present stock of experience, hardly answerable, namely, that of the historical prediction: Are we approaching a state of affairs in which forcible changes of the legal and moral codes (changes not provided for in existing norms) are excluded, or will mankind have to expect over and over again the occurrence of "revolutions" of one kind or another? There is no doubt that a great many people in our contemporary civilization would prefer the first alternative, but from historical experience we can hardly derive arguments for the satisfaction of this longing. Scarcely anybody will believe that mankind is not to experience any further forcible changes of the present standards of law and morals, especially if he thinks of the situation on other continents. But even the question whether the nations within the Western civilization, which believe themselves to be in possession of a permanent high moral standard, are approaching such a stabilized state in the distant future is entirely uncertain.

*Historical experience does not allow us to decide whether mankind will have to expect continually forcible breaks and changes of the legal and moral norms or whether we are approaching a state of stability, in which the further development of the law is accomplished in legalized forms, and that of the ethical principles, by intelligent reasoning.*

4. *Uncertainty of Judgment.* In the preceding chapter we have tried to refute the notion of most philosophers of ethics that *true* moral principles are "given to man by nature" or are in some other manner objectively determined, so that all that would be necessary is to discover them and make people aware of them. The "essential conflict" just discussed contributes to the support of our view. One can point out in detail innumerable cases in which the uncertainty in the judgment of single ways of behavior contradicts the existence of an inborn norm, common to all people.

If, in order to determine the "general opinion," one consults one of the customary textbooks on civic morals, one will find little virtues such as gratefulness, humility, etc., duly praised and recommended. But the attentive student also learns of Goethe's verse, "Only failures are humble . . ."; perhaps he also encounters Schopenhauer's utterance, "Without arrogance, there is no great man"; and he must become completely confused when he reads again that Goethe said to Eckermann that "all mentally and bodily well-equipped men [are] the most unassuming, . . . all mental failures, of a conceited kind." This example of contradictions reflects faintly the conflict between the ethics of the virtuous little man and that of the "hero." But we should not take this example too seriously, for by using a little critique of language, particularly by looking for some reasonable description of the behavior meant by the word "unassuming," one could go a long way in accomplishing agreement of opinions. Even the dilemma in connection with Mandeville's famous *Fable of the Bees,* between the objectionability and the economic usefulness of social vices, does not seem to be unsolvable if some attention is paid to a more careful wording.

But there are more important instances in which a reconciliation cannot so easily be accomplished. The popular notion, represented by the greater part of fiction and poetry, that the presence of certain passionate moods, particularly those sexually influenced, releases one from the observance of many rules which are otherwise supposed to be the basis of acting in good faith is such an example; almost no "serious" philosophy of ethics agrees with this frivolous but widely accepted conception. One human action toward which the judgment in our time seems to be entirely uncertain is that of suicide. From absolute condemnation, which likes to call upon the authority of religious commands but has undoubtedly also a basis in a combination of envy and selfishness, to enthusiastic praise of the spontaneous choice of free death, we encounter all intermediate opinions. As another example we may mention the complex of questions connected with unconscious crime. Undoubtedly, in the course of time an unambiguous evolution of moral feeling has taken place here. Oedipus, who kills his father without recognizing him, in a fight or in self-defense, and who lives with a woman who later proves to be his mother, is for us no abominable criminal. Today he would be acquitted by public opinion as well as by any civilized law court, since to us criminal *intent* seems to be a necessary premise for legal or moral condemnation.

Even among those philosophers whose opinions show kinship in many points there can exist strong contrasts in matters of ethics; witness the philosophy of pity of Schopenhauer and the idolization of force of the later Nietzsche. Also well known are the widely deviating opinions about the relative importance of "good works" and "grace" among representatives of the various Christian denominations.

So far we have restricted our examples to a cultural area that is relatively close to us in time and space. If one transgresses these limits, one finds deviation in moral feeling and sense of justice of a much greater impact. Our Western consciousness of superiority is then by no means always preserved. One may think, e.g., of the unlimited concern for the conservation of every living being that fills the devout Hindu and which is entirely foreign to the Christian Occident. We do not know if, perhaps, some day in our civilization too, possibly after the essential food supply has been secured by the chemical industry, the killing of any nonaggressive animal will be considered wrong and an evil action. Albert Schweitzer's much-discussed philosophy of *Reverence for Life* overshoots the mark by asking protection for every kind of living organism—which is hardly reconcilable with the prayer for our daily bread. If, on the other hand, we look at the morals of primitive peoples of the present and the past and regard our own situation compared to theirs as progress, that does not testify in any way for a "natural provision" of mankind with basic ethical principles either.

The uncertainty of moral judgment is increased to the highest degree once actions performed, not by a single person, but by *larger communities* are considered. There are individuals who in their private lives carefully fulfill all requirements of so-called gentlemanly behavior, but as soon as they represent a group, a community, think almost anything to be allowable, especially in dealing with an opposing group. In the concerted actions of a state, a nation, a race, or even only a so-called social "class," in the opinion of many, even of people not immediately interested in the concrete case, almost all otherwise condemned ways of force, cunning, and even breach of trust are morally admissible. The advantage of the members of the community which one represents, although it may not be meant in a strictly material sense, is taken to be higher than any moral norm. This conception has found its classical systematic exposition in *The Prince* by Machiavelli (1515), who declares explicitly that he who cannot free himself of the customary moral concepts should remain a private man. Modern forms of expression of similar "realistic politics" and of the "dispensation from moral law" are the well-known slogans of "class dictatorship," "sacro egoismo," "right is what is good for one's own country," etc. At least in this sphere of group actions it will have to be admitted that there does not exist any instinct common to all men, or any original intuition of what is good or evil, praiseworthy or condemnable.

*Unprejudiced observation of the often uncertain and changeable moral norms prevailing in our environment, as well as historical and geographical experience, teach us emphatically that moral judgments are not natural constants but rather variables depending upon the social conditions in which a group of people live. There is complete confusion in our time about the moral valuation of actions that are performed on behalf of ideologically bound communities.*

5. *Sociology as Basis.* The problem of how the juridical and moral conceptions are related to the other social conditions in which a human community lives has formed for about a century the object of scientific— sociological—study. It is to be expected that this type of inquiry will gradually take the place of pseudo-scientific "normative" ethics (and in part also, of the "historical"). In France, the tradition of a "science des moeurs" has not been broken since the days of Comte; strictly speaking, it started earlier with Montesquieu, who in his often-quoted work *De l'esprit des lois* (1748) undertook to describe the relations between social conditions and normative systems.

A definition by Anton Menger,

He is ethical who adapts himself to the conditions set by the social powers; he is unethical who offers resistance to them,

can be understood as the claim that customary moral judgments are nothing but statements about the extent of submission to the norms imposed upon society by the ruling classes. This conception finds support in a system that was developed in detail by Vilfredo Pareto, according to whom law and ethics are but a "logomachy," a pseudo-rational dressing of certain claims of power and rule. To this (socialistic) theory of morality it could be objected that it may do justice to the static condition, but it does not explain how the overturn of ruling powers occurs exactly by the general acceptance of other moral norms than the prevailing ones. It is characteristic at least of *some* revolutions that the change of ethical valuations preceded the change in the distribution of power.

It seems that the experiences of every day available to the individual in his profession and his private life, provide the ground upon which the moral judgments grow. Some of the more independent thinkers are led by observations to a tentative proposal of new norms, which are communicated to wider groups of the population through literary works or through direct dispersion among the masses. A wider circle comes to accept the new doctrines by a slow process, if they do not seem to contradict their own observations about the usefulness and expediency of actions. There remain, in addition to the defenders of the existing power, those who do not trust their own observations and rather follow the judgments of the ruling classes without resistance until the change of power has occurred; and finally those for whom better insight, wider historical knowledge, and more comprehensive experience make it impossible to accept the new norms as final solutions. These last form then, after the social change has actually occurred, the nucleus for new, later upheavals.

The prevailing moral conception of a country tends to express itself in legislation, i.e., in the making of laws, the enforcement of laws, and public administration (executive power). The frequently observed contradictions between law and morals, between criminality and immorality, between the written law and "that which was born with us," can be explained in part by the impossibility of codification of certain norms, by the requirement of a rather considerable expense of time and energy for the carrying out of basic changes in the law, and, not least, by linguistic reasons: in the artificial language of law (Chapter 26, 1) one cannot express exactly *the same* as in the ordinary language, in which moral judgments are usually pronounced.

Apart from this, an essential difference between law and morals is that the former considers only specific instances of conduct and primarily prescribes concrete actions (e.g., a precisely limited curtailment of a person's freedom), while ethics restricts itself to the formulation of relatively general principles. A certain transition is formed by the so-called legal principles which do not give formulations of the kind of state laws, but directions for such a formulation. Between the condemnation in principle of theft and the sentencing to imprisonment for three months, with one fasting day every third week, there lies a gap that no penological rule of three can fill. The concrete precepts of civil and criminal law rest upon views of social expediency that are highly questionable and autistic and that vary markedly with time and place. It seems that we still have a long way to go before we arrive at the point where decisions in this field will be derived from unprejudiced, objective observations, carried out with scientific critique.

*The rise and decline of moral conceptions are closely connected with the experiences of daily life of the individual. An approximately stable situation is reached when the moral judgments are adapted to the distribution of power in the society. The derivation of concrete laws from moral principles encounters great difficulties. All scientific—sociological—studies in this direction are still in their infancy.*

6. *The Categorical Imperative.* Kant has given in his *Critique of Practical Reason* a "solution" of the problem of normative ethics. He states a single, quite general principle for moral behavior, from which all norms for practical life are to be derived. The principle is the following:

Act in such a way that the maxim of your will can at any time serve as the principle of a universal law.

This formulation is preceded by some discussions of what may be called a maxim, a principle, a law, etc. The proposition itself is called by Kant a "synthetic statement a priori, based upon no perception, neither pure, nor empirical" and it is also the "only factum of pure reason, which thereby demonstrates itself as originally sovereign (sic volo, sic jubeo)."

What Kant's basic principle, which is usually known as the "categorical imperative," really signifies can be understood only if one applies it to concrete cases. Kant remained unmarried all his life. If one were to take as the maxim that led him never to marry the proposition, "All men ought to remain unmarried," he would have admitted himself that this is not suited as a basis for a general law, since then the human race would die out very quickly. But he might have imagined as the maxim of his conduct the following: "All men who are to an extraordinary extent devoted to philosophical work ought to remain unmarried." This principle may perhaps be suitable for the foundation of a universal law, and hence Kant's behavior would prove compatible with the moral law or the categorical imperative. Kant's formula mentions the maxim of "your will" and not the maxim of behavior, but we know how uncertain and changing the self-motivations of human actions are. Hence in the last analysis the essential point is: one should be able to find *any* maxim from which the action in question follows and which at the same time leads to an acceptable general rule.

The main difficulty, however, of any application of Kant's idea to nontrivial questions is that we lack the criterion for judging in each case whether a suggested universal law is admissible, suitable, or desirable. Schopenhauer, for instance, would not have seen anything wrong in the expectation that the human race would be extinct in the near future. Kant, nevertheless, thinks that "the most ordinary mind can distinguish without any instruction what form of maxim" (and so much the more, what principle) "is suited for a general law, and what is not." For example, one could not set up a norm from which it follows that a deposit whose owner has died without leaving a written will may simply be embezzled. For it can be seen "that such a principle, as a law, would destroy itself, because it would result in there being no deposits at all." This kind of proof does not seem very convincing, but the question itself is in this case not very difficult to settle. On another occasion, Kant declares that the moral law requires us, if asked by a murderer for the whereabouts of our best friend, to answer the truth, even if we know for sure that the latter may lose his life by our answer. But it is not at all evident why it should not be a principle of a universal law that, in order to save a human life, one could conceal something one knows.

Kant's fundamental theorem does not, in our opinion, contribute to the decision of any serious question of moral behavior in a concrete case. This can be illustrated by an example from the life of Kant. We just saw what inexorable strictness he expressed with respect to white lies or even the concealment of the truth in a state of emergency. But when after the publication of his book *Die Religion innerhalb de Grenzen der blossen Vernunft* the Prussian government expressed its displeasure, Kant did not hesitate,

as your royal majesty's most obedient subject, to declare most solemnly: that in the future I shall refrain altogether from any public utterances concerning religion, either natural or revealed, in lectures as well as in writing.

One can imagine many maxims of this conduct which would make a quite reasonable universal law, but one does not have any doubts that from the point of view of the categorical imperative this compliance of a philosopher, who, after all, is supposed to be aware of his mission in the world, could also receive the sharpest condemnation.

Opponents of the Kantian ethics have sometimes claimed that his abovequoted fundamental law has no content at all. That is not our opinion. The sentence expresses that individual conduct is to be judged according to whether it fits into a decently organized community life, and that, therefore, morality is a sociological concept. This idea of course, is not sufficient for determining the behavior in an individual instance, but it represents, by pointing toward the study of social reactions, historically speaking, a great progress as compared to many older, heteronomous, and dogmatic ethical systems (Chapter 25, 4).

*The "fundamental law of pure practical reason," which Kant proposes as the starting point of ethics, does not yield concrete criteria for the judgment of a man's conduct in any situation of life; it presupposes that it is previously known what principles are suited for serving as the bases of general norms. Kant's theorem merely expresses that the moral valuation of any action of an individual is a* sociological *problem.*

7. *Naturalistic Ethics. Statements and Commands.* For building up a system of normative ethics, school philosophy made in the course of time many suggestions that are more or less similar to Kant's approach. All of them have in common that they are based in some way or another upon the supposed existence of an invariable original intuition (Chapter 25, 4) inborn in all men, which in the last analysis imparts to them the knowledge of what is good and what is evil. We have emphasized repeatedly that many decisive observations make such an assumption unacceptable to us. A further remark may be added with respect to other, so-called *naturalistic,* systems of ethics, They are characterized by their attempt to derive moral norms from biological or even physical theories.

The older of these doctrines refute themselves by the simple fact that the scientific theses on which they were based and which they accepted as dogmas are obsolete by now. Thus Herbert Spencer constructed a far-reaching philosophical system based upon the "a priori" true laws of inertia, indestructibility of matter, and conservation of energy, combining them with the law of evolution. All of these theorems have changed their meaning and content with the newer development of science. But it is hardly comprehensible what connection should exist at all between them and any question about ought and may—in the customary sense of these words. The same holds for the various attempts at "justifying" ethics "biologically," mostly based uniquely upon propositions of the theory of descent.

In more recent times, the chemist Wilhelm Ostwald, who called himself a follower of Mach, has actually put up a "basic law" that is to replace Kant's categorical imperative and which he called an "energetical imperative"; it reads, "Do not waste energy!" If one objects to this that often the only happiness of man comes from a certain feeling of waste, Ostwald answers that increased happiness means again an increase of energy—which gives to the physical concept of energy an extension that robs it of all its content. The overrating of the conceptual sphere connected with the word "energy" in Ostwald reaches a degree of lack of linguistic critique other-wise found only with the most extreme metaphysicians:

And thus the concept of energy proves to be in every respect the most uni-versal which science has so far produced. It includes not only the problem of substance, but also that of causality.

Naturally, it also leads to an "energetic world picture" that gives quick an-swers to all questions, even those of conduct; thus ethics would finally have been made a part of physics.

In the conception which this book represents, scientific research, to-ward whatever objects it may be directed, can always only determine rela-tions or connections between groups of phenomena. Its results, which are factual statements and not ought sentences, can only teach what conse-quences certain manners of conduct have. The difficulty here is that with all our statements and systems we can only comprehend special aspects, single artificially abstracted features of the relevant experiences (as far as causes are concerned as well as effects); this is particularly true in the case of those propositions which state something about a so-called totality, e.g., the total-ity of the state, the law, the society.

State, law, and moral systems are complex institutions which have been created by many actions of many men of many generations; among human actions we also count here the setting up of norms, their consolidation, and their defense. To the man who acts, only a small part of the consequences of his conduct can be known in time; some other consequences become known later, but in many points the interconnections remain obscure. The growing stock of true and supposedly true knowledge leads to ever-new manners of conduct and causes changes in the norms. It depends upon the total in-fluences that state and society and the predominant conceptions in them exert upon the individual, in what way he may react to new insights, to the unveiling of new connections, and how he performs, often uncon-sciously, mostly inadvertently, the transition from knowledge of facts to decisions. If we see in social institutions, including the ethical norms, products of human activity, this does not preclude that the individual at any time, whatever he does, acts under the decisive influence of society.

*All attempts at constructing a system of ethics (a system of absolute norms) upon theories of physics or biology must fail, since the propositions of these sciences (as of all others) are factual statements and not ought sentences. The setting up, the acceptance and observance of norms require intentional decisions, which the individual makes under the pressure exerted by his environment, by state and society. In these decisions, scientific (so-ciological) studies are relevant only in so far as they instruct one about the interrelations of various groups of actions and occurrences.*

### CHAPTER 27

# ethics and religion

1. *Religious and Duty Ethics*. The school-philosophy treatment of ethics comprises, on the whole, two quite different problems. The one, which we mainly discussed above, is to construct a system of norms; in the language proper to school philosophy this means to discover the somehow existing, objective, and absolute system of normative ethics. The second problem, considered as a part of metaphysics, consists in studying the "essence" or "real meaning" of morality or of moral actions. One may interpret this as the search for relations between the ways of conduct determined by the norms and other known phenomena.

It is certainly not easy to pick out, from a given accumulation of metaphysical theses, leading ideas that can be expressed in clear and distinct words; this problem of translation is, indeed, unsolvable (Chapter 21, 3). But we believe that we come close to the actual situation if we mention the following three types of answer offered to the question what moral conduct "really" is. In the first place, man acts morally in obeying the rules handed down to him by an extraworldly power and relies upon the rewards promised him for his life after death. In the second place, moral action consists in man's following the moral codes known to him, without any regard to the consequences of his actions, either his own feelings of happiness or any possible transworldly reward. In the third place, conduct is moral when it is directed toward the realization of quite specific worldly purposes; such purposes are, e.g., one's own happiness, the happiness of others, one's own perfection, the progress of human institutions, the promotion of one's own people or of mankind, and many others.

The first of these notions, usually called *religious ethics,* since it forms an essential component of many religious systems, has the advantage of being simple and, in a certain sense, clear. It is usually supplemented by pointing out the sources in which the rules that are given once and for all by authoritative power are to be found. The best-known example is the decalogue of the Jewish tradition. But this tradition does not clearly indicate whether the commandment "Thou shalt not kill" is also applicable to, say, warfare, executions, suicide, mercy killing, etc. The main difficulty is always that no fixed normative systems, however detailed, can *in the long run* suffice to regulate the conduct of men in all possible situations of life. Since the interpretation of laws, the subsumption, etc., as we have seen (Chapter 26, 1), are by no means purely logical processes, but rest upon the adduction of ever-new norms, religious ethics has to assume the continuance of superworldly authority in specific *living persons*. In practice, this has the effect that the development (modification) of the system of norms is slowed down, limited in its range, kept in specific paths, and withdrawn from a part of social influences.

The second of the above-mentioned notions, *the ethic of duty* or of obligations, deviates from the first in that it eliminates the idea of future reward or punishment and attempts to transfer the criterion of moral action completely to subjective consciousness, which in this case is called the "conscience." Nobody can believe that the conscience speaks independently of education, experience, and other influences of the environment, including the experiences of former generations. According to Herbert Spencer, the conscience is "the species' experience of the useful." As a rule, the conscience deems an action virtuous if it does not carry with it the promise of immediate advantage or pleasure in one of the forms familiar to the person in question, e.g., material profit, satisfaction of sensual desire or of instincts of revenge, etc. The particular kind of pleasure that is customarily called "moral satisfaction" is not considered as impairing the moral purity of an action. On the other hand, the favorable judgment of the conscience is strengthened if an action entails some familiar form of feelings of displeasure, such as those due to strain, loss of property, bodily harm, etc. In every case it is seen that the decision of the conscience depends upon the stock of experience of the individual; among persons who belong to widely different social strata there is agreement only in the most trivial instances. It is doubtful whether the Occidental concept of conscience is at all applicable to phenomena such as the nirvana ideal in its highest perfection:

> The nirvana is reached by dissociating oneself from all sensual impressions and all attachments; for him who has reached this highest summit there can be no return, for in nirvana there is no birth, no death, neither does one belong to somebody, nor does anybody belong to the one who has entered nirvana.

In the face of such conduct, which can be called extreme altruism as well as the strongest sort of egotism, the criterion of the ethic of duty seems to break down.

The third type of ethical system, the utilitarian, we shall treat in the following section.

*A heteronomous (authoritative, religious) ethic can be maintained only if one assumes in addition to the original revelation a continuous representation of the authoritative deciding power through all time. The ethic of duty, which assigns the decision on the morality of actions to man's conscience, implies the assumption that all individuals have at their disposal a more or less uniform store of experience; at any rate, it breaks down in the face of certain moral phenomena of the Far Eastern world.*

2. *Utilitarianism. Socrates.* The third of the ethical theories mentioned in the beginning of this chapter, which can be called *utilitarian ethics* in a general sense, regards moral conduct as in some wise *purposeful.* There are the most vigorous debates among the various metaphysical schools concerning the detailed definition of the purpose; but one cannot really speak here of very essential differences. On the one hand, there is the utilitarian conception in the narrower sense of the word, which identifies the moral with the useful, or the hedonistic, according to which the essential aim is the achievement of feelings of pleasure. The other extreme is given by the theories which see the aim of moral conduct in the "perfection" of the individual or the society, in the fulfillment and development of one's own life, i.e., the cultivation and exploitation of all potentialities within the single individual. We cannot find a clear, demonstrable contrast between these apparently so different formulas. Almost any conduct that is justifiable from one of these points of view can also be justified by the others. Those who act consciously in an altruistic way, those who strive to perfect themselves, and those who seek to develop their personality all find some sort of satisfaction for their desire of pleasure and attain personal happiness, and all of these various forms of behavior can even in some sense be called useful.

Most of the theories of school philosophy serve for a *justificatio post festum,* i.e., they set out to prove that the social institutions which have asserted themselves successfully in our civilization for a long time are the only right ones, the only useful, and the only possible. But it cannot be "logically proved" that our form of monogamy is the only solution of the sexual problem, any more than it can be proved that airplanes can be driven only by combustion engines. We do not know whether at some future time airplanes will not fly exclusively by means of steam power or electric batteries or nuclear energy (today's aeronautical engineers may shudder as they read this), or whether a presently unknown form of controlled sex life will not find general acceptance. The customary objection that the "nature" of man, after all, remains always the same carries no weight. For the mechanical and physical foundations upon which today's technology is based also existed thousands of years ago just as today. It is the change in the human *stock of experience* that causes changes in human actions and behavior.

*Socrates' ethics* is frequently summarized by the aphorism, "the good is the true." The sentence belongs to that not rare class of metaphysical propositions in which two words, denoting different things, as the author and the listener or reader are clearly aware, are simply connected by the word "is," although nobody knows what sort of relation is meant here. Further examples of such aggregates are: "the world is our will," "God is the world," "nature is God," "living is perishing," "religion is virtue," "death is life," "one is all, and all is one," etc. The good fortune of these sentences (and the good fortune of metaphysics) rests upon the fact that everybody gives to the identification of the two concepts the interpretation that suits him. Socrates, according to all we know about him, can hardly be claimed as a promoter of metaphysics. He taught the application of common sense to *all* situations of life and believed that the statesman and legislator, like any craftsman, could arrive at rules for his conduct only through careful observation and thinking. School philosophy does not like to have Socrates represent the point of view that virtue is nothing but *knowledge,* a technique, to be acquired by training, practice, and habit, as is geometry or any handicraft; for thus ethics would be entirely taken out of the realm of metaphysics. It seems to us that the doctrines of Socrates are closely related to our conception, according to which any science as soon as it is applied leads to conditional norm sentences (Chapter 26, 2), and that every regulation, if one gives it a justification at all, must take the form of the norms occurring in the positive sciences. The promotion of such ametaphysical doctrines seemed to the Athenian government a "destructive" activity and on this ground it had Socrates sentenced to death. His disciple, Plato, returned to the pre-Socratic metaphysics and thus became the ancestor of the Occidental idealistic philosophy.

*The conception, represented by one wing of school philosophy, that moral action is in a specific sense expedient or useful action does not lead beyond what we had seen previously (Chapter 26, 7), namely, that the observation of norms rests upon intentional decisions, which are guided by positive science only in so far as this points out connections between actions and their consequences. We find that the Socratic ethics, as handed down to us, agrees in essential points with our notion.*

3. *Instinct and Reasoning.* We shall briefly discuss an objection that readily suggests itself and can be brought against our conception, especially where it touches the Socratic doctrine of the knowledge of virtue. It might be said that we reserve too large a role for the intellect, the reasoning insight, in the formation of moral judgments and practical decisions. In reality, it is said, the moral life belongs entirely or almost exclusively

to the realm of feelings, moods, and instincts; no subtle acts of thought, no previous reasoning govern the moral decisions. Some authors, e.g., M. Schlick, even think it necesary to assume here the existence of a kind of preëstablished harmony between the results of unconscious, instinctive processes and the results of reasoning thought.

We agree with Nietzsche's opinion that one speaks of moral feelings and moods only

as though they were so many units; in truth they are streams with a hundred sources and branches. Here too, as so often, the unity of the word does not prove anything about the unity of the thing.

As we have pointed out repeatedly (Chapter 5, Chapter 24), we do not believe that the sharp contrasting of mood, feeling, and instinct on the one hand and intellect on the other is tenable. What is called mood consists of residues of old, diversified experiences, which were mostly assimilated during childhood, and perhaps even sometimes inherited. We know from many autobiographies that most *insignificant* early experiences can influence permanently and decisively one's feelings of later life, and we have to assume that the vast majority of such experiences are forgotten but nevertheless effective, either in the psychoanalytic sense of repressions or otherwise. Lines of thought that recur frequently, from early childhood on, and always in the same way, finally condense into an apparent unit: they become "instinctive." If it is pointed out that morals are usually taught not by explicit instruction through moral codes but rather by the exemplifying conduct of the teacher, we regard this as a particular technique of communication and instruction. Reading, counting, and the first points of arithmetic are also learned almost instinctively by children who grow up in the right environment, yet nobody will deny that these are intellectual abilities. In the practical application of these elements of knowledge in adult life the intellect is not consciously used, but whenever one recognizes the fact that three objects at fixed unit price cost more than two, one makes use of a result of mathematical research that was not reached by mankind until a rather late stage of civilization. Even the simplest and most familiar handling of any household instrument, say the telephone, is based upon a certain knowledge of physics, even though in a concrete single case the act may be done completely "instinctively." It is in this sense that one must understand our formulation that moral decisions are guided by scientific, sociological considerations.

The "rejection of the intellect," which we know as one of the general negativistic tendencies (Chapter 5) and as a certain poetic attitude (Chapter 23, 6), takes a special form in the field of ethics. Attempts are often made to identify a specific moral attitude as that of intellectualism. The naïve, unconsciously and instinctively acting man, whose conduct is determined by habitual and innate drives, along with those acquired in his upbringing, is contrasted to the reflective type of man, who has a purposive expediency in mind, who weighs the consequences of his actions, and even in certain cases bases his conduct upon scientific considerations. There is no doubt that this disjunction—especially in our times—is made with the purpose of distinguishing the naïve type as the more "valuable."

There is no use in arguing about the valuation. No doubt, criteria can be found by which the first type may be rated the higher one, and other arguments in favor of the second. We do not countenance any evaluation without a system of reference. The only question of interest is this: does the abovementioned disjunction point to a real contrast between one moral attitude, resting upon the intellect, and another, resting upon a different foundation? We do not think that this is the case; for habitual action is but an action based upon past reasonings, one's own or another's. It is only the momentary situation of each individual that is different, and in a description of his personality this may be pointed out; but if the actions as such are to be described, along with the external and internal relations in which they take place, it must not be overlooked that they rest upon an earlier activity of the intellect. Even where one speaks of social drives, of faith, or of devotion as the immediate motives, there lie in the background early intellectual efforts dating back to the first attempts to find one's way in the world.

*The subjective conduct of the acting individual may in many cases be explained by habit, instinct, or an attitude of feeling; that does not contradict the assumption that in the formation of the moral norms the intellect has the decisive part.*

4. *Spinoza.* Spinoza's *Ethics,* published in 1677, holds a quite special position in the ethical literature of the Occident. In its external appearance it is an imitation of a mathematical text (*Ethica ordine geometrico demonstrata*); but with respect to the form of language actually used, it must be called metaphysical. As far as the purpose of the author and the content are concerned, it is rationalistic, i.e., it reserves the highest rank for human reason; but the exposition avoids any break with basic religious ideas and it is formulated in such a way that one may speak of a religious ethic. The great attraction that the book has continually exerted upon a great many of the most important thinkers is due to the fact that the system of norms to which it leads corresponds largely to the ideals that have come to be favored in the educated society of the civilized Western world.

Of the method of arranging the material in the form of axioms, theorems, proofs, etc., it must be said that it bears only a very superficial resemblance to the form of presentation used by Euclid. In particular, what was the weakest point in Euclid (and later in Newton) and has been given up entirely by modern axiomatics, namely, the precedence of verbal definitions for the basic concepts appearing in the axioms, plays the primary role in Spinoza's work. It goes without saying that none of his "demonstrations" has any relation to mathematical conclusions. However, we do not wish to give much import to this matter of style.

Of the five parts of the *Ethica* only the last two are devoted to the derivation and discussion of norms of conduct. The first two develop a metaphysical system: "On God" and "On the Nature and the Origin of the Mind." The third, about the "Origin and the Nature of the Affects," is a kind of psychological study of the feelings of pleasure. It is remarkable that this third part of the book is free from any metaphysics and is a purely scientific investigation of human actions and drives:

> Humanas actiones atque appetitus considerabo . . . ac si quaestio de lineis, planis aut de corporibus esset. (I shall consider human actions and strivings . . . as if the question were of straight lines, planes, or bodies.)

Spinoza attempts here, indeed, to give an unprejudiced, factual description of psychological phenomena accessible to observation; it is only the form of exposition that he chose which led him frequently to a much too apodictic manner of expression. On the whole, the problem he posed for himself, namely, to develop a psychology of the drives and affect actions, has until our era of psychoanalysis hardly been much advanced. Incidentally, the theses of the psychoanalysts, although based upon a great wealth of observation, still show a singular tendency toward dogmatism.

Spinoza's ethic has its starting point in the idea that we call good or bad what is useful or harmful for the preservation of our life; what furthers our capacity for action or retards it; and what is thus connected with a sensation of pleasure or displeasure. Virtuous conduct is nothing but to follow the laws of reason, to live, and to safeguard one's real nature (ex ductu rationis agere, vivere, suum esse conservare, haec tria idem significant). The way of life resulting from this conception is a life of moderation, restraint of the drives, forgoing external success, power, and wealth; above all, it is a nonaggressive life of peaceful and loving activity. This norm of individual conduct is supplemented by a theory of social life, which is mainly developed in the later *Tractatus politicus*. In this work Spinoza attempts, again free from any metaphysics, to derive from *observations* those forms of public institutions which are the most useful and hence commendable ones.

We have mentioned above (Chapter 26, 5) that the acceptance or rejection of a new system of norms depends essentially upon whether the arguments offered for its justification agree with the everyday experiences of the individual or not. We may entirely disregard here the deductive proofs or pseudo proofs of Spinoza; nor are we interested in the question whether his theses were entirely new or perhaps anticipated in Christian doctrine or even in certain teachings of classical antiquity. Most people are taught by the daily recurring experience in their own lives and in their immediate environment that certain feelings of happiness are easily accessible through moderation, mastery of the natural drives, conscious (cognitive) conquest of the will, and an attitude of restraint in social intercourse. The reports we have about the personal life of Spinoza particularly corroborate this view. The majority of men, of course, know such a state of restraint and its consequences only as an occasional passing experience, but it is easily imagined or accepted without very careful examination that a life guided consistently by these principles could be a continually happy one. This is the reason why ways of conduct which are similar to the ones Spinoza recommended (and which, to a large extent, can be classified as Christian) are called ideal, dignified, and noble. It is but in agreement with our conception of the relativity of moral codes (Chapter 26, 4) that at the same time and perhaps at the same place quite different and opposite ideals are cherished, e.g., the ideal of the heroic life, etc.

*Spinoza's ethics leads to a system of norms whose justification, stripped of unessential accessories, comes down to the observation that certain ways of conduct are connected with immediate subjective feelings of happiness. It seems that the personal experiences of a large part of mankind are in good agreement with his propositions.*

5. *Religious Systems.* The majority of people become acquainted with rules for their behavior not in the form of scientific systems. We mentioned above (Chapter 27, 3) the role of outright imitation of the examples set by the life of educators (in the widest sense of the word). But even for the part of moral norms that are communicated explicitly by linguistic means, a form has been developed through long tradition, which is clearly distinct from scientific methods. Certain aggregates of interconnected assertions, whose ultimate purpose is to control in a specific way the conduct of large groups of people, are known as *religious systems.* A complex of such sentences, which in their totality form a religious doctrine, is akin to a system of metaphysics, but has also points in common with certain works of art, especially with mythical poetry.

We have emphasized (Chapter 21, 1) that the positivism here represented by us cannot be simply characterized as "anti"-metaphysical. We regard metaphysical systems as "science in the beginning," as the first attempts at a description of the world, which necessarily go far beyond the acquired stock of experience and in this endeavor use linguistic means uncritically. We do not say either that the assertions of religion, even though they may contain expressions that do not seem in any way connectible (reducible to element sentences, Chapter 8, 2), are, in general, without sense or meaning. They originate, in our view, in the human desire for orientation in one's environment, for the description of complicated interrelations that are difficult to comprehend, *with the special aim* of finding useful rules for the community life of man. We quite agree with the strongly "positivistic" remark of Goethe, according to which it is the aim of religion "to further the just and tranquil intercourse of people." Those who study without prejudice the historical course of events will recognize that the present state of moral conduct in almost all countries of the earth was developed under the essential influence of various religious systems.

If one attempts to determine some of the characteristics which, on the whole, are common to most of the religious systems, one may find the following points. It is assumed that the world is created according to an intelligent plan and governed by a just ruler; the most important rules for moral conduct have been communicated to men by revelation or through a special agent; conduct that appears objectionable or commendable according to this standard finds its punishment or reward in the life after death. In addition, there are many details about the creation of the world, about the constitution of world government, the situation in the "other world," the kinds of punishment and reward, and, above all, strongly diverging specifications of the occurrences by which man came to know all this. In the historical development of religions one can generally recognize, although not without exceptions, a trend from more concrete (anthropomorphic) ideas, which closely resemble earthly situations, to those of a more abstract and idealized nature.

The basic assumptions of the religious systems are inductive generalizations of observations, in principle of the same kind as the basic assumptions of any natural science. If all occurrences we know have a cause, all things we deal with a creator, all societies that exist a ruler, the world as a whole must also have an original cause, a creator, and a supreme ruler. A metaphysics that regards the entity to which the word "cause" and other causal expressions point as an "a priori category" endeavors in vain to draw a fundamental dividing line between religious and its own (allegedly) scientific ideas and theories. Connectibility with the language of science and practical life is preserved neither in metaphysical nor in religious systems, nor in the creations of art. Nevertheless, in any of these fields we find assertions which, even though in a vague and rather undetermined form, point to factual situations that can be tested in experience, and sometimes provide the first steps toward a useful description.

*The practically most efficient form of dispersion of ethical doctrines is their incorporation in the framework of religious systems. These systems,*

*like metaphysics and certain creations of art, attempt a broad description
of essential features of the world, which is undertaken from the beginning
with the definite purpose of deriving rules of conduct.*

6. *Philosophical "Justification."* The inquiries of school philosophies into religion deal mainly with the problem of "proving" single propositions of religious doctrine, e.g., the existence of God or of an original
cause. The authors claim, more or less explicitly, that their proofs are
essentially of the same kind as ordinary demonstrations in mathematics.
We have sufficiently pointed out in this book that mathematical proofs are
tautological transformations of assumed basic propositions, that they can
only prove assertions which do not state anything about the world of experience but play their role exclusively within an axiomatic system. If somebody claims that the deflection of a light ray in a magnetic field can be
mathematically proved, he uses a very inexact manner of speaking. All that
is proved is that from (mathematical) assumptions which are derived
from experience—the principles of the electromagnetic theory of light—
there follows a theorem which after retranslation from mathematical to
everyday language states the existence of the light deflection.

Within the field we have now in mind, a mathematization of the basic
propositions is hardly possible; it is not even known what sort of assumptions are to serve as starting points. The so-called *ontological proof* of the
existence of God starts out with the premise, "All men have the idea of a
most perfect being." This is at best an observation on the individual
minds of various men and one would think that from it one could derive
only other psychological facts. But the "proof" continues: If among the
qualities of this highest being the quality of "existence" were lacking, it
would not be the most perfect being; hence the most perfect being must
exist. It is not necessary to enter into any detailed discussion of this play on
words, in which existence is made a quality which itself may again exist or
not exist and whose existence contributes to the perfection of a subject.
Most of the other proofs of the existence of God have the direct form of
inductive generalizations. Everything that is in motion, says Thomas
Aquinas, has a cause that is at rest; the world is in motion; hence there
must be a world cause that is at rest absolutely within itself. The first
elements of linguistic critique, which have been indicated in Part IV, teach
us how to assess such sentences. The so-called pragmatic proof of the
existence of God points in a different direction: The assumption of the
existence of God is useful and life-promoting; hence it is also true.

All of these and similar attempts at a philosophic justification and
support of religion, such as Kant's

even though metaphysics cannot form the foundation of religion, it must always
be one of its most important bulwarks,

must fail. They can be understood only historically out of a social situation which today in most countries no longer exists, namely, the pressure that the church and the powers behind it exerted in many ways upon the philosopher. On the other hand, it was exactly this pressure that had the result that many independent thinkers felt a special attraction in turning against religion and in deprecating its importance. A misunderstanding of a special kind is manifest in the various attempts at the justification of a "religion of reason" or in the creation of a "positive religion," with which Comte thought he had crowned his life's work (Chapter 28, 2).

We see in every religion a specially formulated system of rules of conduct, which carefully take into account the situations occurring in everyday life. An essential characteristic of a religious system is this: it undertakes in principle to answer *all* questions that usually arise, on the average level of education, with respect to personal matters of individual and social life. The believer has for every experience a rule and for every problem a solution. In order to accomplish this result, it was necessary to create a language—for the rules, the answers, and the questions—in which the zone of indeterminacy of all words and all sentences is much wider than even in everyday language (Chapter 3, 2). This holds not only for specific expressions of the religious sphere, such as God and Providence, angel and devil, holy and sinful, cursing and praying, etc., but *every* word, *every* sentence takes a different meaning in a religious text: the coördination to the world of experience is changed and becomes more vague. There are astronomers and geologists who are devout Christians and do not raise objections to the Biblical story of creation; they understand the sentences in the Bible differently—a common denotation for this is "symbolic"—and read them as though they were written in a different language. Theology consists of the futile endeavor to connect the two languages of religion and of science (Chapter 27, 7).

*The various assertions of a religious doctrine do not allow of scientific or philosophical justification. They can be understood only as elements of a comprehensive system, which develops rules for human conduct and for this purpose makes use of a special form of language. The translation into one of the languages of everyday life, science, poetry, or metaphysics, is subject to the unavoidable difficulties of any translation.*

7. *The Religious Drive.* Our conception of religion as a comprehensive system of norms with a peculiar type of rationale cannot of course, do justice to *every* aspect of religion in its relation to man. Particularly it will be noticed that many people have an *immediate urge* for absorbing religious ideas, and also a desire for dealing with those questions and answers in which we see the attempts at systematic justification of the religious rules of conduct. We pointed out earlier an analogous attitude

toward metaphysics, and, indeed, a strict boundary line between meta-physics, religion, and mysticism can hardly be drawn, in so far as religion is taken as a philosophy of life and not merely as a system of norms. We may leave open the question whether this metaphysical and religious longing represents an original drive, common to all men, or whether it has developed under the conditions of Occidental civilization from the instinct of self-preservation and the resulting need for orientation in one's environ-ment. Observations of the primitive and the study of Asiatic religions seem to speak rather for the latter assumption. But no matter, we assert in opposition to all religious, mystical, and metaphysical tendencies our positivistic point of view: We regard it as our task *to explore,* i.e., to con-tinue the scientific development whose beginning was the formation of lan-guage, with the final aim, for all questions posed, of arriving at *connectible* answers.

The psychological foundations of religion have been studied extensively during the last fifty years. William James in his well-known work on *The Varieties of Religious Experience* (1902) stresses again and again the empiricist point of view. In his conclusions, however, he succumbs entirely to the mode of expression of the idealist school philosophers: "God is real since he produces real effects." Sigmund Freud, the creator of psycho-analysis, traces the roots of religion to the subconscious; he calls the religious feeling

a feeling of indissoluble belonging, of being one with the whole of the external world . . . a sensation of eternity . . . a feeling as of something unbounded, limitless, so to speak "oceanic."

Freud locates the origin of this feeling in earliest childhood, in the stage preceding the development of the ego, when the awakening intellect has not yet arrived at a distinction between its own self and the environment and has not yet reached consciousness of the sensations constituting the ego. We may remember that notion introduced by Mach (Chapter 7, 6), which now becomes essential for our whole view: the ego is a practical unit, which was created for vital, but limited, purposes and must be re-placed in the range of more comprehensive questions by the assumption of continuous interconnections among *all* elements of perception. While from a vague feeling of this over-all connection there grows the religious mood, a thoughtful analysis leads to the clarification of innumerable pseudo problems and to essential insights.

A large and extensive field of scientific pseudo problems is represented by *theology.* The interpretation and explication of the "scriptures" consists in reading into primitive expressions which were framed thousands of years ago ideas that are not there, ideas that developed only through the continued preoccupation with these very expressions (translated into modern languages) in a process of constant change and widening of meaning. A well-known example is the beginning of the gospel of St. John, from which gradually the formula "l'être éternel produisant le monde par la parole" was derived. Even more striking is the situation with respect to questions of actual theological theory. In the doctrine of transubstantiation, the question is raised whether something is "really present," while at the same time everybody realizes from the start that these words should not mean in this case what in ordinary language is meant by "really present." Nevertheless, arguments about whether, and to what extent, the expression may be applied to the religious ceremony in question, whether it agrees with the "actual, true, and immanent" meaning of the two words, have been carried on with the greatest amount of sagacity. The physical fights that resulted from this debate are to be understood by the fact that each party regarded its proposition as a component part of a comprehensive system of rules of behavior, thus representing in the last analysis certain material interests.

In our opinion, the existence of God can be proved as little as the principle of conservation of energy. This principle has its place in a tautological system whose purpose it is, in the last analysis, to predict observable phenomena and thus to determine human actions in a certain field. The system in which the statement on the existence of God appears is of a similar kind and tries to direct human conduct in a definite way. The difference is only that practically all observations in the physical world agree with the energy principle and the whole system of physics, while innumerable occurrences of everyday life contradict the religious theories and actually force people to act differently. Whoever installs a lightning rod on his roof or undergoes a surgical operation or practices birth control acts against the letter and the spirit of religion even if *some* of these actions are in our time condoned by complacent churchmen.

Akin to theology are the modern negativistic movements that are known under the names of theosophy and Christian Science. The founder of the latter, Mary Baker Eddy, has written sentences such as this one (1875):

> Christian Science explains all cause and effect as mental, nonphysical . . . All substance, intelligence, wisdom, being, immortality, cause and effect belong to God. These are His attributes, the eternal manifestations of the infinite divine principle, Love.

These sequences of words are sentences only in the sense that they satisfy the routine rules of grammar, but they are not connectible with any constituted language; that, however, does not prevent them from forming a part of a system of moral norms that may rightly enjoy a certain popularity.

The contrast between religion and science is often defined by the formulation that the one deals with "belief," the other with "knowledge."

If this is to make any sense one should be able to describe the difference in the situation of two men, one of whom "knows" that a statement is true, and another who only "believes" it, i.e., is convinced of its truth. Here we are again inclined toward a view which a popular conception of positivism may regard as "antipositivistic." We think that *everything* called "knowledge" is only a belief, an assuming-to-be-true, open to any change on the grounds of future experience.

*The desire for an explanation of the world in religious form may be due to an original instinctual drive. In any case, from the instinct of self-preservation there arises a desire for over-all orientation in the environment at large and for reliable predictions, i.e., anticipations that will agree with future experience. At a later stage, science endeavors to offer such predictions, and where its results are in contradiction to the claims of a religious system, the latter lose out.*

CHAPTER 28

# historical remarks. conjectures and conclusions

1. *The Development up to Kant.* We have seen that the essential function of all science is that it allows the making of *predictions* about future experiences. In the realm of the natural sciences, particularly in physics, where the phenomena treated are accomplished in short intervals of time and are easily repeatable, this statement is rather uncontested. That the same assertion is also true for the humanities, and above all, for history, was one of the results of Part V. If one usually prefers in this case to speak of conjectures rather than of predictions, the reason is that in social phenomena that form the subject matter of the history of mankind the recurrent elements are much more difficult to determine and thus are much less well explored. The subject matter of our book may also be considered as part of sociology; it concerns those endeavors of men which are directed toward information, orientation, and knowledge. All "laws" (recurring elements) we have found in this domain contain implicit predictions of the future. We shall attempt now to bring out a few principal results of this kind and to combine with this a brief recapitulation of what was said before.

Let us first cast a short glance upon the *historical development* of that conception of knowledge with which we feel in closest agreement; scattered indications of it have been given already in the various chapters of the book.

Limiting ourselves to the domain of Occidental culture, we must start with the Greeks. We have pointed out earlier (Chapter 21, 5) that the older pre-Socratic philosophy was essentially metaphysics. It is more difficult to judge the role of the so-called Sophists, who are, as is well known, today an anathema of school philosophy. It seems that the Sophists opposed in many ways the predominant religious and philosophical metaphysics with arguments of common sense, i.e., by appeal to the meaning that the words used possessed in ordinary language. To say the least, they prepared the ground upon which Socrates could develop his effective influence. We see in Socrates, whose historical status has never been completely clarified, a philosopher who freed himself from traditional metaphysical prejudices and argued for a sober way of thinking in *all* fields of life, in agreement with the scientific and technologic state of his time. With Plato, metaphysics gained the upper hand again. Aristotle, who is rightly regarded as the founder of many positive sciences, was also the initiator of the still accepted notion that every science must be based upon metaphysical principles. All idealistic philosophy of modern times goes back to Plato; Aristotle became the father of scholasticism, which believes that one can solve all problems by operations of pure thinking, without extending the stock of experience beyond that contained in Aristotle's writings.

The overcoming of the scholastic method, which had retarded the development of the sciences, was at first impeded by the Catholic Church, which had ascended to great power in Europe, but was finally accomplished by enlightened representatives of the same Church. The English Franciscan friars Roger Bacon, Duns Scotus, and William of Occam in the thirteenth and fourteenth centuries defended with remarkable vigor the need for scientific, empirical research in answering "philosophical" questions of all kinds. Their work was continued by Francis Bacon, Thomas Hobbes, John Locke, Bishop Berkeley, then effectively furthered by the scientific progress achieved by Newton and others, and finally reached a climax in David Hume (1711–1776), the most enlightened thinker in the history of philosophy until the end of the eighteenth century.

Meanwhile, the movement of Enlightenment had also taken root in France, although it followed here a somewhat different course from that in England. While the English thinkers strove primarily toward *empiricism,* i.e., emphasized the role of observation and control by experience, the French were more interested in logical problems, i.e., the critique of language. Outstanding as a unique phenomenon is Descartes (1596–1650), who—within certain limitations inherent in the conditions of his time—asserted the autonomy of human reason, the independence of its decisions of any "higher" authority. Spinoza, who began where Descartes had left off, designed a metaphysical world picture, but, nevertheless, strove in his ethic undoubtedly toward empirical justifications. A short time later, the philosophy of the Enlightenment started in France with Pierre Bayle and Montesquieu, and they were followed by the two founders of positivism and the scientific conception of the world, Condillac and d'Alembert. D'Alembert (1717–1783) conceived the successful idea of an encyclopedia, a comprehensive summary of all knowledge so far secured by mankind. Condillac (1715–1780) was perhaps the first who clearly understood that all studies relating the separate sciences to each other consist primarily of a critique of language. The sentimental philosophy of Rousseau embarked on a sidetrack.

The development that led in England to Hume and in France to Condillac and d'Alembert did not prevent Kant (1724–1804) from regarding as the essential problem of philosophy an answer to the question: How is a priori knowledge about reality, independent of experience and derived from pure reason, possible? The wish for such a possibility was built with great ingenuity into a system of very broad extent. The essential basis for this endeavor was that the philosophy which called itself "critical" made use of the language of science in an entirely uncritical way. The same manner of thinking was inherent in the various later "idealistic" systems, e.g., Schopenhauer's, which shows even in its leading principle, "The world is our will . . . ," upon what sort of linguistic naïveté it is founded (Chapter 2, 4). In Hegel's (1770–1831) "absolute and objective mind," in which nature fulfills itself as incarnated reason, as well as in his "basic postulate," "the world is the contradiction in itself; it is at the same time being and not-being," philosophy performed a somersault and became mere play with words.

*While since the thirteenth century in England, and later also in France, a positive philosophy had developed, based on empiricism, on abandonment of belief in authorities, and on a critical conception of language, the German "idealistic" philosophy of the eighteenth and nineteenth centuries went a step backward in the direction toward a-priorism, metaphysics, and linguistic fetishism.*

2. *The Newer Development.* It is naturally much more difficult to characterize the more recent phases of any development, where we have not as yet gained the necessary perspective. The great accomplishment of Auguste Comte (1798–1857), which has been mentioned above repeatedly, lies behind us as a relatively closed chapter, including its immediate aftereffects. Comte, in the six volumes of his *Cours de philosophie positive,* has created a work that is usually regarded as the foundation of the "positive" world conception, a world picture free from metaphysics and based entirely upon science. The basic idea of his theory of history was pointed out by us earlier (Chapter 18, 3). Comte attached great importance to the construction of a "system" or a "hierarchy" of the sciences, which starts with mathematics and culminates in the social sciences (Chapter 17, 7). He exerted the most lasting influence by giving to sociology, in the widest sense of the word (up to then there had existed only a very one-sided science of economics), a definite position in the realm of scientific endeavors. The supreme rule of practical conduct is for Comte's positivism the ideal of *humanitarianism* and the unlimited devotion to individuals who have earned merit in contributing to progress. In his later years Comte

attempted to give his positivistic doctrine the form of a religious system, and even to introduce a formal cult in which he himself took the place of the High Priest. Such an undertaking could only fail, since, as we have learned, religion is an essentially different language from science and one cannot bridge the gap by the acceptance of similar external forms. The aftereffect of Comte's *philosophie positive* was, and still is today, harmed by the mystic-sentimental turn of the last years of his life.

In England, John Stuart Mill (1806–1873), influenced in his early ideas by Comte, represented an extreme empiricism that did not find the right place in its world picture for the logical aspects of science. Here, Bentham's utilitarianism and the later philosophy of evolution of Herbert Spencer (1820–1903) became the dominating ideas in the conception of science until the end of the nineteenth century.

In Germany the reaction against the excesses of Hegelian dialectics asserted itself in various ways. On the one hand, there appeared an extreme so-called materialism (Vogt, Büchner, Haeckel), which regarded all world riddles as solved by the latest results of natural science. Then there was an accentuated return to Kant, represented by different, mutually antagonistic schools (Fries' school, the neo-Kantians Cohen and Natorp, and later the "old-Kantians" such as Marcus, Riehl, etc.) and by a few individuals who swerved a little farther, such as Vaihinger (Chapter 2, 5), Dilthey (Chapter 17), etc. On the border line between philosophy and poetry lies the work of Friedrich Nietzsche (1844–1900), whose writings before the Zarathustra period exhibit an almost entirely positivistic point of view (Chapter 23, 5).

The decisive turn to a comprehensive positivistic world conception, based on science and a critical attitude toward language, is given for us with the work of Ernst Mach (1838–1916). His ideas are presented and amplified in many of the chapters of this book (see particularly Chapter 7). Some of Mach's theses were developed shortly later in a weaker and more conciliatory form by Henri Poincaré (1854–1912). Mach himself mentions as a school-philosophical parallel to his own work that of Richard Avenarius and, at a certain distance, also of W. Schuppe. But neither the "empirio-criticism" of the former nor the "philosophy of immanence" of the latter could essentially influence the school philosophy of our time, which as we know (Chapter 5), in Germany and elsewhere, is strongly inclined toward negativism.

On the other hand, Mach felt always attracted by the Anglo-Saxon attitude toward science. He dedicated his books to such men as J. B. Stallo, Karl Pearson, William James, and he sponsored a German edition of Stallo's book on *Physical Concepts*. In America, school philosophy had been taken over from Europe with little enthusiasm and soon a countermovement began. Charles S. Peirce (1839–1914), the founder of pragmatism, exerted himself in both directions, in an enlightened view on logic and in the empiricist conception of science. He was followed by William James (1842–1910), who strongly opposed the importation of German idealistic philosophy. In our day, John Dewey, liberally minded, tried to adapt the principles of school philosophy to educational and other practical problems. The physicist P. W. Bridgman devised in his operationalism a theory of knowledge that is closely related to, and in full agreement with, the main teachings of Mach.

The last step so far taken in the direction toward the conceptions represented in this book we see in the work of Ludwig Wittgenstein, who gave a new solution to the perennial problem of the relation of the logical to the empirical, of mathematics to the natural sciences (Chapter 10, 1). The puzzle that bothered Kant all his lifetime, how *pure* natural science is possible, and what one should do to secure for the theorems of positive science or even of metaphysics the apodictic certainty of mathematical statements, is completely settled by Wittgenstein's thesis: that theorems of mathematics and logic, in so far as they are certain (i.e., before they are "applied," or better, *transferred* to a field of application) do not state anything about reality, but form a tautological system of linguistic rules, complete within itself. This idea, which also is the point of view of our book, has been further developed by the members of the so-called Vienna Circle, Carnap, Philipp Frank, Hahn, Neurath, and others. It may not be superfluous to add that the customary use of the term "mathematics" in ordinary language usually covers also certain fields of application in which there can be no question of an apodictic certainty of statements.

*Comte's* philosophie positive *at the beginning of the nineteenth century established the study of the conditions of social life as a new, general science. At the end of the century, the results achieved in the physical sciences were reëxamined and clarified by Mach, who in this way created a firm foundation for the empirical conception of all branches of science. To Ludwig Wittgenstein we owe new, essential insights into the mutual relations between language, logic, and science.*

3. *Separation of the Realm of Science.* The report we gave in the foregoing historical sketch anticipates to a certain extent what we think about possible further developments. *Any* writing of history, however "objective" it may appear from the point of view of the author, contains, as we well know (Chapter 18), a theory of the events and thereby an implicit prediction for the future. It was a gross misunderstanding when Spengler introduced his famous work *The Decline of the West* with the words, "In this book the attempt is dared for the first time to predetermine history."

Let us take as a starting point Comte's idea of the three stages of explanation of the world—the religious, the metaphysical, and the scientific (Chapter 18, 3). It seems to us that this conception is in need of supplementation in several respects. In the first place, even if we limit ourselves completely to the domain of Western civilization, it appears that these three types of attempted intellectual comprehension of the world not only constitute a temporal succession, but have also a continual simultaneous existence. Not in *all* respects has religion been replaced by metaphysics, and metaphysics by science. We do not predict the "End of an Illusion" (religion), which, so far as we can see, seems indispensable to many cultivated and educated men and which seems to draw ever new nourishment from the factual status of the world. We do not believe that the further development will consist in the *complete* annihilation of older forms and their replacement by new ones. We rather see a definite goal in the striving for clear distinction and *conscious delineation*. If Newton in the *scholium generale* of his axiomatic treatment of terrestrial and celestial mechanics could seriously discuss the question whether the concept "Lord" is contained in the concept "God" or not; if the textbooks of physics up to the middle of the nineteenth century could point in their introductions to the "higher," i.e., metaphysical, level on which the explanation of the basic physical concepts is to be found—then this kind of religion and this kind of metaphysics are now at an end and, we believe, will not return. We predict the progressive isolation of an ever more comprehensive realm of thought that is kept free from metaphysics, and in which *connectible* descriptions of the phenomena vital to man are sought.

Another point concerns the range that our judgments, including the present, about future intellectual development may cover. We have become used to regarding a certain group of countries, which stand in permanent intercourse with us, not only as a unit, but as the totality of the intellectual world. It is true that during the last five hundred years the geographic limits of the "intellectual Occident" have been widely extended, and the impression exists that this movement is still in progress today, implicating ever larger parts of Asia and Africa. Nevertheless, the extrapolation to the distant future must be followed by a question mark. At least in Asia we know of independent cultural centers with a long historical tradition and it cannot be anticipated to what extent they may sometimes influence the rest of the world. Also, today still quite insignificant or unknown beginnings may gain important and even dominating positions. The idea that our way of thinking is the only one "possible," that, as is sometimes claimed, even men from Mars could not have a science different from ours, can hardly be justified. At any rate, a concrete prediction of future tendencies must be limited to the range of influence of those phenomena within which we have made our observations and collected our experiences. There is no prophecy of a "Decline of the West" implied by this.

*The course of development of knowledge as hitherto observed shows a tendency toward ever clearer and more determined separation between religious-metaphysical and scientific lines of thought; the range of applicability and validity of the latter expands continually at the expense of the former. One may recognize in the further progress of this trend a characteristic of Western civilization. To what extent, however, this trend may yet spread over the earth can hardly be anticipated.*

4. *Progress in Science and Art.* All discussions about possible trends of evolutions are rendered difficult by the apparently unavoidable confusion with value judgments. The very terms "progress" and "regress" undoubtedly point to valuations. There is far-reaching agreement (if we disregard extreme negativism) about the fact that the *positive sciences* show steady progress, i.e., increasing content, precision, and applicability. From the point of view of the empiricist conception of science this signifies, first, that a growing stock of experience is preserved in memory and in written or oral tradition, and, second, that the human capacities become better adapted to the requirements of scientific work, owing to the influence of improved methods of education and possibly to the influence of heredity. Our view is clearly different from that supported, e.g., in Kant's epistemology, according to which the progress of science consists in a successive replacement of former "errors" by "ultimate truths." We shall say a word further below about the particular case of the social sciences.

The situation is much less clear in the case of *art*. A widely propagated opinion holds that the great works of art of the past are forever unsurpassable. In so far as this is supposed to be an esthetic judgment, i.e., a statement about the subjective feelings of pleasure that a work of art causes, it can be explained mainly by the fact that all such valuations rest to a large extent upon education (Chapter 24, 5), and our education in art can only be oriented along the past accomplishments. Experience, however, teaches that in the course of time new creations of art are again and again accepted among the ranks of the classical and "unsurpassable." It can also hardly be denied that a work of poetry or a painting of the eighteenth century expresses experiences that were not known to men of the Middle Ages or Antiquity—the difference from the growth of science is not as wide as is usually assumed. The forms of expression in art change little, but there is nothing to prevent us from imagining that entirely new forms may sometime develop.

Observation shows that the various branches of intellectual activity by no means progress uniformly at all times. European instrumental music is almost completely a creation of the span of time reaching from the middle of the eighteenth to the middle of the nineteenth century; modern mathematics was conceived almost entirely within the seventeenth, eighteenth, and nineteenth centuries; the development of sculpture took place almost entirely in the first centuries A.D. The two last thirds of the nineteenth century saw a vigorous development of the industrial application of the results of physical science and it seems as though this period still continues, paralleled by an increasing cultivation of biological studies.

A special difficulty presents itself in all questions belonging to the realm of the social sciences. If one considers on the one hand the apparently unreconcilable opposition between the so-called liberal and socialistic doctrines of economics (Chapter 20, 7), and on the other, the state of helplessness and disorder in today's economy in almost all countries, one is hardly inclined to recognize here an analogy with the development of the physical and biological sciences and the practical use that evolved from them. Considerable boldness is needed in order to expect an even moderately adequate solution of these problems in the near future. The main reason for this seems to be that the followers of the classical doctrines do not like to recognize or accept their passing and empirical character and to admit that all theory is but a systematic description of earlier observations, while experience demonstrates that with the course of economic and technological development all premises, including the psychological dispositions of men, change. To mention but one concrete example, the axiom that only "sound egotism" provides a useful incentive for actions that are desirable in the interest of all has been abundantly refuted by the functioning of various public institutions, in which private profit making is now essentially excluded, such as military service, administration of justice, and other executive branches. On the other hand, the often justified distrust of prevalent scientific doctrines led the opponents to exaggerations that go far beyond all boundaries set by experience and thought. While the inherent difficulty of all problems increases more and more, owing to the rationally uncontrolled growth of population and the rise of new technical inventions of greatest impact, the application of common sense and science recedes, giving place to mythical and mystical forms of thought. In conjunction with the above-mentioned theory of power ethics (Chapter 26, 3 and 5), there result those actual conditions that deprive a large part of contemporary mankind of all joy in life.

*Most of the positive sciences grow in the sense that the range and the precision of their statements increase. In the development of art, too, the continually increasing stock of experience of mankind finds its expression. The progress is not uniformly distributed over all periods of time. As to the social sciences and their application to the improvement of our conditions of life, we are passing at present through an extremely critical stage which offers little hope for a decisive contribution to the most important problems in the predictable future.*

5. *Progress in Metaphysics and Ethics.* In the field of the positive sciences, as we have seen, the question of "progress" can at least be formulated in a clear manner, although it cannot always be answered unambiguously. The point there was primarily an increase in the amount and in the range of statements in a system. Even though, of course, we cannot count propositions in the literal sense of the word, it can be decided which of two competing theories dealing with the same factual situation is the more comprehensive and allows of more predictions. The more exact, the nearer to an axiomatized form the complex of statements is, the easier is such a judgment. Lagrange's mechanics accomplishes more than Newton's, because it includes the cases of arbitrarily conditioned, restrained motion, etc.

The further one gets away from exact, in the narrower sense scientific propositions, the more difficult and uncertain becomes the determination of "progress." We agree to a certain extent with the assertion, frequently made by metaphysicians, that there is no progress in metaphysics; it would, however, be more correct to say that the concept of progress cannot be defined in metaphysics. According to our conception, discussed in detail in Part VI, metaphysical statements, in so far as they have any meaning, are within narrow limits connectible, primitive propositions about the observable world. If they are deprived of their primitiveness and their connectibility is extended, they gradually become scientific statements. Above (Chapter 21, 4) we have characterized metaphysics as "science in the beginning." He who, as a matter of principle, stands in the doorway can obviously not progress.

A question that aroused much interest and about which many different opinions were expressed is whether human history indicates a progress of *moral knowledge* and of *moral conduct.* Only the religious systems give a clear and unambiguous answer at least to the first point; for them the source of all moral knowledge is a unique revelation or a completely recorded set of doctrines, and thus there can be no further development of morals. The more positively inclined thinkers differ among themselves in their opinions. Comte held that the human brain has experienced an evolution during historical times and that, accordingly, the intellectual and moral capacities of men have increased. The historian Buckle emphasized with particular stress that such a claim is not supported by the facts of heredity, and the present state of biology is in agreement with his view. The external circumstances, however, under which men live have changed in the course of time, and, according to Buckle, it therefore follows that the same capacities and talents now lead to different conduct.

Our primary assumption in considering all these views is that we do not know of an absolute measure of moral value and thus cannot possibly answer the question whether men in their actual conduct become "better," or the question whether the accepted moral principles "improve." Either through studies of heredity or through sociological studies, claims of the following kind could perhaps be confirmed. This or that specific drive (e.g., the desire for security, stabilization of one's own life and those of one's relatives) has grown in the course of time and approached more closely its satisfaction; another one (e.g., the desire for personal revenge or for personal property of a specific kind) has decreased and now plays a less important role in human conduct. It seems that Durkheim's sociological school, which, however, is not always free from metaphysical influences, comes closest to conceiving the problems in this manner. But even when we have reached at one or another point an unambiguous answer as to the historical past, a prediction of the future will still remain quite uncertain. The closing words of Mach's last work, *Erkenntnis und Irrtum* (1905) may demonstrate, if we confront them with the present state of our environment, how strongly all aspects may change within a relatively short time and within a comparatively limited region. Mach says:

> If we consider the tortures which our ancestors had to suffer from the brutality of their social institutions, their conditions of law and justice, their superstitions, and their fanaticism, if we realize the abundant present inheritance of these goods, and if we imagine how much of this we shall still experience in our descendants, this is a sufficiently powerful incentive for us to coöperate vigorously and vehemently in the realization of the ideal of a moral world order by means of our psychological and sociological knowledge. But once we have created such a moral order, nobody will be able to say any longer that it is not of this world, and nobody will have to look for it any longer in mystical heights or depths.

Who can believe that these words would have been written if Mach had lived through the last few decades?

*Our conception of metaphysics as a starting point and origin of science does not permit the question of "progress" of metaphysical theories. The question whether the moral views and the moral conduct of men show within historical times tendencies toward progress in any sense is one of sociological and biological study and is not yet clarified in almost any single concrete point. So much the more are the foundations for a reasonable prediction for the future lacking.*

6. *A View of the Future.* To the foregoing remarks about our knowledge, or lack of it, of the future of the sciences, arts, metaphysics, and ethics, we wish—at the end—to add a few supplements of a more general kind. A widely held view, upon which we have touched repeatedly (particularly in Chapter 5, and in Chapter 24, 7), denies to everything this book contains any lasting validity and essential usefulness for the *future*.

That which has been puzzled out by the so-called cold intellect, formulated in possibly rigorous sentences, and which refers to the visible, audible, or in any way experienceable, has at best temporary and subordinate significance. In the long run, it is claimed, only that holds and remains which originated in the soul, in the heart, in profound depths and is formulated in a more or less mystical way—in one word: "mind" and not "matter." A much read and popular *Cultural History of Modern Times* (Egon Friedell) concludes with formulations such as this:

> Our intelligible character is, although the root of everything empirical, not empirical itself, not experienceable; it works deep within the interior and in obscurity, the same in essence as that mysterious power which also is enthroned behind the external world . . . The "it" or the thing in itself is the only reality, just because it never appears in "reality" and can never appear there . . . The soul is superreal, matter is subreal. At the same time there appears a dim gleam of light from the other side. The next chapter of European history will be the history of this light.

There is no doubt that such words still today impress many people, educated and uneducated. The source of this effect is the understandable dissatisfaction of most people with the present conditions of life and the false opinion that these conditions are the result of the rule of reason and scientific knowledge. Everybody knows from his own life situations in which reasonable considerations, based upon factual knowledge, have misled him, while at some other time instinctive, apparently unreasonable conduct led to success. He overlooks that in the one case he makes use of a necessarily incomplete theory, whose predictions are *not always* dependable, and that the second represents a reaction, which originates in older, assimilated experiences, in habit, education, and instruction, and which *in rare cases* can be useful. But above all, the idea that the institutions dominating the course of our life today are determined by reason and science is in no way justified.

There is, indeed, only *one* area in which men have become accustomed to a somewhat rational conduct, namely, material technology, based upon the physical (and to a lesser degree the biological) sciences. This is also, so far, the only phenomenon of civilization that gradually and almost without opposition is spreading over the entire inhabited world, a goal that languages, philosophical systems, and religions (one of which even in name expresses its claim to universality), in spite of all their efforts, have not succeeded in reaching and probably never will. In all other realms, even the one closely related to technology—economics—and particularly in politics, there is still rampant an almost unchecked tendency toward irrational conduct, willfully deprived of the control of reason. A large part of the educated men of all countries are today particularly proud of the fact that certain "inalienable" values, such as the national language, a specific political philosophy, a specific national-political goal, are for them *not open to any reasonable discussion.* "One of the strangest applications that man made of his reason," says Lichtenberg, "is to believe that it is a masterpiece to abstain from using it and thus, born with wings, to cut them off."

We recognize the biological value that in an early stage of civilization, a kind of conduct not guided by conscious intelligence may have had for the reaching of specific cultural goals. But if the existing remnants of barbarism, which are conserved by clinging to outgrown mystical and mythical forms of thought, in conjunction with the feelings of displeasure caused by them, serve but to eliminate the application of reason and science where they had asserted themselves so far, then mankind is liable to slip into a vicious circle from which there is no escape.

We do not believe that today's science, i.e., the whole of the communicable, connectibly formulated knowledge we have at our disposal, has in any field reached its end; even the idea of such an end does not seem conceivable to us. Even less do we believe that the quite incomplete sketch that our book has been able to give of some of the basic problems of knowledge is in any sense, however remote, complete or final.

*But we are convinced that the conception presented by us forms a link in the long chain of a development that may be temporarily upset by changing external (political) circumstances, but that progresses in its essential features continually through the course of time, and that presumably* represents the only way by which mankind will approach a gradual decrease in the feelings of uneasiness afflicting it.

7. *Summary.* In conclusion we wish to summarize in brief and as concise sentences as possible some of the main results that the seven parts of this book have presented.

(I) It is the oldest experience and the primitive theories derived from them that are preserved in the traditional stock of language. Through word formulations as well as through various grammatical rules certain typifications of the most frequently occurring relations have been created, and everybody speaking the language must use them. An improvement of knowledge is possible only if one approaches linguistic usage critically and does not regard the existing words and standardized locutions as fixed and unchangeable elements in the construction of a world picture.

(II) The analysis of knowledge leads to the search for the simplest basic sentences upon which further development can rest. We find them in the so-called "protocol sentences," i.e., short linguistic indications of the immediately observed present—without claiming that their range can be delineated *sharply.* That which, by means of a specific set of linguistic rules, can be reduced in principle to protocol sentences is understandable empiricist language. We consider scientific those statements which are connectible with the not explicitly discarded rules of everyday language and with the additional rules of the scientific language. In the "material mode" of expression, the reducibility to protocol sentences appears as an analysis of the world into elements (receptions) in Mach's sense.

(III) The goal of all scientific endeavor is to discover connections between observable phenomena, such that out of a partially given complex the remaining elements can be constructed in thought. Starting from single observations, general propositions are set up in a constructive manner as conjectures (the so-called inductive inference) and these are then, by a continual increase in conciseness of the concepts, built up to tautological (axiomatic) systems, which are disconnected from ordinary language. By means of the (nonrigorous) coördination between the language of the tautologies and that of the protocol sentences, one derives from the sentences deduced within the system statements about reality that can be verified by observation. No theory is uniquely determined by the phenomena; they all contain arbitrary elements. No theory is final; they all are subject to continual testing by new observations.

(IV) The observation of a uniform, stable connection that exists under certain circumstances among specific groups of phenomena leads to the concept of causality. This concept finds its mathematically precise expression in the differential equations of physics, which express the continuous temporal changes of a variable by other observational quantities. Correlations that do not occur without exception but with a stable value of relative frequency lead to the concept of probability, which is given a precise form by the theory of the mathematical "collective." Physics in its present stage makes use of both kinds of description and it cannot be predicted whether one of them will sometime gain and keep the upper hand. None of the popular theories that speak of destruction of causality, of metasciences, of the supernatural, or of miracles can stand a critical linguistic examination.

(V) The whole of science can be resolved (in a vague way) into separate sciences, according to the realms of phenomena that each treats. The idea that there exists a fundamental unbridgeable difference in method or even in the kind of "understanding" between the natural sciences and the humanities is untenable. In history and the social sciences, too, one deals with observations, inductive generalizations, hence theories, and with the first approaches to tautological systems; every result is, in the last analysis, a proposition verifiable in experience. Physics and the branches of knowledge bordering on it are characterized by the fact that they deal with the simplest phenomena, i.e., with those which can be better isolated than all others, and this accounts for the fact that these sciences are more advanced with respect to the accumulation of experiences and to their epistemological elaboration.

(VI) The desire to arrive at practically useful answers (predictions) in the most difficult and most general questions of life leads to the construction of systems of metaphysical propositions, which are characterized by their strictly limited connectibility and allow of a verification by observation only in a very vague form. Progress of research leads in every sphere away from metaphysics, toward the realm of connectible, scientific theories. In the works of poetry, fine arts, music, etc., general contents of experience, condensed into moods and feelings, are communicated by means of special "languages," whose conventions are assimilated in education and instruction. None of these contents can be translated without loss from one language into another one. We do not know of an objective definition of the "beautiful" independent of the apprehending subject. A scientific theory, as well as a work of art, is always only a one-sided hint to possible experiences, never their complete exhaustion.

(VII) From personal commands, which regulate the social life on a primitive stage, there develops the meaning of general, independent ought sentences or norms of conduct. The justification of a system of norms can consist only of sentences that express connections between observable phenomena (actions and their consequences), and which, therefore, belong to the positive sciences, particularly to sociology. The acceptance or rejection of a normative system by a group occurs through a collective act of resolution, in which every individual acts under the influence of the various impacts of society. The alleged existence of an objective scale of moral values, inborn in all men, is not supported by any observation. The religious systems are metaphysical attempts at an explanation of the world, undertaken for the purpose of setting up norms of behavior. We expect from the future that to an ever-increasing extent scientific knowledge, i.e., knowledge formulated in a connectible manner, will control life and the conduct of men.

notes · index

# notes

The initial quotation is from Nietzsche's *Werke,* vol. 2, p. 443, notes to *Human, all too human* (1885). Friedrich Nietzsche, 1844–1900, generally known as the representative of ethical evolutionism and as the herald of *"Herrenmoral"* (heroic ethics) which later became so popular in Germany, started out as an opponent of the German idealistic philosophy and showed in his earlier writings, as far as epistemological questions were concerned, a decidedly positivistic attitude.

## PART I

Georg Christoph Lichtenberg, 1742–1799, physicist, literary author, witty and unprejudiced thinker, is mainly known by his *Fragmente und Bemerkungen vermischten Inhalts,* partially translated in *The reflections of Lichtenberg* (London, 1908). The quotation is from *Vermischte Schriften,* ed. by L. C. Lichtenberg and F. Kries (Göttingen, 1801), vol. 2, p. 57.

Etienne Bonnot de Condillac, 1714–1780, eminent French philosopher of the Enlightenment, was originally under the influence of Locke. His main works are: *Essai sur l'origine des connaissances humaines* (1746); *Traité des systèmes* (1749); *Traité des sensations avec une dissertation sur la liberté* (1754); *La logique* (1780); *La langue des calculs* (1794). The quotation is from *La logique.*

*Chapter 1*

**1.** The general problem of language and science is discussed by Leonard Bloomfield, *Linguistic aspects of science* (International Encyclopedia of Unified Science, vol. 1, no. 4; University of Chicago Press, Chicago, 1939).

**2.** The quotation is from Nietzsche's *Werke,* vol. 1, p. 525.

**3.** For newer approaches to the origin of language see P. B. Ballard, *Thought and language* (London, 1934); L. Bloomfield, *Language* (Holt, New York, 1933); also K. Bühler, *Sprachtheorie* (Fischer, Jena, 1934) (deviating into metaphysics).

Hugo Schuchardt, "Sprachursprung," *Sitzungsberichte der preussischen Akademie der Wissenschaften* (1919).

Ernst Hartig, Gesetz vom Gebrauchswechsel, in *Civilingenieur,* 1880 and 1884.

Hermann Paul, *Prinzipien der Sprachgeschichte* (Halle a/Saale, 1909); contains many points relevant for Chapter 3, 1 and 2.

The quotation is from Nietzsche, *Werke,* vol. 10, p. 202.

**4.** Information about the magic of language will be found *passim* in the literature on primitive culture; see, e.g., J. G. Frazer, *The golden bough* (abridged ed., Macmillan, New York, 1941). There are interetsing remarks in E. Mach, *Erkenntnis und Irrtum* (Leipzig, 1905), pp. 86–105.

**6.** It is a widely held opinion that oral speech contains more than can be given in writing. The critique of scientific theories has nothing to do with this "more." The point of view of the Dutch "significs" (see note to Chapter 3, 3) in this respect is wavering. A detailed study of this question is given in a paper by A. Pentilla and U. Saarnio, *Erkenntnis* **4,** 28 (1934).

**7.** Morris R. Cohen, *Reason and nature* (Harcourt, Brace, New York, 1931), p. xii.

*Chapter 2*

**1.** Philipp Frank, *Das Kausalgesetz und seine Grenzen* (Vienna, 1932). See also the same author's *Modern science and its philosophy* (Harvard University Press, Cambridge, 1949), particularly Chapter 4, "Physical theories of the twentieth century and school philosophy," pp. 90–121.

**2.** The quotations are from Kant, *Critique of pure reason,* trans. by J. M. D. Meiklejohn (London, 1878), pp. 7, 8, "On the difference between analytical and synthetical judgments." Critical remarks to this point in a sense similar to that in the text can be found in E. Cassirer, *Das Erkenntnisproblem* (Berlin, 1921–23), vol. 2, pp. 677 ff.

Aristotle, see note to Chapter 3, 1.

**3.** Kant, *Critique of judgment,* trans. by J. H. Bernard (London, 1892), pp. 54, 90.

William James, *The meaning of truth, A sequel to pragmatism* (New York, 1909), pp. 287 ff.

**4.** F. Mauthner commented in detail on Schopenhauer's characteristic attitude towards language in *Wörterbuch der Philosophie* (Leipzig, 1923–24), pp. 91–150. But in spite of many correct formulations—e.g., ". . . although he masters the German language thoroughly, he becomes, misled by his theories, ever again the superstitious slave of language" (p. 150)—Mauthner does not find the decisive objections.

The quotations are from Schopenhauer, *The world as will and idea,* trans. by R. B. Haldane and J. Kemp (Paul, Trench, Trübner, London), Vol. 2, appendix, "Criticism of the Kantian philosophy," p. 21 and vol. 1, p. 144 (Book II, §22).

**5.** Translation from Hans Vaihinger, *Die Philosophie des Als Ob* (Leipzig, ed. 3, 1918), pp. 512–513; *The philosophy of "as if,"* trans. by C. K. Ogden (Harcourt, Brace, London and New York, ed. 2, 1935), p. 237.

**6.** Translation from E. Husserl, *Logische Untersuchungen,* vol. 2, "Elemente einer phänomenologischen Aufklärung der Erkenntnis," (Halle, 1922), part 2, p. 24; almost the entire three volumes are dedicated to the study of the "Aktcharakter der Bedeutungsverleihung" (roughly, "The action of assignment of meaning").

**7.** Plato, *Republic,* 10th book.

Fritz Mauthner, *Beiträge zu einer Kritik der Sprache* (ed. 3, Leipzig,

1923; 3 vols.), and the above-mentioned (Chapter 2, 4) *Wörterbuch der Philosophie*. A brief summary of Mauthner's ideas can be found in M. Krieg, *Mauthner's Kritik der Sprache, eine Revolution der Philosophie* (Munich, 1914).

*Chapter 3*

**1.** Instead of "logical grammar" the expression "critical grammar" is also used. See, e.g., J. Schächter, *Prolegomena zu einer kritischen Grammatik* (Vienna, 1935); one will find there some remarks touching upon what we have said in the text. A detailed introduction to the problem is given in H. Scholz, "Natürliche Sprachen und Kunstsprachen," *Blätter für Deutsche Philosophie* **12,** 253–281 (1938).

Aristotle, *Topicorum,* lib. I, cap. IV: "Definitio est oratio, quae id, quod definitur, explicat quid sit" (A definition is a discourse which explains what the thing is that should be defined). There is a detailed and partly enlightening treatment of the problems here discussed in W. Dubislav, *Die Definition* (Leipzig, 1931). Documentation of the school-philosophy approach to the definition as an explanation of the "meaning" rather than description of the linguistic usage will be found in J. S. Mill, *A system of logic, ratiocinative and inductive* (1848), vol. 1, pp. 160 ff.; and particularly in C. Sigwart, *Logik* (Freiburg, 1889), vol. 1, p. 170.

**3.** Questions concerning the *meaning* of words and word compounds, such as are treated in Chapter 3, 1–3, have not been classified until quite recently as "grammar," which used to consist only of phonetics, accidence, and syntax. One of the starting points is the work of Raoul de la Grasserie, *Essai d'une sémantique intégrale* (Paris, 1909, 2 vols.). The latest development of semantics follows rather formalistic tendencies; see, e.g., R. Carnap, *Introduction to semantics* (Harvard University Press, Cambridge, 1942). The works of the Dutch school of "significs" are closer to our point of view; see the report of G. Mannoury to the Congress of the Unity of Science Movement in Cambridge, *Erkenntnis* **7,** 180–188 (1939). The school of "General Semantics," with center in Chicago, specializes in the application of semantics to problems of general sociology. Its bible is A. Korzybski, *Science and sanity* (Internat. Non-Aristotelian Library, Lakeville, Conn., ed. 3, 1948).

**7.** Etymology, the history of words, and the evolution of meaning have for a long time been classical subjects of linguistics. Information about the most important basic ideas can be found, e.g., in Hans Sperber, *Einführung in die Bedeutungslehre* (Leipzig, 1923). Many older purely philological works also belong here; e.g., A. Darmesteter, *La vie des mots, étudiée dans leur signification* (Paris, 1899). See also L. Spitzer, *Essays in historical semantics* (S. F. Vanni, New York, 1948).

The idea that the meaning can often be derived from *statistical* considerations is finding its way more and more into linguistic and philological circles. One should not, in this connection, think only of a detailed enumeration of frequencies, as given, e.g., in W. Kaeding, *Häufigkeitsvörterbuch der deutschen Sprache* (Berlin, 1898).

*Chapter 4*

**2.** The works of Mauthner quoted to Chapter 2, 7 are very instructive with respect to the influence of the German (linguistic) syntax upon the philosophy of idealism. A comparative study of such influences in different languages does not seem to exist yet. Some material for this is contained in the excellent *Vocabulaire technique et critique de la philosophie,* by A. Lalande (Paris, 3 vols., 1926–1932).

**3.** Every textbook of Turkish grammar informs about the facts indicated in this Section.

**5.** P. Servien, *Le langage des sciences* (A. Blanchard, Paris, 1931); "Le langage des sciences," *Scientia* **61,** 201, 261 (1937); "Le langage des sciences," in *Travaux du Congrès Descartes* (Paris, 1937), Fasc. V, p. 23: "Nous reservons ce nom de langage des sciences à l'ensemble des phrases qui admettent des équivalentes" (We reserve the expression "scientific language" for those phrases which admit of equivalents).

Karl Pearson, *The grammar of science* (London, 1892); see also note to Chapter 17, 7.

**6.** On the word "transcendental," see Lalande, *Vocabulaire,* p. 903.

**7.** Translation from Nietzsche, *Werke,* vol. 2, p. 250 (*Human, all too human*).

*PART II*

The quotation is intended to render the idea of Aristotle expressed in his *De anima,* lib. III. It also corresponds to the point of view of Locke in *An essay concerning human understanding,* book II, chap. 1, §24: "Thus the first capacity of human intellect is that the mind is fitted to receive the impressions made on it, either through the senses, by outward objects, or by its own operations, when it reflects on them. This is the first step a man makes towards the discovery of any thing, and the ground work whereon to build all those notions which ever he shall have naturally in this world." Similarly Hume, see note to Chapter 7, 5.

*Chapter 5*

**1.** Translation from J. Huizinga, *Im Schatten von Morgen* (Gotthelf Verlag, Bern and Leipzig, 1936), p. 82; *In the shadow of tomorrow* (W. Heinemann, London, 1936), one will find here many further excellent characterizations of what we have called negativism; e.g., on p. 90, "They attack knowledge and concepts, but always by means of pseudo-knowledge and false concepts. In attempting to prove the worthlessness of knowledge one cannot help referring to some knowledge different from that which one rejects." Of course, many similar statements by other contemporary writers could be quoted in addition to Huizinga's book.

Lancelot T. Hogben, *Retreat from reason* (Random House, New York, 1937), with notes by Isabel S. Stearns.

**2.** Delineations and evaluations of what in the history of Greek philosophy is called Skepticism are very fluctuating. It nevertheless seems that there are many points in common between the Skeptics (and similarly, the always abused Sophists) and Positivism as we understand it. See, e.g., M. M. Patrick, *The Greek sceptics* (Columbia University Press, New York, 1929); E. Dühring, *Kritische Geschichte der Philosophie* (Berlin, 1869), pp. 152 ff.

**3.** The well-known principal works of Bergson (most of them also available in English translations) are: *Essai sur les données immédiates de la conscience* (1888); *Matière et mémoire* (1896); *L'évolution créatrice* (1907); *Les deux sources de la morale et de la religion* (1932); *La pensée et le mouvant* (1934). His negativistic point of view may be summarized by the one sentence: "L'intelligence est caracterisée par une incompréhension naturelle de la vie" (The intellect is characterized by a natural lack of comprehension of life), *L'évolution créatrice*, p. 179. An excellent criticism (although not quite free from influences of school philosophy) is rendered by M. Fénart, *Les assertions Bergsoniennes* (J. Vrin, Paris, 1936).

The quotation is from *L'évolution créatrice*, pp. 179 ff.

H. Spencer was the founder of the so-called philosophy of evolution, which was published in many volumes between 1860 and 1893 and at its time found many followers; see Chapter 28, 2. L. Büchner is mainly known for his book, which has had numerous editions since 1855, *Kraft und Stoff oder Grundzüge der natürlichen Weltordnung, nebst einer darauf gebauten Moral oder Sittenlehre* (Leipzig, ed. 21, 1904), a principal work of so-called Materialism; in English, *Force and matter* (London, 1870). E. Haeckel, the well-known biologist, was the founder of a "monistic philosophy" and a monistic "movement," which found their expression mainly in his book *Die Welträtsel, gemeinverständliche Studien über monistische Philosophie* (1899; Bonn, 1903); *The riddle of the universe* (London, 1925).

**4.** On Bergson's theory of duration, see Fénart, pp. 8–35.

Translation from Hegel, *System der Philosophie, Zweiter Teil: Die Naturphilosophie* (Frommann, Stuttgart, 1929), p. 114.

Translation from Ernst Mach, *Beiträge zur Analyse der Empfindungen* (Jena, 1886), pp. 103–112; *Contributions to the analysis of sensations* (Chicago, 1897); more detailed in the later editions; earlier remarks in *Sitzber. Akad. Wiss. Wien* **51** (1865).

**5.** The popular philosophical works of M. Maeterlinck, *Le trésor des humbles* (1896), *La sagesse et la destinée* (1898), *Le mystère de la justice* (1901), *La vie des abeilles* (1901), etc., are particularly characterized by the fact that in them the vocabulary of mysticism is applied to the most modern institutions of today's life.

The literature about Goethe's "Weltanschauung," about Goethe "as physicist," "as scientist," "as mystic," etc., is immense and cannot be mentioned here in detail. One will find valuable material in K. Vorländer, *Kant, Schiller, Goethe* (Leipzig, 1907). Most of the quotations are from *Sprüche in Prosa*, edited with comments by G. v. Loeper (Hempel, Berlin, 1860); partly translated by H. J. Weigand, *Goethe, Wisdom and experience* (Pantheon, New York, 1949).

The basic principles of Anthroposophy are developed again and again in many books and papers by its founder, Rudolf Steiner (1861–1925). Only a part of the books have been translated. We quote for reference *Knowledge of the higher worlds and its attainment* (Anthroposophic Press, New York, n.d.), and *An outline of occult science* (Anthroposophic Press, New York, 1922). Anthroposophy defines itself as a doctrine of the "natural comprehension of supernatural things."

**6.** The philosophic works of L. Klages, *Mensch und Erde* (Jena, 1920); *Vom Wesen des Bewusstseins* (Leipzig, 1921); *Vom kosmogonischen Eros* (Jena, 1922); *Der Geist als Widersacher der Seele* (J. A. Barth, Leipzig, 1929–32), etc., are characterized as to their position toward science by one of his followers, W. Deubel, *Z. Menschenkunde* **6**, 23 (1930–31), as follows: "There is hardly, and has hardly ever existed in history, a thesis, conviction, or method of the intellectual world conception—from religious dogmas and the speculations of Plato, Kant, and Schopenhauer to the purely 'factual' problems, the methodology and theory of psychology, epistemology, physics (Eleatics, sensualism, idealism, materialism, Newton, Einstein)—whose fallaciousness Klages did not reveal by proving the misconception of all 'logocentric' thinking." In English there has appeared L. Klages, *The science of character* (London, 1929).

*Chapter 6*

**1.** The concept of "connectibility" here introduced represents a relativistic form of the point of view of the "Vienna Circle" according to which the metaphysical propositions, i.e., those that are neither statements from experience nor part of a tautological system, are "meaningless." One of the sources of this latter conception is L. Wittgenstein's *Tractatus Logico-Philosophicus* (German and English; London, 1922). See also R. Carnap, "Uberwindung der Metaphysik durch logische Analyse der Sprache," *Erkenntnis* **2**, 219–241 (1931) and the works of the Vienna Circle mentioned below.

**4.** Translation from Heidegger, *Was ist Metaphysik?* (Bonn, 1929); see Carnap, p. 229. Analogous statements can be found in great numbers in Heidegger's and other existentialists' writings; e.g., in "Vom Wesen des Grundes, *Festschrift für Edmund Husserl* (Halle a.d.S., 1929), p. 101: "Freiheit allein kann dem Dasein eine Welt walten und welten lassen. Welt ist nie, sondern weltet" (untranslatable). It seems that the substantivation of verbs (mentioned in Chapter 3, 6) in school philosophy is now paralleled by the reverse process. See also Chapter 22, 3.

**5.** Karl Popper, *Logik der Forschung* (J. Springer, Vienna, 1935), pp. 40 ff.; see also Otto Neurath, "Pseudorationalismus der Falsifikation," *Erkenntnis* **5**, 353 (1935); recent discussions by B. Russell, H. Feigl, and C. G. Hempel in *Rev. Internat. Philosophie* **4**, 3, 41, 64 (1950).

*Chapter 7*

**1.** Mach's doctrine of "elements" was first expounded in context in the *Contributions to the analysis of sensations,* see note to Chapter 5, 4. Some details can be found in Mach's other works, particularly in *The science of mechanics* (Chicago, 1893) and *Prinzipien der Wärmelehre* (Leipzig, 1896); also in the later editions of the *Analyse der Empfindungen; The analysis of sensations* (Chicago and London, rev. ed., 1914). A bibliography of Mach's works is contained in R. v. Mises, "Ernst Mach und die empiristische Wissenschaftsauffassung," *Einheitswissenschaft* **7** ('s Gravenhage, 1938).

R. Carnap, *Der logische Aufbau der Welt* (Berlin, 1928), p. 1, "The aim: constitution of the system of concepts."

**2.** R. Carnap, "Die physikalische Sprache als Universalsprache der Wissenschaft," *Erkenntnis* **2**, 432 (1932).

**4.** Translation from Mach, *Analyse der Empfindungen* (ed. 6), p. 13.

**5.** Thomas Hobbes (1588–1679), *Elementorum philosophiae sectio prima, De corpore* (London, 1655). In the first chapter, on logic, he points out that the concept of a body denotes a complex of phenomena (Sectio secunda, De homine, 1658). David Hume, *Treatise of human nature* (1738), later abridged and reformulated as *Enquiry concerning human understanding* (1748), contains as a "fundamental principle" the proposition that all our ideas are copies of impressions and that we are unable to think anything that we did not previously feel through the senses.

**6.** See Mach, *Analyse der Empfindungen*, pp. 18 ff.

One will find much interesting material about Mach's doctrines in J. Popper-Lynkeus' posthumous paper, "Uber die Grundbegriffe der Philosophie und die Gewissheit unserer Erkenntnisse," *Erkenntnis* **3**, 301–324 (1932–33), and the supplementary commentary to it by H. Löwy, *Erkenntnis* **3**, 324–347 (1932–33).

*Chapter 8*

**1.** The papers of the "Vienna Circle" in connection with the doctrine of protocol statements are essentially the following: R. Carnap, *Der logische Aufbau der Welt,* "Die physikalische Sprache," and "Psychologie in physikalischer Sprache," *Erkenntnis* **3**, 107 (1932–33); E. Zilsel, "Bemerkungen zur Wissenschaftslogik," *Erkenntnis* **3**, 143 (1932–33); R. Carnap, "Erwiderung," *Erkenntnis* **3**, 177 (1932–33); O. Neurath, "Protokollsätze," *Erkenntnis* **3**, 204 (1932–33); R. Carnap, "Über Protokollsätze," *Erkenntnis* **3**, 215 (1932–33); M. Schlick, "Über das Fundament der Erkenntnis," *Erkenntnis* **4**, 79 (1934); M. Schlick, *Gesammelte Aufsätze* (Gerold, Vienna, 1938), pp. 289–310; Otto Neurath, "Radikaler Physikalismus und 'Wirkliche Welt,'" *Erkenntnis* **4**, 346 (1934); B. Juhos, "Kritische Bemerkungen zur Wissenschaftstheorie des Physikalismus," *Erkenntnis* **4**, 397 (1934). For later developments of Carnap's ideas, *Introduction to semantics* (Harvard University Press, Cambridge, 1942); *Meaning and necessity* (University of Chicago Press, Chicago, 1947).

Remarks in this direction are to be found in Philipp Frank's centenary address, "Ernst Mach—The centenary of his birth," *Erkenntnis* **7**, 247 (1938).

G. Mannoury, one of the founders of the "Significs" movement in Holland, introduces the term "I-now language" in an attempt to characterize something similar to what we call "element sentences." See the prepublication from a forthcoming book, *Polar-psychological concept synthesis* in *Etc, A review of general semantics* **7**, 203 (1950).

**3.** Notable contributions to the problems of protocol statements are contained in K. Ajdukiewicz, "Sprache und Sinn," *Erkenntnis* **4**, 100 (1934).

**5.** On Laplace's proposition, see Chapter 15, 2.

**6.** G. C. Lichtenberg (see the first note to Part I), *Vermischte Schriften,* vol. 2, p. 96: "We know only the existence of our impressions, ideas, and thoughts. One should say *it thinks,* just as one says *it thunders.* It is already too much to say *cogito,* if that is to be translated as *I think.* To assume the *I,* to postulate it, is a practical need." With respect to the latter point, see Chapter 7, 6.

Both quotations are translations from Descartes, *Discours de la méthode* (Paris, 1668).

## PART III

The quotation is from Goethe, *Sprüche in Prosa* (see note to Chapter 5, 5), No. 916.

### Chapter 9

**1.** Euclid, *The thirteen books of elements,* translated from the text of Heiberg (Cambridge, 1926), Book I, pp. 1–3.

**2.** Newton's principal work, *Philosophiae naturalis principia mathematica* (Mathematical principles of natural philosophy), appeared in London in 1687. It includes a complete course of mechanics of particles and its application to celestial bodies.

**3.** Mach's criticism of Newton's principles, contained mainly in the *Mechanik* (ed. 8, pp. 237–243) is reproduced here in its essence, but in a slightly changed form; *Science of mechanics* (see note to Chapter 7, 1), pp. 201–244.

**4.** D. Hilbert, *Grundlagen der Geometrie,* published for the first time in 1899; English ed., *The foundations of geometry* (Chicago, 1902). The quotation is from p. 2.

**5.** Gauss's contribution to the beginnings of non-Euclidean geometry is revealed in his correspondence with H. C. Schuhmacher (Altona, 1860–65). See also Sartorius von Waltershausen, *Gauss zum Gedächtnis* (1856).

Kant, *Critique of pure reason* (note to Chapter 2, 2), p. 25.

**6.** On the relation between axioms and experience in geometry see mainly Mach, *Erkenntnis und Irrtum,* particularly pp. 331–440. The earliest discussions concerning this topic are those of Riemann, *Über die Hypothesen, welche der Geometrie zugrunde liegen* (Göttingen, 1867), and several papers by H. v. Helmboltz, *Schriften zur Erkenntnistheorie,* published by P. Hertz and M. Schlick (Berlin, 1921).

**7.** Translation from D. Hilbert, "Axiomatisches Denken," *Math. Ann.* **78,** 405 (1918).

### Chapter 10

**1.** H. Weyl, *Philosophie der Mathematik und Naturwissenschaft* (München und Berlin, 1927), p. 16; *Philosophy of mathematics and natural science* (Princeton University Press, Princeton, 1949).

L. Wittgenstein, see note to Chapter 6, 1.

**2.** H. Rademacher and A. Toeplitz, *Zahlen und Figuren* (J. Springer, Berlin, 1931).

**3.** A textbook of logistic, comprehensible to anyone who can follow abstract chains of inferences, is Hilbert-Ackermann, *Grundzüge der theoretischen Logik* (Berlin, 1928); or W. V. Quine, *Mathematical logic* (Harvard University Press, Cambridge, 1947). Further references are R. Carnap, *The logical syntax of language* (Paul, Trench, Trübner, London, 1937), and *Formalization of logic* (Harvard University Press, Cambridge, 1943). An orientation about the first elements is contained, e.g., in W. Dubislav, *Naturphilosophie* (Junker and Dünnhupt, Berlin, 1933), pp. 2–10.

**4.** Gottfried Wilhelm Leibniz (1646–1716), a contemporary of Newton, was one of the greatest polyhistors of all times. The elements of a logistic symbolism are contained in his *Ars combinatoria* (1866).

In the last few decades symbolic logic has become an extensively studied branch of science. See, in addition to the above-quoted books, A. Tarski, *Introduction to logic and to the methodology of deductive sciences* (Oxford University Press, New York, 1941).

**6.** A. N. Whitehead and B. Russell, *Principia mathematica* (Cambridge, 1910–13). A popular introduction can be found in B. Russell, *Introduction to mathematical philosophy* (London and New York, 1924).

**7.** Translation from F. Gonseth, *Qu'est-ce que la logique?* (Hermann, Paris, 1937), p. 79. A more detailed exposition in the same author's *Les mathématiques et la réalité* (F. Alcan, Paris, 1936).

*Chapter 11*

**1.** A historical discussion of most of the epistemological problems that are relevant to mathematics can be found in L. Brunschvigg, *Les étapes de la mathématique philosophique* (Paris, ed. 3, 1929), which, however, is written entirely from the point of view of school philosophy.

F. Gonseth, see note to Chapter 10, 7.

**2.** Information about the elements of intuitionism (and other conceptions of the foundations of mathematics) can be found in the report by A. Heyting, *Mathematische Grundlagenforschung, Intuitionismus, Beweistheorie* (J. Springer, Berlin, 1934).

**3.** Intuitionism in mathematics was created by L. E. J. Brouwer in his thesis, *Over de grondslagen der wiskunde* (Amsterdam, 1907). Brouwer presented his general philosophical ideas in a paper, "Mathematik, Wissenschaft und Sprache," *Monatsh. Math. Physik* **35** (1929).

**4.** The explanation of the intuitionist view toward the *tertium exclusum* given here is due to Erhardt Schmidt, *Über Gewissheit in der Mathematik* (Berlin, 1930).

**5.** A. Kolmogoroff, "Zur Deutung der intuitionistischen Logik," *Math. Z.* **35**, 58 (1932).

**6.** On the various points of view towards the foundations of mathematics see the lectures by Carnap, Heyting, and v. Neumann, *Erkenntnis* **2**, 91–121 (1931); also detailed bibliography, *ibid.*, pp. 151–155.

K. Gödel, "Über formal unentscheidbare Sätze der 'Principia mathematica,'" *Monatsh. Math. Physik* **37** (1931).

**7.** Whitehead and Russell, see note to Chapter 10, 6.

On the method of mathematical induction, see the easily comprehensible paper by F. Waismann, *Einführung in das mathematische Denken* (Gerold, Vienna, 1936).

H. Poincaré, *La science et l'hypothèse* (Paris, 1912), pp. 20 ff. (see note to Chapter 12, 4).

Goethe to Chancellor v. Müller, June 18, 1826; translation from *Goethe's Gespräche*, edited by F. v. Biedermann (Leipzig, 1910), vol. 3, p. 275.

## Chapter 12

**1.** On the foundations of physicalism, see principally R. Carnap, "Die physikalische Sprache als Universalsprache der Wissenschaft," *Erkenntnis* **2,** 432 (1931); O. Neurath, "Radikaler Physikalismus und 'Wirkliche Welt,' " *Erkenntnis* **4,** 346 (1934).

**2.** Ernst Mach, *Die Geschichte und die Wurzel des Satzes von der Erhaltung der Arbeit* (Prague, 1872; reprinted in Leipzig, 1909). Mach returned often to the topic "description or explanation," e.g. in *Wärmelehre*, pp. 430–437. The phenomenalistic conception at the basis of all of these discussions is reduced to a principle of Leibniz in E. v. Aster, *Naturphilosophie* (E. S. Mittler & Sohn, Berlin, 1932), p. 90.

Karl Pearson, *The grammar of science* (ed. 1, 1892; new ed., J. M. Dent & Sons, London, 1937).

**3.** The idea of the "economy" of science was formulated clearly for the first time in Mach's *Mechanik* (ed. 8, 1883), p. 457. See also Mach, *Die Leitgedanken meiner naturwissenschaftlichen Erkenntnislehre und ihre Aufnahme durch die Zeitgenossen* (Leipzig, 1919).

Translation from E. Husserl, *Logische Untersuchungen* (Halle a.d.S., 1922), p. 194. H. Cornelius, *Psychologie als Erfahrungswissenschaft* (Leipzig, 1897), pp. 82–86, attributes a particularly wide range of influence to the idea of economy.

Translation from H. Buzello, *Kritische Untersuchung von Mach's Erkenntnistheorie* (Kantstudien, Ergänzungsheft 23; Berlin, 1911), pp. 14 ff.

The opening words of the introduction to the second edition of the *Critique of pure reason.*

**4.** The works of Henri Poincaré in which conventionalism is expounded are *Science et hypothèse; La valeur de la science; Science et méthode; Dernières pensées* (all Paris). The first three are included in *The foundations of science*, The Science Press, Lancaster, Pa., 1946.

**5.** The decisive role of the additional axioms is pointed out in R. v. Mises's lectures, "Über die gegenwartige Krise der Mechanik," *Naturwissenschaften* **10,** 25 (1922); "Über kausale und statistische Gesetzmässigkeit in der Physik," *Naturwissenschaften* **18,** 145 (1930) and *Erkenntnis* **1,** 189 (1930).

**6.** Aristotle, *Topicorum*, lib. I, cap. X, distinguishes between two *genera argumentationum dialecticarum:* the *ratiocinatio* (syllogism) and "inductio autem est ex rebus singulis ad universas progressio." Francis Bacon, Lord Verulam (1561–1626), gave in his *Novum organon scientiarum* (the second part of the *Instauratio magna*), published in 1620, a detailed theory of the doctrine of the instances of induction. The parallel is most clearly emphasized by John Stuart Mill, who called his main work (1843) *A system of deductive and inductive logic* (see note to Chapter 3, 1).

Translation from C. Sigwart, *Logik* (Leipzig, ed. 2, 1893), vol. 2, p. 402.

The fact that all physical theories are constructions which are *not uniquely* determined by observations is particularly stressed by A. Einstein, "Physik und Realität," *Z. freie deutsche Forschung* **1**, No. 1, 5–19; No. 2, 1–14 (1938).

## PART IV

Goethe, *Sprüche in Prosa* (Loeper's ed.), No. 641; see note to Chapter 5, 5.

### Chapter 13

**1.** A beautiful example of the confusion of temporal and logical succession is found in Shakespeare, *Hamlet*, act I, scene 3: "And it must follow, as the night the day," that he who is true to himself cannot be false to others.

**2.** On Zeno's paradox of motion, see note to Chapter 21, 5.

**3.** Translation from Heidegger, *Husserl-Festschrift*, p. 107; see note to Chapter 16, 4.

Translation from Hegel, *Encyclopädie der Philosophischen Wissenschaften im Grundrisse* (G. Lasson, Leipzig, ed. 2, 1911), p. 134.

On the philosophical objections to the law of inertia ("cessante causa cessat effectus") see, e.g., Mach, *Mechanik*, pp. 134, 258 ff.; *Science of mechanics* (see note to Chapter 7, 1), pp. 141, 509.

Hume's best-known accomplishment is the clarification of the causality concept, which is contained in the works cited in the note to Chapter 7, 5. One gets the best survey in reading section VII of the *Enquiry*. On Hume's importance in the development of empiricism, see Chapter 28, 1.

Quotation from Hume, *Treatise*, Part III, Sec. 14. See also Cassirer, *Erkenntnisproblem* (see note to Chapter 2, 2), vol. 1, p. 344.

Translation from Leibniz, *La Monadologie* (1714), No. 32.

**4.** E. Zilsel, "Über die Asymmetrie der Kausalität und die Einsinnigkeit der Zeit," *Naturwissenschaften* **15**, 280 (1927).

Philipp Frank, *Das Kausalgesetz und seine Grenzen* (Vienna, 1932), pp. 142–146.

**6.** Kant (see note to Chapter 2, 2), p. 141.

Schopenhauer, *Über die vierfache Wurzel des Satzes vom Grunde*, works, ed. by Frauenstädt (Leipzig, 1873), p. 5; *Two essays by A. Schopenhauer* (London, 1886), p. 5.

Philipp Frank, see note above.

### Chapter 14

**1.** The first determined attempt at reducing the probability concept to that of a relative frequency was made by John Venn, *Logic of chance* (London, 1886). A detailed exposition of all earlier approaches and a foundation of the modern frequency theory is given in R. v. Mises, *Wahrscheinlichkeit, Statistik und Wahrheit* (J. Springer, Vienna, ed. 3, 1951), English transl., *Probability, statistics and truth* (W. Hodge, London, 1939).

**2.** Sigwart (see note to Chapter 12, 6), pp. 305 ff. Typical representatives of the doctrine of subjective probability are J. M. Keynes, *Treatise on probability* (London, 1921); H. Jeffreys, *Scientific inference* (Cambridge, 1931).

Translation from C. Stumpf, "Über den Begriff der mathematischen Wahrscheinlichkeit," *Sitzber. Bayrische Akad. Wiss. phil. hist. Klasse* (1892), p. 41.

A survey of the various aspects of probability theory is given by Ernest Nagel, *Principles of the theory of probability* (International Encyclopedia of Unified Science, vol. 1, no. 6; University of Chicago Press, Chicago, 1939).

**4.** Translation from S. D. Poisson, *Recherches sur la probabilité des jugements* (Paris, 1837), p. 7. This is one of the classical source books of probability calculus.

First publication of the theory: R. v. Mises, *Math. Z.* **5,** 52 (1919). See the book quoted in note to Chapter 14, 1; also R. v. Mises, *Wahrscheinlichkeitsrechnung und ihre Anwendungen* (Vienna, 1931); *Notes on the mathematical theory of probability and statistics* (Graduate School of Engineering, Harvard University, Cambridge, Mass., 1946).

**5.** Many recent papers on probability theory deal with a discussion of the concept of randomness. A survey is contained in v. Mises's book quoted in the note to Chapter 14, 1.

A. Wald, "Die Widerspruchsfreiheit des Kollektivbegriffes," *Ergebnisse eines mathematischen Kolloquiums* (Vienna, 1937), No. 8, pp. 38–72. A. H. Copeland, "Consistency of the conditions determining Kollektivs," *Trans. Am. Math. Soc.* **42,** 333 (1937). W. Feller, "Über die Existenz von sogenannten Kollektiven," *Fundamenta mathematica* **32,** 87 (1939).

H. Poincaré, *Calcul des probabilités* (Paris, 1912), Introduction, pp. 1 ff. Also *Science et hypothèse* (see note to Chapter 12, 4), pp. 213–245.

**6.** P. S. Laplace, *Essai philosophique sur les probabilités* (Paris, ed. 4, 1819); in English, *A philosophical essay on probabilities* (New York, 1902). A. A. Markoff, *Lehrbuch der Wahrscheinlichkeitsrechnung* (Leipzig and Berlin, 1912), p. 199. E. v. Hartmann, *Philosophie des Unbewussten* (Leipzig, ed. 11, 1904), vol. 1, p. 36. Here the probability that a physical phenomenon can be due to mental causes is computed in a specific case as 0.5904!

E. Zilsel, *Das Anwendungsproblem, ein philosophischer Versuch über das Gesetz der grossen Zahlen und die Induktion* (Leipzig, 1916). H. Reichenbach, *Wahrscheinlcihkeitslehre* (A. W. Sijthoff, Leiden, 1935), especially Chapter 9, "Das Anwendungsproblem," pp. 325–364. In the English edition, *The theory of probability* (University of California Press, Berkeley and Los Angeles, 1949), Chapter 11.

The application of the probability calculus, called error theory, was developed by Legendre and Gauss. It solves the problem of determining for certain numbers, computed from observations, so-called probable limits of errors. The attempt at making the error theory, which itself *presupposes* a rigorously founded probability theory, afterwards the basis of all theories, or even of all knowledge, is one of the most flagrant examples of "borderline transgression." See also Chapter 15, 5.

Bernoulli's law and its importance within probability theory are discussed in most papers on the foundation of probability calculus. See R. v. Mises's book quoted in the note to Chapter 14, 1, chap. 4.

G. Pólya, "Heuristic reasoning and the theory of probability," *Am. Math. Monthly* **48**, 450 (1941); also R. Carnap, "The two concepts of probability," *Philos. Phenomenol. Research* **5**, 513 (1945).

### Chapter 15

**1.** On the attempts at physics "with a memory" see Vito Volterra, *Drei Vorlesungen über neuere Fortschritte der mathematischen Physik* (Leipzig and Berlin, 1914), pp. 155–181. The original paper by Volterra is in *Rendiconti Accademia dei Lincei* (5), 22 (1st sem.), 9.

**2.** Laplace, *Essai*, see note to Chapter 14, 6.

**3.** On the concept of the intervention of statistics, here discussed, see the two lectures quoted in the note to Chapter 14, 4, and v. Mises's book quoted in the note to Chapter 14, 1, pp. 207–265.

**4.** Boltzmann's theory, first comprehensively expounded in L. Boltzmann, *Vorlesungen über Gastheorie* (Leipzig, 1896), is presented in most textbooks on theoretical physics.

**5.** There exists a great number of introductions into the problems of quantum theory and wave mechanics, written for the nonmathematician. Most of them are unreliable with respect to the logical foundation. Satisfactory and most enlightening information is given in P. W. Bridgman, *The logic of modern physics* (New York, 1927), and in Philipp Frank's books quoted in the note to Chapter 2, 1. P. Jordan, *Anschauliche Quantentheorie* (see note to Chapter 19, 5) contains an exposition intended for physicists, representing a rather unclear "positivistic" point of view.

**7.** On this section see also Philipp Frank, "Was bedeuten die gegenwärtigen physikalischen Theorien für die allgemeine Erkenntnislehre?", *Naturwissenschaften* **17**, 971, 987 (1929), *Erkenntnis* **1**, 126 (1930), now in *Modern science and its philosophy* (note to Chapter 2, 1). See also v. Mises's lecture, "Über das naturwissenschaftliche Weltbild der Gegenwart," *Naturwissenschaften* **18**, 885 (1930). A comprehensive attempt at interpreting the methods and concepts of contemporary physics from the point of view of school philosophy was made by E. Cassirer, *Determinismus und Indeterminismus in der modernen Physik, Historische und systematische Studien zum Kausalproblem* (Elander, Goteborg, 1937).

### Chapter 16

**1.** Hume, see note to Chapter 7, 5, Sec. X of the *Enquiry*.

**2.** The contemporary school sympathizing with astrology is represented by, for example, M. E. Winkel, *Naturwissenschaft und Astrologie* (Augsburg, 1928); also A. Speiser, *Die mathematische Denkweise* (Zurich, 1932), pp. 98–108, 116 (for the quotations from Kepler). A host of books, current magazines, and newspaper articles could be quoted to prove the present popularity of astrology.

**3.** Well-known representatives of "Ausdruckskunde" are at present: L. Klages (see note to Chapter 5, 6), *Einführung in die Psychologie der Hand-*

*schrift* (Stuttgart-Heilbronn, 1924); *The science of character* (London, 1929); R. Kassner (particularly fantastic), *Zahl und Gesicht* (Leipzig, 1919); *Grundlagen der Physiognomik* (Leipzig, 1922).

·E. Kretschmer, *Körperbau und Charakter, Untersuchungen zum Konstitutionsproblem und zur Lehre von den Temperamenten* (Berlin, 1921); *Physique and character* (New York and London, 1926).

**5.** Charles Richet, *Notre sixième sens* (Paris, n. d.). The book presents a wealth of material in critical and well-ordered form. At present a large group of scholars in the United States is studying so-called extrasensory perception and related phenomena. See J. B. Rhine and others, *Extra-sensory perception after sixty years* (Holt, New York, 1940); also the current volumes of the *Journal of Parapsychology*.

**6.** On the notions of teleology and finality see P. Frank, *Das Kausalgesetz* (note to Chapter 13, 4), pp. 89–130.

H. Driesch, *Ordnungslehre, ein System des nichtmetaphysischen Teiles der Philosophie, mit besonderer Berücksichtigung der Lehre vom Werden* (Jena, 1912).

**7.** Jakob Moleschott, *Der Kreislauf des Lebens* (1852), is the supposed founder of Materialism in Germany. Karl Vogt is known for his exaggerated formulations in the polemic paper, *Köhlerglaube und Wissenschaft* (1855). About Büchner and Haeckel see note to Chapter 5, 3.

Nietzsche, *Werke*, vol. 5, p. 165.

Mach, *Mechanik*, p. 443; *Science of mechanics* (see note to Chapter 7, 1), p. 464.

## PART V

The motto is one of the 25 theses which Brentano defended at his installation in Würzburg, *Ad disputationem qua theses . . . defendit Franciscus Brentano* (Aschaffenburg, 1866). Francis Brentano (1838–1917), originally a theologian and student of Greek metaphysics, gradually adopted an empiricist conception of science and became one of the founders of modern positivism. He is best known as the author of *Psychologie vom empirischen Standpunkt* (Leipzig, 1874, 1911). Available in English is his work, *The origin of the knowledge of right and wrong* (Westminster, 1902).

### Chapter 17

**1.** Friedrich Albert Lange, *Geschichte des Materialismus und Kritik seiner Bedeutung in der Gegenwart* (Iserlohn, 1886; later more complete editions); latest English edition, with comments by Bertrand Russell, *History of materialism and criticism of its present importance* (London, 1925).

Comte, *Philosophie positive,* see note to Chapter 19, 5.

John Stuart Mill (1806–1873), a leader of early English positivism (see also Chapter 12, 6 and Chapter 28, 2), wrote *The positive philosophy of Auguste Comte* (New York, 1887).

**2.** The writings relevant here and in the following are: W. Windelband, *Geschichte und Naturwissenschaft* (Strassburg, 1894); Wilhelm Dilthey, collected works, esp. vol. 1, *Einleitung in die Geisteswissenschaften* (Leipzig and Berlin, ed. 2, 1923), French edition, *Introduction à l'étude des sciences humaines* (Paris, 1942); Heinrich Rickert, *Die Grenzen der Naturwissenschaftlichen Begriffsbildung* (Tübingen, ed. 2, 1913); Johann Gustav Droysen, *Grundriss der Historik* (Leipzig, 1868; new ed., Halle, 1925); see also E. Spranger, *Die Grundlagen der Geschichtswissenschaft* (Berlin, 1905). M. Schlick, *Erkenntnis* **4**, 390 (1934) and J. Kraft, *Die Unmöglichkeit der Geisteswissenschaft* (Leipzig, 1934) are essentially in agreement with our point of view.

Translation from Emil du Bois-Reymond, *Über die Grenzen des Naturerkennens, die sieben Welträtsel* (Leipzig, ed. 10, 1907), p. 16.

**3.** Translation from Rickert, p. 293.

Translation from Dilthey, p. 9.

**4.** Schopenhauer, *The world as will and idea,* Supplements, Chap. 38. History "lacks the fundamental character of a science, the subordination of the known . . . Therefore it is knowledge, but not science. For it never derives the particular from the general."

**5.** Translation from T. Mommsen, *Römische Geschichte* (Berlin, 1856), vol. 3, p. 264; in English, *The provinces of the Roman empire* (London, 1909).

Translation from Jacob Burckhardt, *Weltgeschichtliche Betrachtungen* (1905; new ed., Leipzig, 1935), p. 6; in English, *Force and freedom, reflections on history* (Pantheon, New York, 1943).

**6.** Dilthey, p. 9.

**7.** Schopenhauer's system of the sciences is expounded in detail in *The world as will and idea,* Supplements, Chap. 12. For earlier attempts at classification, see Karl Pearson, *The grammar of science* (new ed., Dent, London, 1937), pp. 312–335.

On the contemporary discussion of the "system" of the sciences, in connection with the present movement toward "Unification of Science," see Otto Neurath, "The departmentalization of unified science," *Erkenntnis* **7**, 240 (1938). Closer to the older point of view is W. Ostwald, *Die Pyramide der Wissenschaften* (Stuttgart and Berlin, 1929); *The system of the sciences* (Houston, 1915). An extensive discussion on the problem of unification of science will be found in *Philos. Phenomenol. Research* **6**, 493–553 (1946).

The contents of Chapter 17, more than any other part of this book, are motivated particularly by the intellectual conditions at *German* universities. In other countries there is a less outspoken *ideological* opposition between the natural sciences and the humanities. The customary delineation of the concept "science" in English and French creates a more natural situation. Nevertheless, the detailed discussion did not seem to be superfluous from the point of view of the task of this book.

*Chapter 18*

**1.** This and analogous quotations from Goethe can be found frequently in his "Gespräche." For example (complete ed. by Biedermann, Leipzig, 1910, vol. 3, p. 489): "I did not grow as old as I am in order to care for world history, which is the most absurd thing there is." The quotation in the text is also a translation from vol. 3, p. 137.

Schopenhauer (see note to Chapter 17, 7).

E. Zilsel, "Geschichte und Biologie, Überlieferung und Vererbung," *Arch. Sozialwiss. Sozialpolitik* **65**, 475 (1931).

H. Hahn, "Logik, Mathematik und Naturerkenntnis," *Einheitswissenschaft,* No. 2 (Gerold, Vienna, 1933), p. 26.

**2.** Eduard Meyer, *Zur Theorie und Methodik der Geschichte* (1902), quoted from Rickert (see note to Chapter 17, 2), p. 291.

In connection with many of the questions here discussed one can find interesting remarks which, however, are frequently influenced by conceptions of school philosophy, in Theodor Lessing, *Geschichte als Sinngebung des Sinnlosen* (Munich, ed. 4, 1927).

**3.** Oswald Spengler, *Der Untergang des Abendlandes, Umriss einer Morphologie der Weltgeschichte* (1918; Munich, 1923), 2 vols.; in English, *The decline of the West* (Knopf, New York, 1947). There exists an extraordinary amount of literature about the problematical character of this book, which combines Hegel's metaphysics with modern negativistic tendencies to form an ingenious theory of history. Many of Spengler's ideas are amplified, and at the same time moderated, by Arnold J. Toynbee, whose comprehensive work, *A study of history* (abridgment of volumes 1–6 by D. C. Somervell, Oxford University Press, New York and London, 1947) is considered the outstanding present-day exposition of world history.

Henry Thomas Buckle, *History of civilization in England* (1857–61; new ed., New York, 1920).

**4.** E. Littré, *Dictionnaire de la langue française* (Paris, 1878–9); Lalande, see note to Chapter 4, 2. Dagobert D. Runes, *The dictionary of philosophy* (Philosophical Library, New York, 1942).

The voluminous literature about "historicism" cannot be quoted here; see, e.g., E. Troeltsch, *Der Historismus und seine Überwindung* (Berlin, 1924); English ed., *Christian thought, its history and application* (London, 1923).

**5.** E. Spranger, *Lebensformen* (Halle, ed. 3, 1922).

E. Mach, *Populär-wissenschaftliche Vorlesungen* (Leipzig, 1896), p. 215; *Popular scientific lectures* (Chicago, ed. 2, 1898).

C. Bühler, *Der menschliche Lebensablauf als psychologisches Problem* (Leipzig, 1933).

**6.** Nietzsche, *Werke*, vol. 16, p. 10.

**7.** Wilhelm Wundt, *Völkerpsychologie* (Ethnopsychology) (Leipzig, 1900 ff.), 10 vols.; vol. 1, *Language*, p. 11.

*Chapter 19*

**1.** T. Ribot, *La psychologie allemande contemporaine, école expérimentale* (Paris, 1879), and S. Hall, *Founders of modern psychology* (London, 1912), give an account of the beginnings of experimental psychology. The present-day activity in this field, which is particularly extensive in the United States, is best reflected in the numerous periodicals devoted to it, e.g., *Journal of Applied*

*Psychology, Journal of Abnormal and Social Psychology, Journal of Comparative and Physiological Psychology, Journal of Consulting Psychology, Journal of Experimental Psychology,* and many others.

**2.** On the Weber-Fechner law see T. Fechner, *Elemente der Psychophysik* (Leipzig, 1877). For more recent criticism, see Y. Renquist, *Erkenntnis* **3,** 348 (1932–3), and J. F. Brown, *Erkenntnis* **4,** 46 (1934).

**3.** On the physicalistic conception of psychology see particularly R. Carnap, "Psychologie in physikalischer Sprache," *Erkenntnis* **3,** 107 (1932–3); O. Neurath, "Radikaler Physikalismus und 'Wirkliche Welt,' " *Erkenntnis* **4,** 346 (1934). Also B. Juhos, *Erkenntnis* **4,** 397 (1934); C. G. Hempel, "Analyse logique de la psychologie," *Revue de Synthèse* **10,** 27 (1935). The original behaviorism was represented by William James (1842–1910). He states in *Principles of psychology* (London, 1901), vol. 2, p. 451, "If we fancy some strong emotion, and then try to abstract from our consciousness of it all the feelings of its bodily symptoms, we find we have nothing left behind, no 'mind-stuff.' " The experiences of actors would perhaps yield profitable material for the study of this side of behaviorism.

**4.** The best information about the basic ideas of psychoanalysis is found in Sigmund Freud, *Vorlesungen zur Einführung in die Psychoanalyse* (1917; Leipzig, Vienna, Zurich, 1922); *A general introduction to psychoanalysis* (translation of the revised edition; Liveright, New York, 1935).

E. Bleuler, *Naturgeschichte der Seele und ihres Bewusstwerdens* (Berlin, ed. 2, 1932).

**5.** The best-known contemporary representative of vitalism is H. Driesch; see, e.g., his *Philosophie des Organischen* (Leipzig, ed. 4, 1928), and *Geschichte des Vitalismus* (Leipzig, 1922); *The history and theory of vitalism* (London, 1914); *Der Mensch und die Welt* (Leipzig, 1928); *Man and the universe* (London, 1929).

P. Jordan, *Anschauliche Quantentheorie* (Berlin, 1936). This book, which is mainly intended for the theoretical physicist, contains an appendix, "Atome und Organismen," pp. 271–319, in which the author speaks, as he puts it, along the lines of the "positivistic method" about problems such as causality, finality, structure of the real world, the problem of observation of living substances, etc. Neither these discussions nor the same author's "Quantenphysikalische Bemerkungen zur Biologie und Psychologie," *Erkenntnis* **4,** 215 (1934), it seems to us, fulfills the necessary requirements of "connectibility."

**6.** W. Whewell, *History of the inductive sciences, from the earliest to the present time* (New York, ed. 3, 1866), 3 vols. This work, which is an excellent source of information for the older history of the natural sciences, is also particularly interesting with respect to its classification of the sciences, which was adequate at its time, but today seems to us somewhat strange; see Chapter 17, 7.

Alexis Carrel, *Man the unknown* (Harper, New York and London, 1935).

**7.** On the contemporary situation with respect to the problems in genetics see, e.g., E. Guyénot, *L'hérédité* (Paris, ed. 2, 1931); or M. Caullery, *Les conceptions modernes de l'hérédité* (Paris, 1936). For information on modern points of view in genetics, see some chapters in G. L. Jepsen, E. Mayr, and

G. G. Simpson, eds., *Genetics, paleontology, and evolution* (Princeton University Press, Princeton, 1949). The elements of Mendel's theory are contained in every textbook; see, e.g., L. T. Hogben, *Introduction to mathematical genetics* (Norton, New York, 1946). The statistical laws discovered in the period from 1866 to 1870 by Gregor Mendel remained long unnoticed and became known only about 1930 through publications by H. de Vries, O. Correns, and E. v. Tschermak.

Hugo de Vries, *The mutation theory* (Chicago, 1909–10).

Concerning an exact formulation of the biological problems, see the papers of the Copenhagen Congress for the Unity of Science by J. B. S. Haldane, N. Rashevsky, and others, *Erkenntnis* **6**, 346 ff. (1936).

*Chapter 20*

**1.** Othmar Spann, Gesellschaftslehre, quoted from O. Neurath, *Empirische Soziologie* (Vienna, 1931), p. 51.

**2.** W. Sombart, *Die drei Nationalökonomien, Geschichte und System der Lehre von der Wirtschaft* (Munich, 1930).

**3.** On the historical development of economics see, e.g., C. Gide and C. Rist, *Histoire des doctrines économiques depuis les physiocrates jusqu'à nos jours* (Paris, ed. 5, 1929); E. Dühring, *Kritische Geschichte der Nationalökonomie und des Sozialismus von ihren Anfängen zur Gegenwart* (Leipzig, ed. 4, 1900).

Adam Smith (1723–1790), *Inquiry into the nature and cause of the wealth of nations* (1776); David Ricardo (1772–1823), *Principles of political economy and taxation* (1812).

Karl Marx, *Das Kapital, Kritik der Politischen Ökonomie; Capital, a critique of political economy,* trans. by E. Untermann (Chicago, 1926).

F. v. Gottl, *Die Herrschaft des Wortes. Untersuchungen zur Kritik des Nationalökonomischen Denkens* (1901); reprinted in *Wirtschaft als Leben* (Jena, 1925), pp. 79–335.

**4.** H. H. Gossen (1810–1858), *Entwicklung der Gesetze des menschlichen Verkehrs und der daraus fliessenden Regeln des menschlichen Handelns* (Brunswick, 1854). This work remained unnoticed for a long time, but has become since the eighties the subject of a steadily increasing amount of literature. At present, studies in this direction are labeled econometry, and are reflected, for instance, in the international periodical *Econometrica*.

The principal work of the "Austrian School": E. v. Böhm-Bawerk, *Positive Theorie des Kapitals* (Jena, ed. 4, 1921), 2 vols.; *The positive theory of capital* (New York, 1923).

F. Kaufmann, *Methodenlehre der Socialwissenschaft* (Vienna and Leipzig, 1936), particularly pp. 255–290; *Methodology of the social sciences* (Oxford University Press, London and New York, 1944) (not the same book).

The principal classical works of mathematically oriented economics are: A. A. Cournot, *Recherches sur les principes mathématiques de la théorie des richesses* (1863); W. S. Jevons, *The theory of political economy* (London, ed. 4, 1911); Leo Walras, *Elements d'économie pure* (Paris, new ed. 4, 1926);

V. Pareto, *Manuale d'economia politica* (Milan, 1906; French ed. 2, Paris, 1927).

John von Neumann and O. Morgenstern, *Theory of games and economic behavior* (Princeton University Press, Princeton, 1944).

**5.** Auguste Compte, *Cours de philosophie positive* (Paris, 1830–42; ed. 2, 1862), 6 vols. The fundamentals of sociology are discussed mainly in vol. 4.

Otto Neurath, *Empirische Soziologie* (Vienna, 1931).

A. C. Kinsey, *Sexual behavior in the human male* (Saunders, Philadelphia, 1948), a typical example of accumulation of statistical data.

**6.** A. Quetelet, *Physique sociale ou essai sur le développement des facultés de l'homme* (Brussels and Paris, ed. 2, 1869), 2 vols.

T. R. Malthus (1766–1834), *An essay on the principle of population* (1798; ed. 6, 1826).

**7.** Technocracy is defined by Webster as "1. Government or management of the whole of society by technical experts or in accordance with principles established by technicians; 2. An organization of technicians that studies the possibilities of such management." An insight into the lines of thought of the technocrats can be found in J. Werner, *Technokratie* (Brunn, 1933), 4 pamphlets.

O. Neurath, see note to Chapter 20, 5 and "Was bedeutet rationale Wirtschaftsbetrachtung?", *Einheitswissenschaft* 4 (Vienna, 1935).

Mohammed, according to A. Weber, *Allgem. Volkswirtschaftslehre* (Munich and Leipzig, 1928), p. 9.

A principal representative of social romanticism is W. Sombart in his later works, e.g., *Deutscher Sozialismus* (Charlottenburg, 1934); pp. 244–266, a temperamental polemic against modern technology.

On the polemic of neoliberalism against collectivist theories of economics see, e.g., Louis Rougier, *Les mystiques économiques, comment on passe des démocraties libérales aux Etats totalitaires* (Flammarion, Paris, 1938); W. Lippmann, *La cité libre* (Paris, 1938); L. v. Mises, *Human action, a treatise on economics* (Yale University Press, New Haven, 1949); F. A. Hayek (editor), *Collectivist economic planning* (Routledge, London, 1935).

## PART VI

The motto is from Ernst Mach, *Erkenntnis und Irrtum*, p. 4.

### Chapter 21

**1.** From a good description of Hegel's dialectic method by E. v. Hartmann, *Über die dialektische Methode* (Berlin, 1868), pp. 35 ff., the following excerpts may be of interest here: "The mind moves by means of abstracts, of fixed and one-sided concepts, along the guiding line of the formal rules of identity and contradiction. If, however, one singles out any one specific concept and studies it thoroughly, it turns out that this concept cannot remain what it was, but breaks through the boundaries prescribed to it by the mind, annihilates itself (by means of the contradictions contained in itself), and continues in the negative direction thus begun until it reaches its natural limit, i.e., until it has transformed itself into its complete opposite. If one then studies this opposite concept (which is also known to the mind), the same phenomenon can be observed: it also annihilates itself and transforms itself back into its opposite . . . Hence the truth of the concept is that it separates itself into an absolute contradiction, but also that it finds in this contradiction of its self-created opposition again its absolute identity. This identity is no longer the cheap abstract identity of the mind, which belongs to the one-sided mental concept due to the constancy forced upon it arbitrarily, but it is rather the concrete identity of reason, which contains in itself the abundance of the opposition as negated, i.e., at the same time as annihilated and preserved." One of Hegel's contemporary opponents was O. F. Gruppe (1804–1876), who in his book, *Antäus, ein Briefwechsel über speculative Philosophie in ihrem Conflict mit Wissenschaft und Sprache,* Berlin 1831 (new ed., Munich, 1914), offers some interesting starting points for critical linguistic study of philosophic problems.

A recent attempt to rationalize the dialectic method is by Gaston Casanova, *Mathématiques et matérialisme dialectique* (Editions sociales, Paris, 1947).

The translation is from Schopenhauer, *Werke,* vol. 2, p. 331.

**2.** Translation from Kant, *Prolegomena zu einer künftigen Metaphysik, die als Wissenschaft wird auftreten können* (1783), *Werke,* ed. by Rosenkranz (Leipzig, 1838), 12 vols., vol. 3, pp. 16, 25, 22, 147.

**3.** About the point of view of logical empiricism, see note to Chapter 6, 1 for references.

Heidegger, see note to Chapter 6, 4.

**4.** Translation from Hegel, *System der Philosophie,* second part, "Die Naturphilosophie," ed. by Michelet (Stuttgart, 1929), pp. 140, 319.

**5.** The historical remarks of this section are based upon generally known expositions of the history of philosophy; see, e.g., K. Vorländer, *Geschichte der Philosophie* (Leipzig, ed. 6, 1921), 2 vols., or Will Durant, *The story of philosophy* (new ed., Simon and Schuster, New York, 1933).

The paradox of Zeno concerning the race between Achilles and the tortoise is solved by noting that the infinitely many terms $1 + \frac{1}{2} + \frac{1}{4} + \frac{1}{8} +$ etc. have a finite sum, namely, 2, and this leads to the concept of the infinite convergent series. Nevertheless, school philosophy continues to talk about "unavoidable antinomies"; thus, K. Jaspers, *Psychologie der Weltanschauungen* (Berlin, ed. 3, 1925), p. 234, says: "The moving object must be thought of as in one place. But since it moves, it must likewise at a small period of time be at a different place. While changing, something is, and, since it changes, at the same time it is not."

**6.** Translation from L. Nelson, "Die kritische Methode und das Verhältnis der Psychologie zur Philosophie," *Abhandlungen der Friesschen Schule,* new series, No. 1 (1904), p. 8.

Edmund Husserl (1859–1935) was, so far, the last in the long series of German idealist philosophers, modifying once more the layout, the style, and the attributes of the metaphysical system. His main work is *Ideen zu einer Phänomenologie und einer phänomenologischen Philosophie* (Halle, 1928);

trans. as *Ideas: general introduction to pure phenomenology* (Macmillan, London and New York, 1931). The quotations are from one of his last papers, "Die Krisis der europäischen Wissenschaften und die transzendentale Phänomenologie," *Philosophia* **1**, 134, 175 (1936). See also the note to Chapter 2, 6.

Wittgenstein, *Tractatus* (see note to Chapter 6, 1), p. 186. The quoted statement, one of the last of the *Tractatus,* starts with the proposition: "For an answer which one cannot pronounce, one cannot pronounce the question either," a sentence which we have to consider as absolutely unconnectible.

## Chapter 22

**1.** Kant, *Critique of pure reason,* Introduction to the first edition. The later quotations are from the second edition, pp. 3–4, 5, 7.

**2.** In the voluminous Kant literature, which cannot be quoted here, it has often been pointed out that the meaning of the a priori is frequently changing in Kant—which is also evident from our quotations. Sometimes the purely psychological point of view is predominant, according to which a priori is that which is immediately evident, and sometimes the epistemological one, of validity without exception. The controversies among the later commentators are thus easily understandable.

Johan Friedrich Herbart (1776–1841) had a strong leaning toward empiricism, but succumbed to the influence of school philosophy. His main work, *Allgemeine Metaphysik nebst den Anfängen der philosophischen Naturlehre* (1829), contains, in spite of its continual stressing of scientific purposes, many bizarre ideas.

J. F. Fries, in his *Neue Kritik der reinen Vernunft* (1807), and *Psychische Anthropologie* (1821), gives, from the positivistic point of view, the most acceptable interpretation of Kant's doctrines, somehow related to today's intuitionism (Chapter 11, 3).

Hermann Cohen, the founder of the Marburg school of Neo-Kantianism, conceived a system of philosophy in three parts: *Die Logik der reinen Erkenntnis* (Berlin, ed. 3, 1922); *Die Ethik des reinen Willens* (Berlin, ed. 4, 1923); *Aesthetik des reinen Gefühls* (Berlin, ed. 2, 1923). This system forms, in a different direction from Hegel's, an extreme accomplishment of idealistic philosophy.

P. Natorp, *Die logischen Grundlagen der exakten Wissenschaften* (Leipzig and Berlin, 1910), pp. 392–404.

Husserl, *Ideen* (see note to Chapter 21, 6), pp. 38–39. About the polemic between Husserl and Schlick, see Schlick, *Allgemeine Erkenntnislehre* (Berlin, ed. 2, 1925), pp. 127 ff.

**4.** The beginnings of the so-called Gestalt psychology were the studies of C. v. Ehrenfels, *Vierteljahrschrift für wissenschaftliche Philosophie,* vol. 14 (1890); they started from suggestions in Mach's *Analysis of sensations.* Decisive results were achieved by M. Wertheimer since 1910. A survey can be found in M. Wertheimer, *Uber Gestaltstheorie* and *Drei Abhandlungen zur Gestaltstheorie* (Erlangen, 1925). The alleged contrast to empiricism is particularly stressed by W. Köhler, *Psychologische Probleme* (Berlin, 1933), pp. 93–140;

*Dynamics in psychology* (Liveright, New York, 1940). For an introduction to the present state of problems, see D. Katz, *Gestalt psychology, its nature and significance* (Ronald, New York, 1949).

E. Mach, *Analyse de Empfindungen* (ed. 6), pp. 90 ff., 170 ff., 232 ff., etc.

**5.** The origin of the saying about the "whole that is more than the sum of its parts" is hardly traceable today; at any rate, the biologists use it and related forms continuously. B. Dürkens, *Entwicklungsbiologie und Ganzheit* (Leipzig, 1937), speaks in this connection of a "mental revolution of gigantic dimensions." About the factual basis see, e.g., Jepsen, Mayr, and Simpson, *Genetics*, etc., mentioned in note to Chapter 19, 7.

**6.** H. Driesch, *Ordnungslehre* (see note to Chapter 16, 6), p. 258.

O. Spann, *Tote und lebendige Wissenschaft* (Jena, 1921), pp. 4–5.

Max Adler, *Kant und der Marxismus* (Berlin, 1925), p. 16.

## Chapter 23

**1.** "Ungeheures Welt-, Staats- und Kirchengebäude": An expression of Stefan George in the introduction to his Dante translation, *Works,* vol. 10, p. 5.

The most important works of L. Lévy-Bruhl in this connection are: *Les fonctions mentales dans les societés inférieures, L'âme primitive, La mentalité primitive, Le surnaturel et la nature dans la mentalité, La mythologie primitive* (all Alcan, Paris).

G. F. Lipps, *Mythenbildung und Erkenntnis* (Leipzig and Berlin, 1907).

**3.** F. Gonseth, *Les mathématiques et la realité* (Paris, 1936), p. 51.

**4.** Comments on the theory of poetry as developed in this chapter have been given by Van Meter Ames, *Kenyon Review* **6,** 101 (1944), and by Werner Richter, *Germanic Review* **21,** 94 (1946).

**5.** R. M. Rilke, translated by M. D. Herter Norton, *The notebooks of Malte Laurids Brigge* (Norton, New York, 1949), p. 26.

Nietzsche, *Werke,* vol. 4 (Aurore), pp. 40–41.

**6.** Thomas Mann, *Death in Venice,* trans. by H. T. Lowe-Porter (Knopf, New York, 1930), pp. 23–24.

**7.** Plato, *The Republic,* book 10.

R. M. Rilke, *Sonnets to Orpheus,* trans. by J. B. Leishman, Hogarth Press, London, 1946), Sonnet XIX.

## Chapter 24

**1.** L. Lévy-Bruhl, see note to Chapter 23, 1.

Dante, *Divina Commedia,* Paradiso, X, 75 ff.

**3.** G. T. Fechner, *Vorschule der Aesthetik* (Leipzig, 1876), vol. 1, p. 263.

Kant, *Critique of aesthetic judgment,* trans. by J. C. Meredith (Oxford, 1911), p. 80.

Rilke, *Duino Elegies,* trans. by B. J. Morse (Silurian Press, South Wales, England, n.d.), p. 5.

**4.** The doctrine of proportions as a basis of aesthetics has found for centuries ever new expositions. A critical survey, which also in many points coincides with the discussions of the text, is found in E. Kulke, *Kritik der Philosophie des Schönen,* with introductory letters by E. Mach and F. Jodl (Leipzig, 1906).

A new approach to this problem is given by G. D. Birkhoff, *Aesthetic measure* (Harvard University Press, Cambridge, 1933).

**5.** Quotation from Fechner (see note to Chapter 24, 3), p. 89.

E. v. Hartmann, *Grundriss der Aesthetik* (new ed., Leipzig, 1909).

Josef Popper, *Die technischen Fortschritte nach ihrer ästhetischen und kulturellen Bedeutung* (Leipzig, 1888).

**6.** J. Strzygowski, *Die Krisis der Geisteswissenschaften, vorgeführt am Beispiel der Forschung über bildende Kunst* (Vienna, 1923), p. 127. The quoted schema is a translation from the article, "Bildende Kunst," of the same author in *Das Jahr 1913, ein Gesamtbild der Kulturentwicklung,* ed. by Sarason (Leipzig and Berlin, 1913), p. 485.

**7.** F. Kuntze in a review of Bruno Bauch, *Kantstudien* **33**, 151 (1928).


## PART VII

The motto is from Montaigne, *Essais,* Livre I, Ch. XXIII, appendix to the manuscripts. Michel de Montaigne (1533–1592) was one of the early predecessors of the French Enlightenment. His principal work is his *Essais* (1580, augmented 1588; modern English edition with commentaries, Heritage Press, New York, 1947).

*Chapter 25*

**1.** Blaise Pascal (1623–1662), the great mathematician, in his early philosophical writings a follower of Descartes' "clarity," attempted in the *Pensées,* which remained unfinished, an apology of Christian religion. Modern English edition, *Thoughts,* trans. by W. F. Trotter (New York, 1910).

**2.** Schopenhauer, *passim;* particularly in the second volume of *The world as will and idea.* Thomas Hobbes, *Elementorum Philosophiae, sectio prima, de corpore* (London, 1655). E. Mach, *Analyse der Empfindungen* (ed. 6), p. 82, see note to Chapter 5, 4.

**3.** Similar lines of thought in K. Menger, *Moral, Wille und Weltgestaltung, Grundlegung zur Logik der Sitten* (Vienna, 1934), pp. 6 ff.

**5.** *Travaux du Congrès Descartes* (Paris, 1937), fasc. X, pp. 3, 7.

**6.** The remarks in the text concerning the so-called problem of the freedom of the will correspond more or less to Hume's conceptions in the *Enquiry,* chap. viii (see note to Chapter 7, 5). The present point of view of school philosophy can be found by leafing through any one of the currently used philosophy texts; or Wilhelm Wundt, *Ethik* (Stuttgart, ed. 5, 1923–4), 3 vols. M. Schlick, *Fragen der Ethik* (Vienna, 1930), p. 105, calls the continuation of such discussions of the free will and similar problems one of the "greatest scandals of philosophy."

**7.** Bergson, *Les deux sources de la morale et de la religion* (Paris, 1937), pp. 287 ff.

*Chapter 26*

**1.** R. Ihering, *Geist des Römischen Rechtes auf den verschiedenen Stufen seiner Entwicklung* (Leipzig, 1852 ff.). A comprehensive discussion of the questions dealt with in this chapter can be found in Julius Stone, *The province and function of law* (Harvard University Press, Cambridge, 1950).

**2.** Hans Kelsen, *Der soziologische und juristische Staatsbegriff* (Tübingen, ed. 2, 1928), pp. 76, 80; *Reine Rechtslehre* (Vienna and Leipzig, 1934); *General theory of law and state* (Harvard University Press, Cambridge, 1945). R. Stammler, *Lehrbuch der Rechtsphilosophie* (Leipzig, ed. 2, 1922), and *Die Lehre vom richtigen Rechte* (Halle, 1926), offer expositions of the philosophy of law very much worth reading. His discussions, although they are all within the framework of the school-philosophy conception of language, are rather close to positive scientific studies.

**4.** *The fable of the bees, or: Private vices, publick benefits,* published anonymously in 1714, 2nd part, 1724, by Bernard de Mandeville (1670–1733). He demonstrates, particularly in the extensive comments, the many contradictions that arise from the observation of actual social life and the assumptions of an "objectively right" moral code. Modern English edition, Oxford, 1924.

Nicolo Macchiavelli (1469–1527), *Il Principe* (Venice, 1515), a critical discussion of moral codes concerning public life, which is far ahead of its time. Modern English edition, *The Prince* (Crofts, New York, 1947). There are many counter writings, e.g., Frederick the Great, *Antimachiavel ou examen du Prince de Machiavel* (1740). Also often defended, e.g., by L. v. Ranke, *Zur Kritik neuerer Geschichtsschreiber* (Leipzig, ed. 2, 1874). Freer conceptions of the "dispensation from the moral law" in Burckhardt (note to Chapter 17, 5), p. 243.

**5.** Charles, Baron de Montesquieu (1689–1755), *L'esprit des lois* (Geneva, 1748), develops the ideal of a free society on the basis of observations of the actual social life; modern English edition, *The spirit of the laws,* (Hafner, New York, 1949). Historical and positive development of the present situation in L. Lévy-Bruhl, *La morale et la science de moeurs* (Alcan, Paris, 1937).

Anton Menger, *Neue Sittenlehre* (Jena, 1905), p. 3; positivistic discussion from the point of view of political socialism.

Vilfredo Pareto, *Les systèmes socialistes* (Paris, 1902), 2 vols.; *Trattato di sociologia generale* (Florence, ed. 2, 1924), 2 vols.; English edition, *The mind and society* (Harcourt, Brace, New York, 1935), 4 vols.

See in this connection J. Popper-Lynkeus, *Philosophie des Strafrechts* (Vienna, 1924).

**6.** Kant, *Critique of practical reason, Werke,* vol. 8, p. 141.

Kant describes his apology in the preface to a later work. To the words, "Your Royal Majesty's most obedient subject," he adds as a footnote, "This expression, too, was chosen by me quite carefully, in order not to waive the freedom of my judgment in this religious problem *forever,* but only so long as His Majesty was alive."

**7.** Herbert Spencer, see note to Chapter 5, 3, *Principles of morality* (1879–1893).

Wilhelm Ostwald (1853–1932) was a chemist of great merits; see also note to Chapter 17, 7. *Der energetische Imperativ, Erste Reihe* (Leipzig, 1912); *Vorlesungen über Naturphilosophie* (Leipzig, ed. 3, 1905), p. 153; English, *Natural philosophy* (New York, 1910).

*Chapter 27*

**1.** In the dictionaries of philosophy (see, e.g., those quoted in the note to Chapter 4, 2) different definitions of ethics and its subdivisions can be found, corresponding to the slightly varying conceptions in the various systems of school philosophy. A small dictionary which reflects rather the positivistic point of view is Clauberg and Dubislav, *Systematisches Wörterbuch der Philosophie* (Leipzig, 1923).

**2.** The historical figure of Socrates is not very clear, owing to conflicting traditions. See the thorough study of Heinrich Maier, *Sokrates, sein Werk und seine geschichtliche Stellung* (Tübingen, 1913); for the questions relevant here, see particularly pp. 339–358.

**3.** M. Schlick (note to Chapter 25, 6), p. 72.

Nietzsche, *Werke,* vol. 2, p. 30.

**4.** Baruch d'Espinoza (1632–1677). Benedicti de Spinoza, *Opera posthuma* (Amsterdam, 1677), containing *Ethica ordine geometrico demonstrata,* his main systematic work, new English edition: *Ethics* (Hafner, New York, 1949).

*Tractatus politicus, in quo demonstratur, quomodo societas . . . debet institui, ne in tyrannidem labatur. . .* ; in English, *A treatise on politics* (London, 1854).

**5.** Those who want to get a general picture, without going into special studies, of the point of view of the German (Protestant) scholars (at the beginning of the twentieth century) toward questions of the relations among religion, metaphysics, and science, will find information in the collective volume, *Weltanschauung, Philosophie und Religion in Darstellungen von W. Dilthey . . . M. Frischeisen-Köhler* (Berlin, 1911). The reader will be able to judge for himself how little all of these discussions would hold up under a critical linguistic analysis. For the Catholic conceptions, see, e.g., A. Ehrhard, *Der Katholizismus und das 20. Jahrhundert im Lichte der kirchlichen Entwicklung der Neuzeit* (Stuttgart and Vienna, 1902), and the following polemic book of the same author: *Liberaler Katholizismus? Ein Wort an meine Kritiker* (Stuttgart and Vienna, 1902). For the point of view of modern American writers, see the note to Chapter 27, 7.

**6.** The ontological proof of the existence of God stems from Bishop Anselm of Canterbury (1033–1109). The first sentence of Spinoza's *Ethics* also corresponds to it: "Per causam sui intellego id, cuius essentia involvit existentiam; sive id, cuius natura non potest concipi, nisi existens" (As cause of itself I consider that whose essence implies existence, or that whose nature cannot be conceived except as existent). The point of view of contemporary school philosophy toward such play with words may be seen from the following quotation from W. Wundt's contribution to *Die Kultur der Gegenwart* (Berlin and Leipzig, 1907), part I, chap. vi, "Systematische Philosophie," p. 112: "In addition to the transition from the theological to the more general philosophical form of the concept, it is the replacement of the proof by a definition which marks the essential progress here (scil., Spinoza). A concept that, in virtue of the logical evidence of its characteristic properties, proves itself, does not need a proof; all one needs to do is to define it by means of those necessary properties in order to see that it must have reality." This juggling with definitions and proofs was taken up again as recently as 1943 by an American philosopher: Mortimer J. Adler, "The demonstration of God's existence," *The Thomist* **5**, 188 (1943).

Kant, *Critique of pure reason,* pp. 513–514.

The opposition to religion, usually labeled by the name "atheism," is a widespread cultural phenomenon which is often mentioned in connection with positivistic conceptions. One of its most outstanding representatives was Voltaire, e.g., in his *Dictionnarie philosophique* (1769). For an exhaustive historical report, see F. Mauthner, *Der Atheismus und seine Geschichte im Abendlande* (Stuttgart and Berlin, 1920–23), 4 vols. See also Josef Popper-Lynkeus, *Über Religion* (Vienna and Leipzig, 1924).

**7.** William James, *The varieties of religious experience* (New York and London, 36th impression, 1928), p. 517. A more objective exposition is given by J. B. Pratt, *The religious consciousness* (New York, 1920).

Sigmund Freud, *Das Unbehagen in der Kultur* (Leipzig, Vienna, Zurich, 1930); *Civilization and its discontents* (London, 1930); *Die Zukunft einer Illusion* (London, 1927); *The future of an illusion* (London, 1928). We purposely quote an author who surely is far from metaphysical and theistic tendencies.

Mary Baker Eddy, *Science and health, with key to the Scriptures* (Boston, 1875), pp. 114, 275.

The theory of ethics as developed in this book (whose German edition appeared in 1939) has been the subject of an extensive study from the point of view of unorthodox Christian theology by W. F. Zuurdeeg, *A research for the consequences of the Vienna Circle philosophy for ethics* (Thesis, Amsterdam, 1946).

*Chapter 28*

**1.** The best-known expositions of the history of philosophy are almost all written from the point of view of present school philosophy and therefore agree with each other in most of their judgments, particularly in the condemnation of positivistic tendencies. A somewhat more independent conception is evident in Eugen Dühring (see note to Chapter 5, 2), who, forced into opposition by personal events, in his later works voices heretical and in part strange opinions; see, e.g., *Logik und Wissenschaftstheorie, denkerisches Gesamtsystem verstandessouveräner Geisteshaltung* (Leipzig, 1905).

Socrates, see note to Chapter 27, 2.

Roger Bacon (1214–1294) marks the beginning of the consideration of empirical science in philosophy; some accomplishments in optics are also due to him; works: *Opus maius, Opus minus, Opus tertium.* John Duns Scotus (1265?–1308), works published by Wadding (Lyons, 1639, new ed., Paris, 1891–95), strove for a separation of the areas of science and faith (Chapter 28, 3). William of Occam or Ockham (about 1300–1350) was known as the renewer of nominalism (Chapter 21, 5). "Occam's razor" is his proposition: "Entia non sunt multiplicanda praeter necessitatem" (New concepts should not be introduced where they are not necessary).

Francis Bacon, Lord Verulam, see note to Chapter 12, 6. Thomas Hobbes, see notes to Chapter 7, 5 and Chapter 25, 2. John Locke (1632–1704), *Essay concerning human understanding* (1690) is the first empirical epistemology. George Berkeley (1684–1753), *Treatise on the principles of human knowledge* (1710), is a combination of empirical and metaphysical points of view, but contains some of the basic ideas of Mach's doctrine of the elements; see Mach, *Analyse der Empfindungen* (ed. 6), pp. 295, 299. David Hume, see notes to Chapter 7, 5 and Chapter 13, 3.

Pierre Bayle (1647–1706), polyhistor, author of the *Dictionnaire historique et critique.* François Marie Arouet Voltaire (1694–1778) spread the ideas of Newton and Locke in France. Montesquieu, see note to Chapter 26, 5. Jean le Rond d'Alembert (1717–1783), great mathematician, author of the *Discours préliminaire,* of the great encyclopedia (1751).

**2.** On the human side of the last phase of Comte's life, see E. Littré, *Auguste Comte et la philosophie positive* (Paris, 1863), and the (hostile) paper, H. Gruber, S.J., *August Comte der Begründer des Positivismus, sein Leben und seine Lehre* (Freiburg i.B., 1889).

John Stuart Mill, see notes to Chapter 3, 1, Chapter 12, 6, and Chapter 17, 1.

Jeremy Bentham (1748–1832), jurist and philanthropist, is the originator of the concept "greatest happiness for the greatest number."

Spencer, Vogt, Büchner, Haeckel, see notes to Chapter 5, 3, and Chapter 16, 7.

Fries, Cohen, Natorp, see note to Chapter 22, 2.

Richard Avenarius (1843–1896), founder of "Empiriocriticism." Main work: *Philosophie der reinen Erfahrung,* (Leipzig, 1907–08), 2 vols.

J. B. Stallo, *The concepts and theories of modern physics* (New York, 1882); German edition with preface by Mach, *Die Begriffe und Theorien der modernen Physik* (Leipzig, 1911).

Charles S. Peirce's work remained little noticed until recently. It is now available in *Collected papers* (Harvard University Press, Cambridge, 1931–35), 6 vols.

William James, main works in addition to those mentioned in notes to Chapter 2, 3 and Chapter 27, 7: *The principles of psychology* (1890), *Pragmatism* (1907), *Essays in radical empiricism* (1912).

John Dewey, who follows Spencer in his appreciation of evolutionism, is an extremely prolific author; *Democracy and education* (1916), *The quest of certainty* (1930), etc.

Henri Poincaré, see note to Chapter 12, 4. Of newer French authors developing Poincaré's ideas we mention M. Boll, *La science et l'esprit positif chez les penseurs contemporains* (Paris, 1921); General Vouillemin, *Qu'est-ce, au fond, que la science?* (Paris, 1924).

P. W. Bridgman, *The logic of modern science,* 1927 (Reprint: Macmillan, New York, 1946) developed, essentially independently of Mach and the Vienna Circle, a consistent, positivistic view of physical concepts and theories. His approach, known as operationalism, reduces all acceptable concepts in physics to actions, measurements, operations; it is in close agreement with the point of view represented in this book.

Ludwig Wittgenstein, see notes to Chapter 6, 1 and Chapter 21, 7.

In addition to the writings of the members of the Vienna Circle frequently mentioned in this book, we may cite the programmatic paper, *Wissenschaftliche Weltauffassung* (Verein Ernst Mach, Vienna, 1929), and the historical exposition in the first chapter of the book by Philipp Frank, *Modern science and its philosophy* (Harvard University Press, Cambridge, 1949). The traditions of the Vienna Circle are now continued in the *Institute for the Unity of Science* in Cambridge, Massachusetts, under the direction of Philipp Frank. The communications of the Institute appear in the periodical *Synthèse* (Bussum, Netherlands). A number of articles revealing the present stage appeared in *Synthèse* **7**, 457–533 (1948–49).

**5.** Emile Durkheim, *De la division du travail social* (Paris, 1893); *Les règles de la méthode sociologique* (Paris, 1895); *Les formes eléméntaires de la vie religieuse* (Paris, 1912). In these and other writings the predominant idea is to give a systematic *description* of the social phenomena, based upon clear concepts, if possible—after the model of the theories of the natural sciences.

Mach, *Erkenntnis und Irrtum*, p. 455.

**7.** Egon Friedell, *Kulturgeschichte der Neuzeit* (Munich, 1927–31), vol. 3, p. 579.

# index

A CATALOGUE OF SELECTED DOVER BOOKS
IN ALL FIELDS OF INTEREST

# A CATALOGUE OF SELECTED DOVER BOOKS
## IN ALL FIELDS OF INTEREST

WHAT IS SCIENCE?, *N. Campbell*
The role of experiment and measurement, the function of mathematics, the nature of scientific laws, the difference between laws and theories, the limitations of science, and many similarly provocative topics are treated clearly and without technicalities by an eminent scientist. "Still an excellent introduction to scientific philosophy," H. Margenau in *Physics Today*. "A first-rate primer . . . deserves a wide audience," *Scientific American*. 192pp. 5⅜ x 8.
Paperbound $1.25

THE NATURE OF LIGHT AND COLOUR IN THE OPEN AIR, *M. Minnaert*
Why are shadows sometimes blue, sometimes green, or other colors depending on the light and surroundings? What causes mirages? Why do multiple suns and moons appear in the sky? Professor Minnaert explains these unusual phenomena and hundreds of others in simple, easy-to-understand terms based on optical laws and the properties of light and color. No mathematics is required but artists, scientists, students, and everyone fascinated by these "tricks" of nature will find thousands of useful and amazing pieces of information. Hundreds of observational experiments are suggested which require no special equipment. 200 illustrations; 42 photos. xvi + 362pp. 5⅜ x 8.
Paperbound $2.00

THE STRANGE STORY OF THE QUANTUM, AN ACCOUNT FOR THE GENERAL READER OF THE GROWTH OF IDEAS UNDERLYING OUR PRESENT ATOMIC KNOWLEDGE, *B. Hoffmann*
Presents lucidly and expertly, with barest amount of mathematics, the problems and theories which led to modern quantum physics. Dr. Hoffmann begins with the closing years of the 19th century, when certain trifling discrepancies were noticed, and with illuminating analogies and examples takes you through the brilliant concepts of Planck, Einstein, Pauli, Broglie, Bohr, Schroedinger, Heisenberg, Dirac, Sommerfeld, Feynman, etc. This edition includes a new, long postscript carrying the story through 1958. "Of the books attempting an account of the history and contents of our modern atomic physics which have come to my attention, this is the best," H. Margenau, Yale University, in *American Journal of Physics*. 32 tables and line illustrations. Index. 275pp. 5⅜ x 8.
Paperbound $1.75

GREAT IDEAS OF MODERN MATHEMATICS: THEIR NATURE AND USE, *Jagjit Singh*
Reader with only high school math will understand main mathematical ideas of modern physics, astronomy, genetics, psychology, evolution, etc. better than many who use them as tools, but comprehend little of their basic structure. Author uses his wide knowledge of non-mathematical fields in brilliant exposition of differential equations, matrices, group theory, logic, statistics, problems of mathematical foundations, imaginary numbers, vectors, etc. Original publication. 2 appendixes. 2 indexes. 65 ills. 322pp. 5⅜ x 8.
Paperbound $2.00

THE MUSIC OF THE SPHERES: THE MATERIAL UNIVERSE — FROM ATOM TO QUASAR, SIMPLY EXPLAINED, *Guy Murchie*
Vast compendium of fact, modern concept and theory, observed and calculated data, historical background guides intelligent layman through the material universe. Brilliant exposition of earth's construction, explanations for moon's craters, atmospheric components of Venus and Mars (with data from recent fly-by's), sun spots, sequences of star birth and death, neighboring galaxies, contributions of Galileo, Tycho Brahe, Kepler, etc.; and (Vol. 2) construction of the atom (describing newly discovered sigma and xi subatomic particles), theories of sound, color and light, space and time, including relativity theory, quantum theory, wave theory, probability theory, work of Newton, Maxwell, Faraday, Einstein, de Broglie, etc. "Best presentation yet offered to the intelligent general reader," *Saturday Review*. Revised (1967). Index. 319 illustrations by the author. Total of xx + 644pp. 5⅜ x 8½.
Vol. 1 Paperbound $2.00, Vol. 2 Paperbound $2.00,
The set $4.00

FOUR LECTURES ON RELATIVITY AND SPACE, *Charles Proteus Steinmetz*
Lecture series, given by great mathematician and electrical engineer, generally considered one of the best popular-level expositions of special and general relativity theories and related questions. Steinmetz translates complex mathematical reasoning into language accessible to laymen through analogy, example and comparison. Among topics covered are relativity of motion, location, time; of mass; acceleration; 4-dimensional time-space; geometry of the gravitational field; curvature and bending of space; non-Euclidean geometry. Index. 40 illustrations. x + 142pp. 5⅜ x 8½. Paperbound $1.35

HOW TO KNOW THE WILD FLOWERS, *Mrs. William Starr Dana*
Classic nature book that has introduced thousands to wonders of American wild flowers. Color-season principle of organization is easy to use, even by those with no botanical training, and the genial, refreshing discussions of history, folklore, uses of over 1,000 native and escape flowers, foliage plants are informative as well as fun to read. Over 170 full-page plates, collected from several editions, may be colored in to make permanent records of finds. Revised to conform with 1950 edition of Gray's Manual of Botany. xlii + 438pp. 5⅜ x 8½. Paperbound $2.00

MANUAL OF THE TREES OF NORTH AMERICA, *Charles Sprague Sargent*
Still unsurpassed as most comprehensive, reliable study of North American tree characteristics, precise locations and distribution. By dean of American dendrologists. Every tree native to U.S., Canada, Alaska; 185 genera, 717 species, described in detail—leaves, flowers, fruit, winterbuds, bark, wood, growth habits, etc. plus discussion of varieties and local variants, immaturity variations. Over 100 keys, including unusual 11-page analytical key to genera, aid in identification. 783 clear illustrations of flowers, fruit, leaves. An unmatched permanent reference work for all nature lovers. Second enlarged (1926) edition. Synopsis of families. Analytical key to genera. Glossary of technical terms. Index. 783 illustrations, 1 map. Total of 982pp. 5⅜ x 8.
Vol. 1 Paperbound $2.25, Vol. 2 Paperbound $2.25,
The set $4.50

IT'S FUN TO MAKE THINGS FROM SCRAP MATERIALS,
*Evelyn Glantz Hershoff*
What use are empty spools, tin cans, bottle tops? What can be made from
rubber bands, clothes pins, paper clips, and buttons? This book provides
simply worded instructions and large diagrams showing you how to make
cookie cutters, toy trucks, paper turkeys, Halloween masks, telephone sets,
aprons, linoleum block- and spatter prints — in all 399 projects! Many are easy
enough for young children to figure out for themselves; some challenging
enough to entertain adults; all are remarkably ingenious ways to make things
from materials that cost pennies or less! Formerly "Scrap Fun for Everyone."
Index. 214 illustrations. 373pp. 5⅜ x 8½.                    Paperbound $1.50

SYMBOLIC LOGIC and THE GAME OF LOGIC, *Lewis Carroll*
"Symbolic Logic" is not concerned with modern symbolic logic, but is instead
a collection of over 380 problems posed with charm and imagination, using
the syllogism and a fascinating diagrammatic method of drawing conclusions.
In "The Game of Logic" Carroll's whimsical imagination devises a logical game
played with 2 diagrams and counters (included) to manipulate hundreds of
tricky syllogisms. The final section, "Hit or Miss" is a lagniappe of 101 additional puzzles in the delightful Carroll manner. Until this reprint edition,
both of these books were rarities costing up to $15 each. Symbolic Logic:
Index. xxxi + 199pp. The Game of Logic: 96pp. 2 vols. bound as one. 5⅜ x 8.
                                                             Paperbound $2.00

MATHEMATICAL PUZZLES OF SAM LOYD, PART I
*selected and edited by M. Gardner*
Choice puzzles by the greatest American puzzle creator and innovator. Selected
from his famous collection, "Cyclopedia of Puzzles," they retain the unique
style and historical flavor of the originals. There are posers based on arithmetic,
algebra, probability, game theory, route tracing, topology, counter and sliding
block, operations research, geometrical dissection. Includes the famous "14-15"
puzzle which was a national craze, and his "Horse of a Different Color" which
sold millions of copies. 117 of his most ingenious puzzles in all. 120 line
drawings and diagrams. Solutions. Selected references. xx + 167pp. 5⅜ x 8.
                                                             Paperbound $1.00

STRING FIGURES AND HOW TO MAKE THEM, *Caroline Furness Jayne*
107 string figures plus variations selected from the best primitive and modern
examples developed by Navajo, Apache, pygmies of Africa, Eskimo, in Europe,
Australia, China, etc. The most readily understandable, easy-to-follow book in
English on perennially popular recreation. Crystal-clear exposition; step-by-
step diagrams. Everyone from kindergarten children to adults looking for
unusual diversion will be endlessly amused. Index. Bibliography. Introduction
by A. C. Haddon. 17 full-page plates, 960 illustrations. xxiii + 401pp. 5⅜ x 8½.
                                                             Paperbound $2.00

PAPER FOLDING FOR BEGINNERS, *W. D. Murray and F. J. Rigney*
A delightful introduction to the varied and entertaining Japanese art of
origami (paper folding), with a full, crystal-clear text that anticipates every
difficulty; over 275 clearly labeled diagrams of all important stages in creation.
You get results at each stage, since complex figures are logically developed
from simpler ones. 43 different pieces are explained: sailboats, frogs, roosters,
etc. 6 photographic plates. 279 diagrams. 95pp. 5⅝ x 8⅜. Paperbound $1.00

PRINCIPLES OF ART HISTORY,
*H. Wölfflin*

Analyzing such terms as "baroque," "classic," "neoclassic," "primitive," "picturesque," and 164 different works by artists like Botticelli, van Cleve, Dürer, Hobbema, Holbein, Hals, Rembrandt, Titian, Brueghel, Vermeer, and many others, the author establishes the classifications of art history and style on a firm, concrete basis. This classic of art criticism shows what really occurred between the 14th-century primitives and the sophistication of the 18th century in terms of basic attitudes and philosophies. "A remarkable lesson in the art of seeing," *Sat. Rev. of Literature.* Translated from the 7th German edition. 150 illustrations. 254pp. 6⅛ x 9¼.          Paperbound $2.00

PRIMITIVE ART,
*Franz Boas*

This authoritative and exhaustive work by a great American anthropologist covers the entire gamut of primitive art. Pottery, leatherwork, metal work, stone work, wood, basketry, are treated in detail. Theories of primitive art, historical depth in art history, technical virtuosity, unconscious levels of patterning, symbolism, styles, literature, music, dance, etc. A must book for the interested layman, the anthropologist, artist, handicrafter (hundreds of unusual motifs), and the historian. Over 900 illustrations (50 ceramic vessels, 12 totem poles, etc.). 376pp. 5⅜ x 8.          Paperbound $2.25

THE GENTLEMAN AND CABINET MAKER'S DIRECTOR,
*Thomas Chippendale*

A reprint of the 1762 catalogue of furniture designs that went on to influence generations of English and Colonial and Early Republic American furniture makers. The 200 plates, most of them full-page sized, show Chippendale's designs for French (Louis XV), Gothic, and Chinese-manner chairs, sofas, canopy and dome beds, cornices, chamber organs, cabinets, shaving tables, commodes, picture frames, frets, candle stands, chimney pieces, decorations, etc. The drawings are all elegant and highly detailed; many include construction diagrams and elevations. A supplement of 24 photographs shows surviving pieces of original and Chippendale-style pieces of furniture. Brief biography of Chippendale by N. I. Bienenstock, editor of *Furniture World.* Reproduced from the 1762 edition. 200 plates, plus 19 photographic plates. vi + 249pp. 9⅛ x 12¼.          Paperbound $3.50

AMERICAN ANTIQUE FURNITURE: A BOOK FOR AMATEURS,
*Edgar G. Miller, Jr.*

Standard introduction and practical guide to identification of valuable American antique furniture. 2115 illustrations, mostly photographs taken by the author in 148 private homes, are arranged in chronological order in extensive chapters on chairs, sofas, chests, desks, bedsteads, mirrors, tables, clocks, and other articles. Focus is on furniture accessible to the collector, including simpler pieces and a larger than usual coverage of Empire style. Introductory chapters identify structural elements, characteristics of various styles, how to avoid fakes, etc. "We are frequently asked to name some book on American furniture that will meet the requirements of the novice collector, the beginning dealer, and . . . the general public. . . . We believe Mr. Miller's two volumes more completely satisfy this specification than any other work," *Antiques.* Appendix. Index. Total of vi + 1106pp. 7⅞ x 10¾.
                    Two volume set, paperbound $7.50

THE BAD CHILD'S BOOK OF BEASTS, MORE BEASTS FOR WORSE CHILDREN, and A MORAL ALPHABET, *H. Belloc*
Hardly and anthology of humorous verse has appeared in the last 50 years without at least a couple of these famous nonsense verses. But one must see the entire volumes — with all the delightful original illustrations by Sir Basil Blackwood — to appreciate fully Belloc's charming and witty verses that play so subacidly on the platitudes of life and morals that beset his day — and ours. A great humor classic. Three books in one. Total of 157pp. 5⅜ x 8.
Paperbound $1.00

THE DEVIL'S DICTIONARY, *Ambrose Bierce*
Sardonic and irreverent barbs puncturing the pomposities and absurdities of American politics, business, religion, literature, and arts, by the country's greatest satirist in the classic tradition. Epigrammatic as Shaw, piercing as Swift, American as Mark Twain, Will Rogers, and Fred Allen, Bierce will always remain the favorite of a small coterie of enthusiasts, and of writers and speakers whom he supplies with "some of the most gorgeous witticisms of the English language" (H. L. Mencken). Over 1000 entries in alphabetical order. 144pp. 5⅜ x 8.
Paperbound $1.00

THE COMPLETE NONSENSE OF EDWARD LEAR.
This is the only complete edition of this master of gentle madness available at a popular price. *A Book of Nonsense, Nonsense Songs, More Nonsense Songs and Stories* in their entirety with all the old favorites that have delighted children and adults for years. The Dong With A Luminous Nose, The Jumblies, The Owl and the Pussycat, and hundreds of other bits of wonderful nonsense. 214 limericks, 3 sets of Nonsense Botany, 5 Nonsense Alphabets, 546 drawings by Lear himself, and much more. 320pp. 5⅜ x 8.
Paperbound $1.00

THE WIT AND HUMOR OF OSCAR WILDE, *ed. by Alvin Redman*
Wilde at his most brilliant, in 1000 epigrams exposing weaknesses and hypocrisies of "civilized" society. Divided into 49 categories—sin, wealth, women, America, etc.—to aid writers, speakers. Includes excerpts from his trials, books, plays, criticism. Formerly "The Epigrams of Oscar Wilde." Introduction by Vyvyan Holland, Wilde's only living son. Introductory essay by editor. 260pp. 5⅜ x 8.
Paperbound $1.00

A CHILD'S PRIMER OF NATURAL HISTORY, *Oliver Herford*
Scarcely an anthology of whimsy and humor has appeared in the last 50 years without a contribution from Oliver Herford. Yet the works from which these examples are drawn have been almost impossible to obtain! Here at last are Herford's improbable definitions of a menagerie of familiar and weird animals, each verse illustrated by the author's own drawings. 24 drawings in 2 colors; 24 additional drawings. vii + 95pp. 6½ x 6.
Paperbound $1.00

THE BROWNIES: THEIR BOOK, *Palmer Cox*
The book that made the Brownies a household word. Generations of readers have enjoyed the antics, predicaments and adventures of these jovial sprites, who emerge from the forest at night to play or to come to the aid of a deserving human. Delightful illustrations by the author decorate nearly every page. 24 short verse tales with 266 illustrations. 155pp. 6⅝ x 9¼.
Paperbound $1.50

THE PRINCIPLES OF PSYCHOLOGY,
*William James*
The full long-course, unabridged, of one of the great classics of Western literature and science. Wonderfully lucid descriptions of human mental activity, the stream of thought, consciousness, time perception, memory, imagination, emotions, reason, abnormal phenomena, and similar topics. Original contributions are integrated with the work of such men as Berkeley, Binet, Mills, Darwin, Hume, Kant, Royce, Schopenhauer, Spinoza, Locke, Descartes, Galton, Wundt, Lotze, Herbart, Fechner, and scores of others. All contrasting interpretations of mental phenomena are examined in detail—introspective analysis, philosophical interpretation, and experimental research. "A classic," *Journal of Consulting Psychology.* "The main lines are as valid as ever," *Psychoanalytical Quarterly.* "Standard reading . . . a classic of interpretation," *Psychiatric Quarterly.* 94 illustrations. 1408pp. 5⅜ x 8.
Vol. 1 Paperbound $2.50, Vol. 2 Paperbound $2.50,
The set $5.00

VISUAL ILLUSIONS: THEIR CAUSES, CHARACTERISTICS AND APPLICATIONS,
*M. Luckiesh*
"Seeing is deceiving," asserts the author of this introduction to virtually every type of optical illusion known. The text both describes and explains the principles involved in color illusions, figure-ground, distance illusions, etc. 100 photographs, drawings and diagrams prove how easy it is to fool the sense: circles that aren't round, parallel lines that seem to bend, stationary figures that seem to move as you stare at them — illustration after illustration strains our credulity at what we see. Fascinating book from many points of view, from applications for artists, in camouflage, etc. to the psychology of vision. New introduction by William Ittleson, Dept. of Psychology, Queens College. Index. Bibliography. xxi + 252pp. 5⅜ x 8½.                                     Paperbound $1.50

FADS AND FALLACIES IN THE NAME OF SCIENCE,
*Martin Gardner*
This is the standard account of various cults, quack systems, and delusions which have masqueraded as science: hollow earth fanatics. Reich and orgone sex energy, dianetics, Atlantis, multiple moons, Forteanism, flying saucers, medical fallacies like iridiagnosis, zone therapy, etc. A new chapter has been added on Bridey Murphy, psionics, and other recent manifestations in this field. This is a fair, reasoned appraisal of eccentric theory which provides excellent inoculation against cleverly masked nonsense. "Should be read by everyone, scientist and non-scientist alike," R. T. Birge, Prof. Emeritus of Physics, Univ. of California; Former President, American Physical Society. Index. x + 365pp. 5⅜ x 8.                                     Paperbound $1.85

ILLUSIONS AND DELUSIONS OF THE SUPERNATURAL AND THE OCCULT,
*D. H. Rawcliffe*
Holds up to rational examination hundreds of persistent delusions including crystal gazing, automatic writing, table turning, mediumistic trances, mental healing, stigmata, lycanthropy, live burial, the Indian Rope Trick, spiritualism, dowsing, telepathy, clairvoyance, ghosts, ESP, etc. The author explains and exposes the mental and physical deceptions involved, making this not only an exposé of supernatural phenomena, but a valuable exposition of characteristic types of abnormal psychology. Originally titled "The Psychology of the Occult." 14 illustrations. Index. 551pp. 5⅜ x 8.                     Paperbound $2.25

FAIRY TALE COLLECTIONS, *edited by Andrew Lang*
Andrew Lang's fairy tale collections make up the richest shelf-full of traditional
children's stories anywhere available. Lang supervised the translation of stories
from all over the world—familiar European tales collected by Grimm, animal
stories from Negro Africa, myths of primitive Australia, stories from Russia,
Hungary, Iceland, Japan, and many other countries. Lang's selection of translations are unusually high; many authorities consider that the most familiar
tales find their best versions in these volumes. All collections are richly deco-
rated and illustrated by H. J. Ford and other artists.

THE BLUE FAIRY BOOK. 37 stories. 138 illustrations. ix + 390pp. 5⅜ x 8½.
Paperbound $1.50

THE GREEN FAIRY BOOK. 42 stories. 100 illustrations. xiii + 366pp. 5⅜
x 8½.
Paperbound $1.50

THE BROWN FAIRY BOOK. 32 stories. 50 illustrations, 8 in color. xii +
350pp. 5⅜ x 8½.
Paperbound $1.50

THE BEST TALES OF HOFFMANN, *edited by E. F. Bleiler*
10 stories by E. T. A. Hoffmann, one of the greatest of all writers of fantasy.
The tales include "The Golden Flower Pot," "Automata," "A New Year's Eve
Adventure," "Nutcracker and the King of Mice," "Sand-Man," and others.
Vigorous characterizations of highly eccentric personalities, remarkably imaginative situations, and intensely fast pacing has made these tales popular all
over the world for 150 years. Editor's introduction. 7 drawings by Hoffmann.
xxxiii + 419pp. 5⅜ x 8½.
Paperbound $2.00

GHOST AND HORROR STORIES OF AMBROSE BIERCE,
*edited by E. F. Bleiler*
Morbid, eerie, horrifying tales of possessed poets, shabby aristocrats, revived
corpses, and haunted malefactors. Widely acknowledged as the best of their
kind between Poe and the moderns, reflecting their author's inner torment
and bitter view of life. Includes "Damned Thing," "The Middle Toe of the
Right Foot," "The Eyes of the Panther," "Visions of the Night," "Moxon's
Master," and over a dozen others. Editor's introduction. xxii + 199pp. 5⅜
x 8½.
Paperbound $1.25

THREE GOTHIC NOVELS, *edited by E. F. Bleiler*
Originators of the still popular Gothic novel form, influential in ushering in
early 19th-century Romanticism. Horace Walpole's *Castle of Otranto*, William
Beckford's *Vathek*, John Polidori's *The Vampyre*, and a *Fragment* by Lord
Byron are enjoyable as exciting reading or as documents in the history of
English literature. Editor's introduction. xi + 291pp. 5⅜ x 8½.
Paperbound $2.00

BEST GHOST STORIES OF LEFANU, *edited by E. F. Bleiler*
Though admired by such critics as V. S. Pritchett, Charles Dickens and Henry
James, ghost stories by the Irish novelist Joseph Sheridan LeFanu have
never become as widely known as his detective fiction. About half of the 16
stories in this collection have never before been available in America. Collec-
tion includes "Carmilla" (perhaps the best vampire story ever written), "The
Haunted Baronet," "The Fortunes of Sir Robert Ardagh," and the classic
"Green Tea." Editor's introduction. 7 contemporary illustrations. Portrait of
LeFanu. xii + 467pp. 5⅜ x 8.
Paperbound $2.00

EASY-TO-DO ENTERTAINMENTS AND DIVERSIONS WITH COINS, CARDS, STRING, PAPER AND MATCHES, *R. M. Abraham*
Over 300 tricks, games and puzzles will provide young readers with absorbing fun. Sections on card games; paper-folding; tricks with coins, matches and pieces of string; games for the agile; toy-making from common household objects; mathematical recreations; and 50 miscellaneous pastimes. Anyone in charge of groups of youngsters, including hard-pressed parents, and in need of suggestions on how to keep children sensibly amused and quietly content will find this book indispensable. Clear, simple text, copious number of delightful line drawings and illustrative diagrams. Originally titled "Winter Nights' Entertainments." Introduction by Lord Baden Powell. 329 illustrations. v + 186pp. 5⅜ x 8½.                                                         Paperbound $1.00

AN INTRODUCTION TO CHESS MOVES AND TACTICS SIMPLY EXPLAINED, *Leonard Barden*
Beginner's introduction to the royal game. Names, possible moves of the pieces, definitions of essential terms, how games are won, etc. explained in 30-odd pages. With this background you'll be able to sit right down and play. Balance of book teaches strategy — openings, middle game, typical endgame play, and suggestions for improving your game. A sample game is fully analyzed. True middle-level introduction, teaching you all the essentials without oversimplifying or losing you in a maze of detail. 58 figures. 102pp. 5⅜ x 8½.                                                         Paperbound $1.00

LASKER'S MANUAL OF CHESS, *Dr. Emanuel Lasker*
Probably the greatest chess player of modern times, Dr. Emanuel Lasker held the world championship 28 years, independent of passing schools or fashions. This unmatched study of the game, chiefly for intermediate to skilled players, analyzes basic methods, combinations, position play, the aesthetics of chess, dozens of different openings, etc., with constant reference to great modern games. Contains a brilliant exposition of Steinitz's important theories. Introduction by Fred Reinfeld. Tables of Lasker's tournament record. 3 indices. 308 diagrams. 1 photograph. xxx + 349pp. 5⅜ x 8.       Paperbound $2.25

COMBINATIONS: THE HEART OF CHESS, *Irving Chernev*
Step-by-step from simple combinations to complex, this book, by a well-known chess writer, shows you the intricacies of pins, counter-pins, knight forks, and smothered mates. Other chapters show alternate lines of play to those taken in actual championship games; boomerang combinations; classic examples of brilliant combination play by Nimzovich, Rubinstein, Tarrasch, Botvinnik, Alekhine and Capablanca. Index. 356 diagrams. ix + 245pp. 5⅜ x 8½.                                                         Paperbound $1.85

HOW TO SOLVE CHESS PROBLEMS, *K. S. Howard*
Full of practical suggestions for the fan or the beginner — who knows only the moves of the chessmen. Contains preliminary section and 58 two-move, 46 three-move, and 8 four-move problems composed by 27 outstanding American problem creators in the last 30 years. Explanation of all terms and exhaustive index. "Just what is wanted for the student," Brian Harley. 112 problems, solutions. vi + 171pp. 5⅜ x 8.                           Paperbound $1.35

SOCIAL THOUGHT FROM LORE TO SCIENCE,
*H. E. Barnes and H. Becker*
An immense survey of sociological thought and ways of viewing, studying,
planning, and reforming society from earliest times to the present. Includes
thought on society of preliterate peoples, ancient non-Western cultures, and
every great movement in Europe, America, and modern Japan. Analyzes hundreds of great thinkers: Plato, Augustine, Bodin, Vico, Montesquieu, Herder,
Comte, Marx, etc. Weighs the contributions of utopians, sophists, fascists and
communists; economists, jurists, philosophers, ecclesiastics, and every 19th
and 20th century school of scientific sociology, anthropology, and social psychology throughout the world. Combines topical, chronological, and regional
approaches, treating the evolution of social thought as a process rather than
as a series of mere topics. "Impressive accuracy, competence, and discrimination . . . easily the best single survey," *Nation*. Thoroughly revised, with new
material up to 1960. 2 indexes. Over 2200 bibliographical notes. Three volume
set. Total of 1586pp. 5⅜ x 8.
Vol. 1 Paperbound $2.75, Vol. 2 Paperbound $2.75, Vol. 3 Paperbound $2.50
The set $8.00

A HISTORY OF HISTORICAL WRITING, *Harry Elmer Barnes*
Virtually the only adequate survey of the whole course of historical writing
in a single volume. Surveys developments from the beginnings of historiog-
raphy in the ancient Near East and the Classical World, up through the
Cold War. Covers major historians in detail, shows interrelationship with
cultural background, makes clear individual contributions, evaluates and
estimates importance; also enormously rich upon minor authors and thinkers
who are usually passed over. Packed with scholarship and learning, clear, easily
written. Indispensable to every student of history. Revised and enlarged up
to 1961. Index and bibliography. xv + 442pp. 5⅜ x 8½.    Paperbound $2.50

JOHANN SEBASTIAN BACH, *Philipp Spitta*
The complete and unabridged text of the definitive study of Bach. Written
some 70 years ago, it is still unsurpassed for its coverage of nearly all aspects
of Bach's life and work. There could hardly be a finer non-technical introduction to Bach's music than the detailed, lucid analyses which Spitta provides
for hundreds of individual pieces. 26 solid pages are devoted to the B minor
mass, for example, and 30 pages to the glorious St. Matthew Passion. This
monumental set also includes a major analysis of the music of the 18th century:
Buxtehude, Pachelbel, etc. "Unchallenged as the last word on one of the
supreme geniuses of music," John Barkham, *Saturday Review Syndicate*. Total
of 1819pp. Heavy cloth binding. 5⅜ x 8.
Two volume set, clothbound $13.50

BEETHOVEN AND HIS NINE SYMPHONIES, *George Grove*
In this modern middle-level classic of musicology Grove not only analyzes all
nine of Beethoven's symphonies very thoroughly in terms of their musical
structure, but also discusses the circumstances under which they were written,
Beethoven's stylistic development, and much other background material. This
is an extremely rich book, yet very easily followed; it is highly recommended
to anyone seriously interested in music. Over 250 musical passages. Index.
viii + 407pp. 5⅜ x 8.
Paperbound $2.00

THREE SCIENCE FICTION NOVELS,
*John Taine*
Acknowledged by many as the best SF writer of the 1920's, Taine (under the name Eric Temple Bell) was also a Professor of Mathematics of considerable renown. Reprinted here are *The Time Stream*, generally considered Taine's best, *The Greatest Game*, a biological-fiction novel, and *The Purple Sapphire*, involving a supercivilization of the past. Taine's stories tie fantastic narratives to frameworks of original and logical scientific concepts. Speculation is often profound on such questions as the nature of time, concept of entropy, cyclical universes, etc. 4 contemporary illustrations. v + 532pp. 5⅜ x 8⅜.

Paperbound $2.00

SEVEN SCIENCE FICTION NOVELS,
*H. G. Wells*
Full unabridged texts of 7 science-fiction novels of the master. Ranging from biology, physics, chemistry, astronomy, to sociology and other studies, Mr. Wells extrapolates whole worlds of strange and intriguing character. "One will have to go far to match this for entertainment, excitement, and sheer pleasure . . ."*New York Times*. Contents: The Time Machine, The Island of Dr. Moreau, The First Men in the Moon, The Invisible Man, The War of the Worlds, The Food of the Gods, In The Days of the Comet. 1015pp. 5⅜ x 8.

Clothbound $5.00

28 SCIENCE FICTION STORIES OF H. G. WELLS.
Two full, unabridged novels, *Men Like Gods* and *Star Begotten*, plus 26 short stories by the master science-fiction writer of all time! Stories of space, time, invention, exploration, futuristic adventure. Partial contents: *The Country of the Blind, In the Abyss, The Crystal Egg, The Man Who Could Work Miracles, A Story of Days to Come, The Empire of the Ants, The Magic Shop, The Valley of the Spiders, A Story of the Stone Age, Under the Knife, Sea Raiders,* etc. An indispensable collection for the library of anyone interested in science fiction adventure. 928pp. 5⅜ x 8.

Clothbound $4.50

THREE MARTIAN NOVELS,
*Edgar Rice Burroughs*
Complete, unabridged reprinting, in one volume, of Thuvia, Maid of Mars; Chessmen of Mars; The Master Mind of Mars. Hours of science-fiction adventure by a modern master storyteller. Reset in large clear type for easy reading. 16 illustrations by J. Allen St. John. vi + 490pp. 5⅜ x 8½.

Paperbound $1.85

AN INTELLECTUAL AND CULTURAL HISTORY OF THE WESTERN WORLD,
*Harry Elmer Barnes*
Monumental 3-volume survey of intellectual development of Europe from primitive cultures to the present day. Every significant product of human intellect traced through history: art, literature, mathematics, physical sciences, medicine, music, technology, social sciences, religions, jurisprudence, education, etc. Presentation is lucid and specific, analyzing in detail specific discoveries, theories, literary works, and so on. Revised (1965) by recognized scholars in specialized fields under the direction of Prof. Barnes. Revised bibliography. Indexes. 24 illustrations. Total of xxix + 1318pp.
Vol. 1 Paperbound $2.00, Vol. 2 Paperbound $2.00, Vol. 3 Paperbound $2.00,

The set $6.00

HEAR ME TALKIN' TO YA, *edited by Nat Shapiro and Nat Hentoff*
In their own words, Louis Armstrong, King Oliver, Fletcher Henderson, Bunk Johnson, Bix Beiderbecke, Billy Holiday, Fats Waller, Jelly Roll Morton, Duke Ellington, and many others comment on the origins of jazz in New Orleans and its growth in Chicago's South Side, Kansas City's jam sessions, Depression Harlem, and the modernism of the West Coast schools. Taken from taped conversations, letters, magazine articles, other first-hand sources. Editors' introduction. xvi + 429pp. 5⅜ x 8½. Paperbound $2.00

THE JOURNAL OF HENRY D. THOREAU
A 25-year record by the great American observer and critic, as complete a record of a great man's inner life as is anywhere available. Thoreau's Journals served him as raw material for his formal pieces, as a place where he could develop his ideas, as an outlet for his interests in wild life and plants, in writing as an art, in classics of literature, Walt Whitman and other contemporaries, in politics, slavery, individual's relation to the State, etc. The Journals present a portrait of a remarkable man, and are an observant social history. Unabridged republication of 1906 edition, Bradford Torrey and Francis H. Allen, editors. Illustrations. Total of 1888pp. 8⅜ x 12¼. Two volume set, clothbound $25.00

A SHAKESPEARIAN GRAMMAR, *E. A. Abbott*
Basic reference to Shakespeare and his contemporaries, explaining through thousands of quotations from Shakespeare, Jonson, Beaumont and Fletcher, North's *Plutarch* and other sources the grammatical usage differing from the modern. First published in 1870 and written by a scholar who spent much of his life isolating principles of Elizabethan language, the book is unlikely ever to be superseded. Indexes. xxiv + 511pp. 5⅜ x 8½. Paperbound $2.75

FOLK-LORE OF SHAKESPEARE, *T. F. Thistelton Dyer*
Classic study, drawing from Shakespeare a large body of references to supernatural beliefs, terminology of falconry and hunting, games and sports, good luck charms, marriage customs, folk medicines, superstitions about plants, animals, birds, argot of the underworld, sexual slang of London, proverbs, drinking customs, weather lore, and much else. From full compilation comes a mirror of the 17th-century popular mind. Index. ix + 526pp. 5⅜ x 8½. Paperbound $2.50

THE NEW VARIORUM SHAKESPEARE, *edited by H. H. Furness*
By far the richest editions of the plays ever produced in any country or language. Each volume contains complete text (usually First Folio) of the play, all variants in Quarto and other Folio texts, editorial changes by every major editor to Furness's own time (1900), footnotes to obscure references or language, extensive quotes from literature of Shakespearian criticism, essays on plot sources (often reprinting sources in full), and much more.

HAMLET, *edited by H. H. Furness*
Total of xxvi + 905pp. 5⅜ x 8½. Two volume set, paperbound $4.75

TWELFTH NIGHT, *edited by H. H. Furness*
Index. xxii + 434pp. 5⅜ x 8½. Paperbound $2.25

LA BOHEME BY GIACOMO PUCCINI,
*translated and introduced by Ellen H. Bleiler*
Complete handbook for the operagoer, with everything needed for full enjoyment except the musical score itself. Complete Italian libretto, with new, modern English line-by-line translation—the only libretto printing all repeats; biography of Puccini; the librettists; background to the opera, Murger's La Boheme, etc.; circumstances of composition and performances; plot summary; and pictorial section of 73 illustrations showing Puccini, famous singers and performances, etc. Large clear type for easy reading. 124pp. 5⅜ x 8½.
Paperbound $1.00

ANTONIO STRADIVARI: HIS LIFE AND WORK (1644-1737),
*W. Henry Hill, Arthur F. Hill, and Alfred E. Hill*
Still the only book that really delves into life and art of the incomparable Italian craftsman, maker of the finest musical instruments in the world today. The authors, expert violin-makers themselves, discuss Stradivari's ancestry, his construction and finishing techniques, distinguished characteristics of many of his instruments and their locations. Included, too, is story of introduction of his instruments into France, England, first revelation of their supreme merit, and information on his labels, number of instruments made, prices, mystery of ingredients of his varnish, tone of pre-1684 Stradivari violin and changes between 1684 and 1690. An extremely interesting, informative account for all music lovers, from craftsman to concert-goer. Republication of original (1902) edition. New introduction by Sydney Beck, Head of Rare Book and Manuscript Collections, Music Division, New York Public Library. Analytical index by Rembert Wurlitzer. Appendixes. 68 illustrations. 30 full-page plates. 4 in color. xxvi + 315pp. 5⅜ x 8½.
Paperbound $2.25

MUSICAL AUTOGRAPHS FROM MONTEVERDI TO HINDEMITH,
*Emanuel Winternitz*
For beauty, for intrinsic interest, for perspective on the composer's personality, for subtleties of phrasing, shading, emphasis indicated in the autograph but suppressed in the printed score, the mss. of musical composition are fascinating documents which repay close study in many different ways. This 2-volume work reprints facsimiles of mss. by virtually every major composer, and many minor figures—196 examples in all. A full text points out what can be learned from mss., analyzes each sample. Index. Bibliography. 18 figures. 196 plates. Total of 170pp. of text. 7⅞ x 10¾.
Vol. 1 Paperbound $2.00, Vol. 2 Paperbound $2.00,
The set $4.00

J. S. BACH,
*Albert Schweitzer*
One of the few great full-length studies of Bach's life and work, and the study upon which Schweitzer's renown as a musicologist rests. On first appearance (1911), revolutionized Bach performance. The only writer on Bach to be musicologist, performing musician, and student of history, theology and philosophy, Schweitzer contributes particularly full sections on history of German Protestant church music, theories on motivic pictorial representations in vocal music, and practical suggestions for performance. Translated by Ernest Newman. Indexes. 5 illustrations. 650 musical examples. Total of xix + 928pp. 5⅜ x 8½.
Vol. 1 Paperbound $2.00, Vol. 2 Paperbound $2.00,
The set $4.00

THE METHODS OF ETHICS, *Henry Sidgwick*
Propounding no organized system of its own, study subjects every major methodological approach to ethics to rigorous, objective analysis. Study discusses and relates ethical thought of Plato, Aristotle, Bentham, Clarke, Butler, Hobbes, Hume, Mill, Spencer, Kant, and dozens of others. Sidgwick retains conclusions from each system which follow from ethical premises, rejecting the faulty. Considered by many in the field to be among the most important treatises on ethical philosophy. Appendix. Index. xlvii + 528pp. 5⅜ x 8½.
Paperbound $2.50

TEUTONIC MYTHOLOGY, *Jakob Grimm*
A milestone in Western culture; the work which established on a modern basis the study of history of religions and comparative religions. 4-volume work assembles and interprets everything available on religious and folkloristic beliefs of Germanic people (including Scandinavians, Anglo-Saxons, etc.). Assembling material from such sources as Tacitus, surviving Old Norse and Icelandic texts, archeological remains, folktales, surviving superstitions, comparative traditions, linguistic analysis, etc. Grimm explores pagan deities, heroes, folklore of nature, religious practices, and every other area of pagan German belief. To this day, the unrivaled, definitive, exhaustive study. Translated by J. S. Stallybrass from 4th (1883) German edition. Indexes. Total of lxxvii + 1887pp. 5⅜ x 8½. Four volume set, paperbound $10.00

THE I CHING, *translated by James Legge*
Called "The Book of Changes" in English, this is one of the Five Classics edited by Confucius, basic and central to Chinese thought. Explains perhaps the most complex system of divination known, founded on the theory that all things happening at any one time have characteristic features which can be isolated and related. Significant in Oriental studies, in history of religions and philosophy, and also to Jungian psychoanalysis and other areas of modern European thought. Index. Appendixes. 6 plates. xxi + 448pp. 5⅜ x 8½.
Paperbound $2.75

HISTORY OF ANCIENT PHILOSOPHY, *W. Windelband*
One of the clearest, most accurate comprehensive surveys of Greek and Roman philosophy. Discusses ancient philosophy in general, intellectual life in Greece in the 7th and 6th centuries B.C., Thales, Anaximander, Anaximenes, Heraclitus, the Eleatics, Empedocles, Anaxagoras, Leucippus, the Pythagoreans, the Sophists, Socrates, Democritus (20 pages), Plato (50 pages), Aristotle (70 pages), the Peripatetics, Stoics, Epicureans, Sceptics, Neo-platonists, Christian Apologists, etc. 2nd German edition translated by H. E. Cushman. xv + 393pp. 5⅜ x 8.
Paperbound $2.25

THE PALACE OF PLEASURE, *William Painter*
Elizabethan versions of Italian and French novels from *The Decameron*, Cinthio, Straparola, Queen Margaret of Navarre, and other continental sources — the very work that provided Shakespeare and dozens of his contemporaries with many of their plots and sub-plots and, therefore, justly considered one of the most influential books in all English literature. It is also a book that any reader will still enjoy. Total of cviii + 1,224pp.
Three volume set, Paperbound $6.75

THE WONDERFUL WIZARD OF OZ, *L. F. Baum*
All the original W. W. Denslow illustrations in full color—as much a part of "The Wizard" as Tenniel's drawings are of "Alice in Wonderland." "The Wizard" is still America's best-loved fairy tale, in which, as the author expresses it, "The wonderment and joy are retained and the heartaches and nightmares left out." Now today's young readers can enjoy every word and wonderful picture of the original book. New introduction by Martin Gardner. A Baum bibliography. 23 full-page color plates. viii + 268pp. 5⅜ x 8.
Paperbound $1.50

THE MARVELOUS LAND OF OZ, *L. F. Baum*
This is the equally enchanting sequel to the "Wizard," continuing the adventures of the Scarecrow and the Tin Woodman. The hero this time is a little boy named Tip, and all the delightful Oz magic is still present. This is the Oz book with the Animated Saw-Horse, the Woggle-Bug, and Jack Pumpkinhead. All the original John R. Neill illustrations, 10 in full color. 287pp. 5⅜ x 8.
Paperbound $1.50

ALICE'S ADVENTURES UNDER GROUND, *Lewis Carroll*
The original *Alice in Wonderland*, hand-lettered and illustrated by Carroll himself, and originally presented as a Christmas gift to a child-friend. Adults as well as children will enjoy this charming volume, reproduced faithfully in this Dover edition. While the story is essentially the same, there are slight changes, and Carroll's spritely drawings present an intriguing alternative to the famous Tenniel illustrations. One of the most popular books in Dover's catalogue. Introduction by Martin Gardner. 38 illustrations. 128pp. 5⅜ x 8½.
Paperbound $1.00

THE NURSERY "ALICE," *Lewis Carroll*
While most of us consider *Alice in Wonderland* a story for children of all ages, Carroll himself felt it was beyond younger children. He therefore provided this simplified version, illustrated with the famous Tenniel drawings enlarged and colored in delicate tints, for children aged "from Nought to Five." Dover's edition of this now rare classic is a faithful copy of the 1889 printing, including 20 illustrations by Tenniel, and front and back covers reproduced in full color. Introduction by Martin Gardner. xxiii + 67pp. 6⅛ x 9¼.
Paperbound $1.50

THE STORY OF KING ARTHUR AND HIS KNIGHTS, *Howard Pyle*
A fast-paced, exciting retelling of the best known Arthurian legends for young readers by one of America's best story tellers and illustrators. The sword Excalibur, wooing of Guinevere, Merlin and his downfall, adventures of Sir Pellias and Gawaine, and others. The pen and ink illustrations are vividly imagined and wonderfully drawn. 41 illustrations. xviii + 313pp. 6⅛ x 9¼.
Paperbound $1.50

*Prices subject to change without notice.*

Available at your book dealer or write for free catalogue to Dept. Adsci, Dover Publications, Inc., 180 Varick St., N.Y., N.Y. 10014. Dover publishes more than 150 books each year on science, elementary and advanced mathematics, biology, music, art, literary history, social sciences and other areas.